Aldehydes—
Photometric Analysis

THE ANALYSIS OF ORGANIC MATERIALS

An International Series of Monographs

edited by R. BELCHER and D. M. W. ANDERSON

Aldehydes—Photometric Analysis

Volume 2

EUGENE SAWICKI

and

CAROLE R. SAWICKI

Raleigh,
North Carolina
U.S.A.

1975

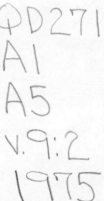 Academic Press
London · New York · San Francisco
A Subsidiary of Harcourt Brace Jovanovich, Publishers

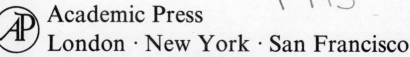

ACADEMIC PRESS INC. (LONDON) LTD.
24/28 Oval Road,
London NW1

United States Edition published by
ACADEMIC PRESS INC.
111 Fifth Avenue
New York, New York 10003

Library of Congress Catalog Card Number: 75 11373
ISBN: 0-12-620502-7

Printed in Great Britain by
Page Bros (Norwich) Ltd, Norwich

PREFACE

In this second volume we will consider the background and experimental details of colorimetric, fluorimetric and phosphorimetric methods of analysis for aldehydes ranging from β-formylacrylic acid through vanillin. Analytical methods for more than 44 aldehydes are discussed in this volume; over 100 detailed procedures are given for the analysis of these aldehydes. In addition, the ultraviolet-visible spectral, fluorescence and phosphorescence properties of these aldehydes have been discussed. Many more characterization and assay methods could be developed from the information presented. Some novel methods of assay have also been introduced in these volumes.

Let us emphasize that the value of these volumes lies not only in the ready availability of this knowledge for use, but its potentiality in environmental and biochemical analysis. Much of this potentiality has been realized, as shown to some extent in the present volumes and to a larger extent in the subsequent volumes. Many of the methods are being applied in the advancing forefronts of environmental and biochemical (especially) analysis of a wide variety of aldehyde precursors. Some of them are being used as a cutting edge of some of the investigations into aging, cancer, mental health, memory, emphysema, liver damage, etc.

It is hoped that these volumes will prove to be of value to the many people interested in the analysis of environmental pollutants and plant, animal and human tissue. It is also hoped that they will be effective in stimulating and fertilizing the minds of research scientists in the environmental and biochemical fields into origination of new ideas, facts, theories and analytical procedures.

June 1974

EUGENE SAWICKI
CAROLE R. SAWICKI

To the little ones:
Tomorrow can be even nicer.

CONTENTS

24. 3-FORMYLACRYLIC ACID

$$\underset{\underset{\text{H}}{|}}{\text{OC}}\text{—CH=CH—COOH}$$

I. PHYSICAL AND SPECTRAL PROPERTIES

M.p. 55°. B.p. 145°/10 mm. Very soluble in alcohol, water, ether; slightly soluble in chloroform and benzene; insoluble in heptane.

Furfural undergoes autoxidation in contact with air. One of the products is 3-formylacrylic acid. This aldehyde is identified by elution of the sample on Celite with solvents of increasing polarity, e.g. heptane, butanol, ethanol, water; elution of the appropriate fractions on silica gel impregnated with $0.5 \text{ N } H_2SO_4$ with $CHCl_3$–butanol (3:1) as eluent; and UV spectral examination.[1] This acid can also be determined in the presence of furfural.[2] The 2,4-dinitrophenylhydrazones are formed. The furfural hydrazone is insoluble in cold 0.1 N NaOH. The alkaline solution of the dinitrophenylhydrazone of the acid is then assayed at 456 nm.

REFERENCES

1. V. G. Kul'nevich, G. F. Muzychenko and I. A. Vishnyakova. *Z. Anal. Khim.* **23**, 1396 (1968).
2. V. I. Mil'man, V. A. Smirnov and O. B. Krayanskii. *Izv. Vyssh. Ucheb. Zaved., Pishch. Teknol.* 167 (1969).

25. FUMARALDEHYDE

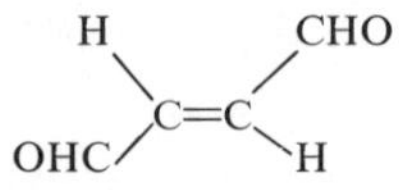

$$\begin{array}{ccc} H & & CHO \\ \diagdown & & \diagup \\ & C{=}C & \\ \diagup & & \diagdown \\ OHC & & H \end{array}$$

I. PHYSICAL AND SPECTRAL PROPERTIES

The aldehyde absorbs in isooctane at λ_{max} 225 and 354 nm and mε 17 and 0·071 respectively.[1] It and other α,β-unsaturated aldehydes can be determined with p-aminophenol by the following procedure. If the final solution contains 6% trichloroacetic acid the colour, which develops at once, is stable for at least two hours. Cysteine and glutathione hinder the reaction. Malealdehydic acid, cinnamaldehyde and furfural also react. Acrolein reacts but its colour fades quickly. Saturated aldehydes do not interfere.

p-*Aminophenol determination of fumaraldehyde*.[2] To 1 ml of test solution add 1 to 2 ml of 40% trichloroacetic acid. Dilute to 8 ml with water and add 2 ml of 3% p-aminophenol in 6% aq trichloroacetic acid. Read the absorbance at 434 nm.

Some of the reagents used in the determination of glyoxal could be used here, e.g. p-nitrophenylhydrazine and 2,4-dinitrophenylhydrazine. Many of the reactions and reagents utilized for the determination of glyoxal could be used in the analysis of this dialdehyde.

REFERENCES

1. D. L. Hufford, D. S. Tarbell and T. R. Koszalka. *J. Am. Chem. Soc.* **74**, 3014 (1952).
2. F. L. Breusch and E. Ulosoy. *Z. Physiol. Chem.* **291**, 64 (1952); through *Chem. Abstr.* **48**, 12211 (1954).

26. FURFURAL

I. PHYSICAL AND SPECTRAL PROPERTIES

M.p. $-36.5°$; b.p. 161.7; D_4^{20} 1.1594; n_D^{20} 1.52608. 8.3% soluble in water at $20°$. Very soluble in alcohol and ether. Easily distilled with steam.

As will be shown, furfural is found in many mixtures, occurs in small quantities in many foodstuffs, and is found in appreciable amounts in cigarette smoke. Fed to rats it produces liver cirrhosis[1] and with benzo[a]-pyrene has a co-carcinogenic effect on the respiratory tract of hamsters.[2]

The ultraviolet absorption spectra of furfural are given in Table 1. Furfural can be determined in mixtures through use of its ultraviolet absorption spectra. Table 2.

The photometric analysis of furfural and other furfurals is of some importance since these aldehydes are readily derived from the carbohydrates.

Table 1. Ultraviolet absorption spectra of furfural

Solvent	λ_{max}	mε	Ref.
Hexane	275, 335s	13, 0.04	3
Dioxane	270, 313	14.8, 0.06	4
Alcohol	229, 275, 335	3, 16, 0.06	5–7
Water	230, 275	4, 14–15	8–15
1.3% Aq HCl[a]	228, 277	4, 16	16
Aq buffer, pH 3–10	277	16.8[b]	17
76% H_2SO_4	250, 310	4, 16	18
28.3 N H_2SO_4	315	22.5	19
89% H_2SO_4[c]	315	21.8	20

[a] After heating for 1 h λ_{max} 228, 277 and mε 2.5 and 13, respectively.
[b] Fresh solution used, since absorbance decreases with age of solution.
[c] Spectrum shifts to longer wavelength and increased millimolar absorptivity with an increase in the sulphuric acid concentration.[21, 22]

Table 2. Determination of furfural in mixtures at λ_{max} 278 after distillation

Mixture	Ref.
Acetone condensates	23
Cheese, soft curd	24
Furfuryl alcohol	25
Oak wood hydrolysate	26
Spirits	27, 28
Tollens distillate	30
Wine	31
Wood and starch hydrolysates	32
Wood smoke	33[a]

[a] Furfural identified by colour tests after TLC.

II. REAGENTS

Table 3. Photometric determination of furfural

Reagent	λ_{max} (mε)	Ref.
m-Aminophenol	515[a]	33–35
Aniline	500–525	36–63
Anthrone	610 (13·8)	64–66
Anthrone	F460/505	67, 68
4-Azobenzenehydrazinesulphonic acid	575 (~80)	69
Azulene	492 (42)	70
Barbituric acid	366	16, 71
Bisulphite	277[b]	72–74
p-Bromoaniline	520	62, 75
Camphor–H_2SO_4	480	76
Cyclopentanone	574	77
Dimedone	F395/460	78
Dimedone–alkali	F465/520	78
N,N-Dimethyl-p-phenylenediamine	495	79, 80
2,4-Dinitrophenylhydrazine	412 (12)	81
Orcinol	598 (10)	82, 83
m-Phenylenediamine	558	79
Phloroglucinol	622 (2·7)[c]	85
Phloroglucinol + ammonia	412	86
Pyrogallol	496 (30)	
Schiff's reagent	560	87
Thiobarbituric acid	418	88

[a] Beer's law obeyed from 1 to 20 μg.   [c] Chromogen can be extracted into n-butanol.
[b] λ_{max} of furfural.

As will be shown in the precursor volume many carbohydrates can be determined by the same reagents used for the furfurals.

The many reagents used in the analysis of furfural are compared in Table 3. It is difficult to compare these methods in terms of sensitivity since the apparent molar absorptivity is rarely reported for a procedure. Most of the methods have not been optimized and could be considerably improved through a proper study of the variables.

A. Aromatic amines

The most popular method for the determination of furfural consists of its reaction with an excess quantity of an aromatic amine in acidic solution. This reaction of aniline with furfural to give a red chromogen was discovered in 1870 by Stenhouse.[101] In later years it was shown to be a general reaction of aromatic amines with furfural to give a polymethine cation, IV.[102-105] The mechanism of the reaction is shown in Fig. 1.[62, 63, 106, 107] The fading of the colour is postulated as being due to the formation of colourless heterocyclic compounds, such as VII, VIII or IX. In strongly acid solution an arylamine is split off and a pyridinium chloride, VIII, is formed,[105, 108] while in neutral or alkaline solution a dihydropyridine, IX, is formed,[106, 109, 110] and in some cases a pyrrole derivative, VII, is formed.[111-113]

Other compounds that can be assayed in the reaction include α-Furyl-CH=CH—CHO,[114, 115] α-Furyl-CH=CH—CH=CH—CHO,[115] and α-Furyl-CH=C(CN)—COOCH$_3$.[113]

The colour obtained in the furfural determination can be stabilized with oxalic acid and disodium phosphate,[42] thiourea, or stannous chloride.[35, 62, 116] With aniline, p-anisidine and p-bromoaniline as reagents the maxima is found at 525 nm, with benzidine at 575 nm. Many other aromatic amines give maxima within this range.[62] Aniline, p-anisidine and p-bromoaniline were found to be the most suitable of the arylamines studied. 5-Methylfurfural and 5-hydroxymethylfurfural give yellow to orange colours which do not interfere. Stannous chloride catalyzes the furfural reaction. Formaldehyde interferes in the p-bromoaniline procedure.

The chromogen formed with aniline in the analytical procedure is 1-phenylimino-5-phenylamino-2-hydroxypenta-2,4-diene hydrochloride, IV, Ar = C$_6$H$_5$, which is stated to have λ_{max} 520 nm and an extinction coefficient of about 67000 in 0·024 M alcoholic sulphuric acid.[63] Unfortunately, the millimolar absorptivitiy is not reported in most analytical procedures so comparisons of sensitivity are difficult to make. However, in the aniline determination of furfural the yield of chromogen in most, if not all, of the methods could be considerably improved.

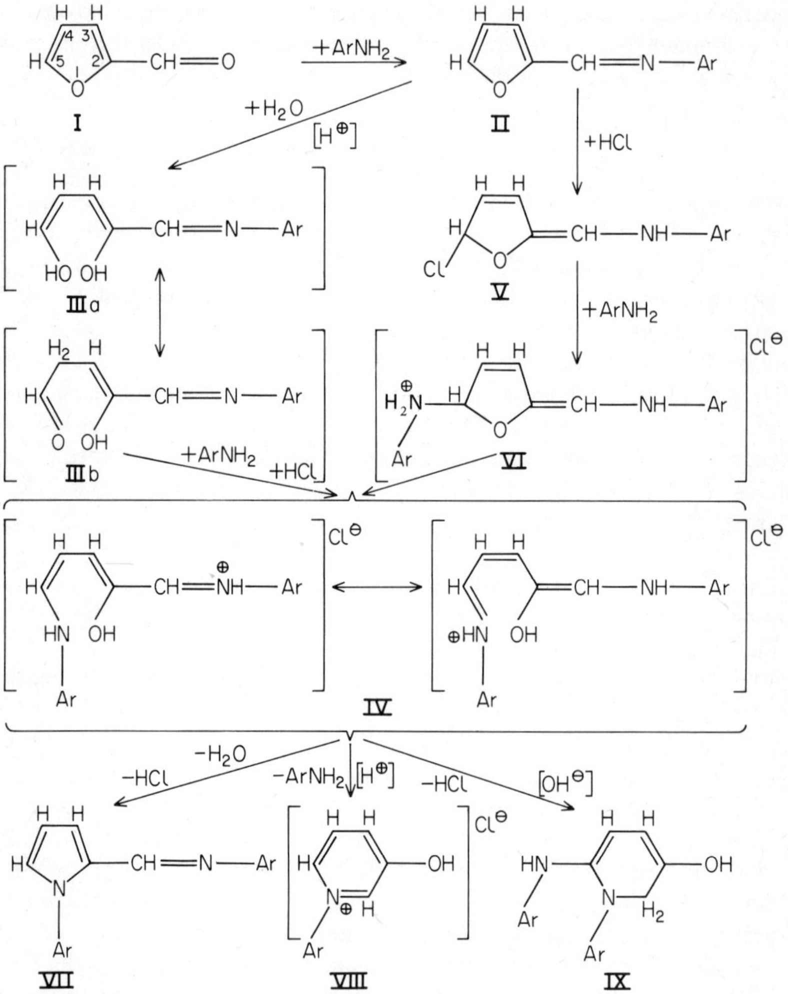

FIG. 1. Mechanism for reaction of furfural with an aromatic amine in the formation and decolorization of the chromogen **IV**.[62]

Some of the mixtures which have been analysed for furfural by some of the methods to be discussed are shown in Table 4.

Table 4. Determination of furfural in various mixtures

Mixture[a]	Procedure	Ref.
Air	Aniline → colorimetry (C)	42
Air	Aniline → C	84, 89
Air	Collect in EtOH → UV	90
Apricot extract	Steam distn → UV	91
Aq solutions	Aniline → C	37
Asphalt	Steam distn → UV	92
Beer	Aniline → C	39
Bisulphite solutions	UV	73, 74
Cheeses	Steam distn → UV	24
Cordials and liquors	Aniline → C	93
Furfuryl alcohol	UV	25
Hydrocarbon oil	Aniline → C	50, 51
Liquified petroleum gas	Aniline → C	41
Lubricating oil	Aniline → C	45, 60
Mexican lime oil	Barbituric acid → UV	71
Oakwood hydrolysates	UV	26
Oil	Extn → UV	72
Oil, lubricating	Aniline → C	94
Orange juice	Distn → aniline → C	95–97
Pentosans	Distn → UV	98–100
Petroleum products	Phloroglucinol → C	86
Spirits	UV	27, 28
Starch hydrolysates	UV	31
Tollens distillates	UV	29
Water	UV	92
Wine	Steam distn → UV	31
Wood hydrolysates	Steam distn → UV	26, 31
Wood pulp	Distn → UV	100
Wood smoke	TLC → UV	32

[a] Many more furfural precursors discussed in aldehyde precursor volume.

B. *m*-Aminophenol

Furfural in spirits has been determined with *m*-aminophenol by the following procedure. A polymethine cation is formed. The mechanism of this reaction has been discussed in terms of a general reaction with aromatic amines.

m-*Aminophenol determination of furfural*.[35] To 1 ml of the test solution add 10 ml of the reagent (1 g *m*-aminophenol in 5 ml of 95% ethanol, dilute to

30 ml with n-butanol and add 0·15 ml of 0·4 g stannous chloride in 3 ml of conc. HCl and 27 ml of water) and set aside for 5 h at 20°. Filter, and measure the absorbance at 515 nm.

C. Aniline

Aniline determination of furfural in hydrocarbon oil.[50, 51] Carry out the determinations under conditions such that the samples, standards and reagents before mixing are at a uniform temp. as are the cell contents during an absorbance reading. Pipette 5 ml of the test solution into a 25 ml volumetric flask followed by 8 ml of toluene, 10 ml of aniline acetate solution (100 ml of pure aniline in 900 ml of glacial acetic acid). Dilute to the mark with toluene. Invert the flask and shake. Read the absorbance at 520 nm at maximum reading (about 4 min). For most accurate work do not let temperature vary by more than 1°.

Furfural in refined mineral oil is determined by the following procedure.

Aniline determination of furfural in mineral oil.[94] Shake a test sample containing 7 to 40 µg of furfural in about 10 ml of light petroleum for 3 min with 10 ml of 0·5 M KCl, 10 ml anhydrous acetic acid and 1 ml of freshly distilled aniline. When the phases have separated, draw off the lower coloured layer, dilute to 25 ml with water, and keep in the dark at 20° for 20 min. Measure the absorbance at 515 nm.

Furfural has also been measured in commercially processed orange juice with the aniline reagent.[95] Examination of canned and bottled orange juice stored at various temperatures for up to 16 weeks showed that the furfural content is approximately doubled for every 5° rise in storage temperature, Fig. 2. Although furfural is not responsible for the flavour change, organoleptic evaluation showed that when the level of furfural exceeded 55 µg l^{-1} of juice, a taste panel observed a difference in flavour in comparison to controls at a significance of $p < 0.001$.

Similarly, furfural has also been measured in stored grapefruit juice with the aniline reagent.[97] When the level of furfural exceeded a value of approximately 175 µg l^{-1} in canned grapefruit juice or 150 µg l^{-1} in glass-packed juice, a taste panel observed a highly significant difference in flavour.

As a necessity in the pursuit of these various studies an improved colorimetric method has been developed for the determination of furfural in citrus juices.[116] A reliable quantitative method for evaluating deterioration of citrus juice during canning or storage is needed by the canning industry and citrus juice researchers. Since there appears to be a consistent correlation between onset of flavour change and furfural content, furfural concentration has been suggested as an index of deterioration in processed citrus juices.

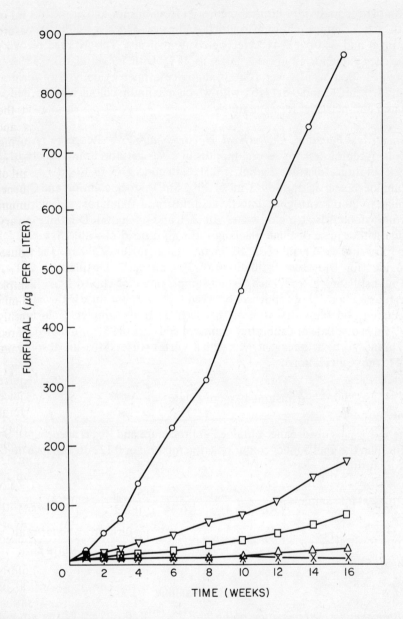

FIG. 2. Increase in furfural content in glass-packed orange juice over a 18-week period at 5°(×), 10°(Δ), 16°(□), 21°(∇), and 30°(○).[95]

Statistical analysis of furfural recoveries from orange and grapefruit juices with the stannous chloride method indicates $33.85 \pm 1.35\%$ recovered (orange) and $34.01 \pm 2.44\%$ recovered (grapefruit). The average recovery efficiency value for all juices is taken as 34%; with aq standards, 38% was obtained. Best results were obtained for colorimetric analysis of furfural using 1% $SnCl_2$ and 0.6 N HCl, with which maximum colour was reached at 50 min and persisted for 25 minutes.

Aniline determination for furfural in citrus juice.[116] Reagents: Aniline, distilled—colourless for several months in a refrigerator. Stannous chloride stock solution—dissolve 2 g $SnCl_2 \cdot 2H_2O$ in conc. HCl to 10 ml 1% $SnCl_2$ in aniline–acetic acid; dilute 1 ml of 20% $SnCl_2$ stock solution and 2 ml of aniline to 20 ml with glacial acetic acid. Furfural standards; a. Calibration furfural standards; 1 mg/ml water. 10, 2, 1 and 0.5 µg/ml. Dilutions can be made with a juice distillate (lacking furfural) instead of water. Samples for recovery studies: 600 ml of 25, 50, 75 and 100 µg furfural/200 ml. The 600 ml provides for triplicate distillations of 200 ml each. Distillation: Collect 10 ml distillate[117] from each 200 ml sample in an ice-chilled 12 × 125 mm test tube. Do not rinse condenser between replicates but rinse with water and methanol and blow dry with air between different samples. Colorimetry. To 2 ml of distillate or calibration standard add 2 ml of 95% ethanol and 1 ml of aniline–acetic acid reagent. Mix with a Vortex stirrer. Measure absorbance at 515 nm. Calculations:

$$\mu g \text{ furfural}/10 \text{ ml distillate} = \frac{5A_{sample}}{A_{cal}},$$

where A_{sample} is absorbance obtained in procedure and A_{cal} is absorbance/µg furfural in the final 5 ml of colour reaction mixture or 0.122 absorbance units per µg furfural

$$\mu g/200 \text{ ml sample} = \frac{5}{RE} \times \frac{A_{sample}}{A_{cal}} = \frac{5}{0.34} \times \frac{A_{sample}}{0.122} = 120.5\, A_{sample}$$

$$\text{ppb furfural} = \frac{25}{RE} \times \frac{A_{sample}}{A_{cal}} = 603\, A_{sample} = \frac{\mu g \text{ furfural}}{kg \text{ juice}} = \frac{\mu g \text{ furfural}}{\text{litre juice}}$$

D. *p*-Bromoaniline

p-Bromoaniline determination of furfural.[49, 75] Reflux 5 ml of the aq test solution with 3 ml of conc. hydrochloric acid and 25 ml of xylene for 150 min in an all-glass apparatus. Cool, separate the xylene layer and dry it with anhydrous sodium sulphate. To a 1 ml aliquot of the xylene solution add

5 ml of reagent (2 g *p*-bromoaniline in 95 ml of 95 % acetic acid saturated with urea). Read the absorbance at 520 nm at 30 to 50 min after the last addition.

E. Anthrone

Anthrone can also be used to determine furfural or pentoses.[118] The calibration graph is rectilinear for 1–10 µmol of furfural or pentose. The following procedure is recommended:

Fluorimetric determination of furfural (or pentoses) with anthrone.[118] Cool 1 ml of aq test solution containing 2 to 15 µg of furfural in ice and mix with 10 ml of 0·01 % anthrone in 65 % H_2SO_4. Heat at 100° for 15 min, cool for 10 min and read fluorescence at $F465/506$.

It has been shown that anthrone reacts with furfural in strong acid to give a blue solution.[64] This reaction has been investigated. The chromogen has been isolated and synthesized, and found to be 10-furfurylideneanthrone, Fig. 3.[66] The cation of this compound is the blue compound absorbing at 600 nm.

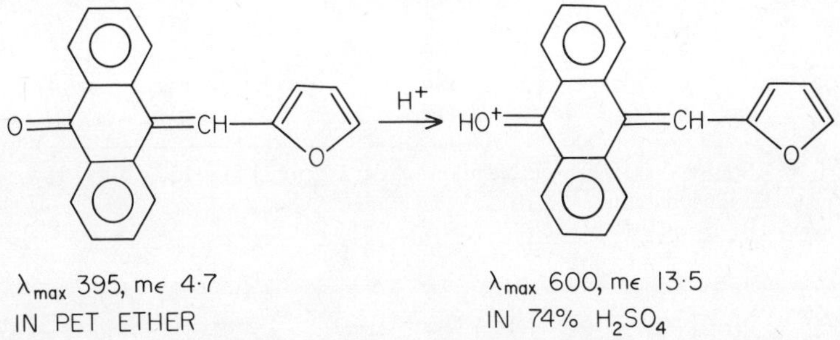

λ_{max} 395, mε 4·7 λ_{max} 600, mε 13·5
IN PET ETHER   IN 74% H_2SO_4

FIG. 3. Absorption spectral data in neutral and acid solution of a chromogen obtained in the determination of furfural with anthrone.[66]

On this basis anthrone can also be used to determine furfural. Beer's law is obeyed in the following procedure.

Anthrone determination of furfural.[64] Mix 1 ml of aq test solution with 10 ml of 0·1 % anthrone in conc H_2SO_4–85 % H_3PO_4 (3:2) with cooling. Let the mixture stand for 40 minutes. Read the absorbance at 600 nm.

Anthrone reacts with furfural in sulphuric acid to give a fluorogen in addition to the blue chromogen.[67, 68] The same type of excitation and emission spectra are obtained from furfural and pyruvaldehyde and their precursors.[67] Data are given in Table 69 of the crotonaldehyde section (Vol. 1, Chapter 18). The procedure is also given in that chapter. 5-Methyl-furfural and 5-hydroxymethylfurfural react more poorly than furfural.

F. 4-Azobenzenehydrazine sulphonic acid

This reagent has been reacted with a group of furylpolyenals to give highly coloured blue hydrazone cations with millimolar absorptivities ranging from about 63 for furfural to about 80 for the longer chain α-furylpolyenals.[69] The results obtained with the different aldehydes are compared in Table 5. A practical analytical procedure has not yet been developed using this reaction. The reaction with furfural is shown in Fig. 4.

Table 5. Azobenzenehydrazinesulphonic acid determination of α-furylpolyenals[69]

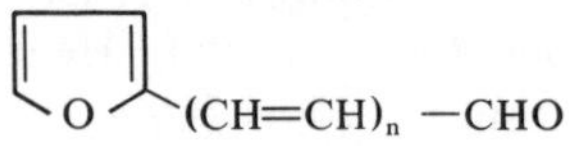

$$\text{(furan ring)}\,O\!-\!(CH\!=\!CH)_n\,-\!CHO$$

n	Free aldehyde λ_{max}	Chromogen λ_{max}
0	270	575
1	312[a]	595
2	346	610
3	366	617
4	389	612
5	412	615

[a] 5-Methyl-2-thiopheneacrolein absorbs at λ_{max} (mε) 213 (10·2), 278 (7·1), 325 (26·9) in ether.[119]

FIG. 4. Reaction of furfural with 4-phenylazophenylhydrazine-N-sulphonic acid.

G. Azulenes

Azulene and its alkyl derivatives can be condensed with aromatic and heteroaromatic aldehydes to form diarylmethane cations.[110] The derivative from furfural was prepared by heating 144 mg furfural, 192 mg azulene, 0·5 ml 70–72% perchloric acid and 8 ml acetic acid to the boiling point and allowing to cool. This perchlorate was found to absorb at 505 nm with mε 36 in acetic acid.

Azulene has been applied to the determination of furfural, its derivatives and their precursors.[70] With furfural the red chromogen, X, λ_{max} 492, mε 42, is formed.

X

In the following procedure the colour is stable for 24 hours. Twelve determinations of furfural give a percent derivation of ± 1.02. Beer's law is obeyed from 0·17 ($A = 0.1$) to 4·8 μg. Sugars and aliphatic aldehydes react weakly, Table 6.

Table 6. Azulene determination of furfurals[70]

Compound[a]	λ_{max} (nm)	$\varepsilon \cdot 10^{-3}$	Relative intensity at 492 nm
Furfural	492	42	100
5-Hydroxymethylfurfural	500	42	100
3-α-Furylacrolein	560 br[b]	46	46
5-Methylfurfural	535	64	75
1,1,3,3-Tetramethoxypropane	472	12	19
1,3,3-Trimethoxy-1-propene	472	11	17
Rhamnose	533	5	7
Ribose	500	2	4
Galactose	500	0·4	1

[a] Formaldehyde, pyruvaldehyde, crotonaldehyde, and acrolein give molar absorptivities less than 2000 in the 450 to 800 nm region.
[b] br = broad band composed of two component bands.

Azulene determination of furfural and its derivatives.[70] To 2 ml of aq test solution containing 0·2 to 5 μg of a furfural add with mixing, 3 ml of reagent (0·1 % azulene in acetic acid) followed by 3 ml of conc sulphuric acid. Mix and allow to stand for 5 min and then cool under the tap. Read the absorbance at the wavelength maximum.

H. Cyclopentanone

Furfural has also been determined by cyclopentanone.[77] The following type of reaction takes place, Fig. 5.

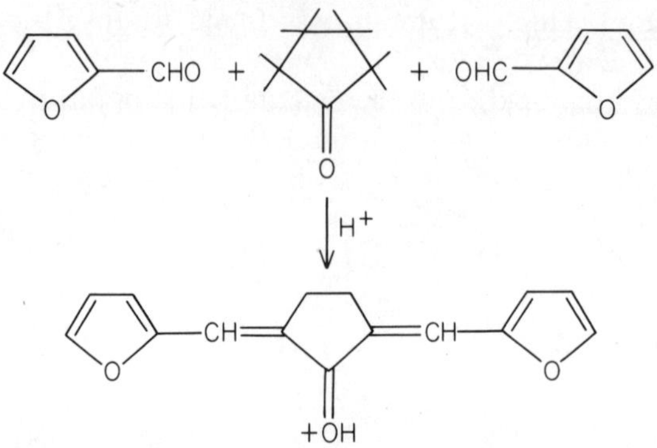

FIG. 5. Reaction of furfural with cyclopentanone in acid solution.

Cyclopentanone determination of furfural.[77] To 1 ml of aq test solution containing 0·5 to 30 µg of furfural add 0·5 ml of 0·01 M cyclopentanone, 0·2 ml of 50% KOH solution and, after 5 min, 2 ml each of 50% aq H_2SO_4 and conc H_2SO_4. Measure the absorbance at 574 nm.

I. 1,3-Diketones

Furfural can be determined with dimedone as can other aldehydes.[78] 1,3-cyclohexanedione can also be used. Since the procedure was standardized with formaldehyde, before use for the determination of furfural conditions should be optimized. The fluorogens **XI**a and b are formed.

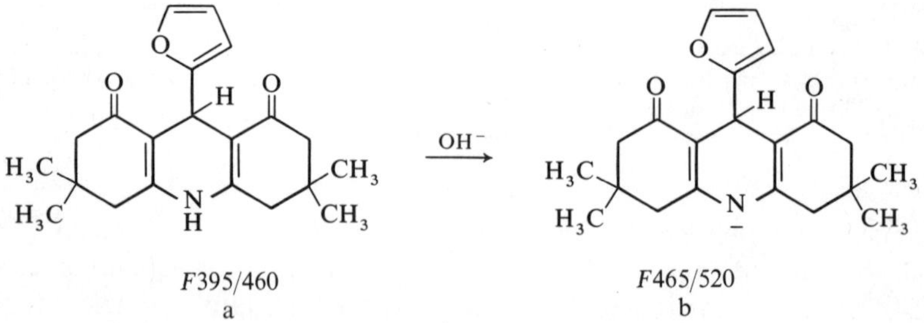

F395/460
a

F465/520
b

XI

The 2 procedures forming **XI**a and **XI**b are described in the acetaldehyde section. The results obtained with various aldehydes in the first procedure (**XI**a as fluorogen) are given in Table 21 of the aliphatic aldehydes section; the results obtained in the second procedure (**XI**b as fluorogen) are given in Table 7 of this section.

Table 7. Fluorimetric determination of aldehydes at $F465/520$ with dimedone by procedure II* [78]

Compound	Detn limit, μg	Relative fluor. intensity
Formaldehyde	0·04	100
Furfural	0·08	54
Benzaldehyde	0·2	22
Acetaldehyde	0·2	19
Propionaldehyde	0·2	19
Glyoxal	0·3	14
n-Valeraldehyde	0·3	13
4-Pyridinecarboxaldehyde	0·4	10
Pyruvaldehyde	0·4	8
Glycolaldehyde	0·6	7
D-Erythrose	0·6	7
Hexanal	0·8	5
iso-Valeraldehyde	1·0	4
1,1,3,3-Tetramethoxypropane	4·0	1
Methacrolein	8·0	0·5
Acrolein	8·0	0·5
Glyceraldehyde	14	0·3
Crotonaldehyde		0·0

* Final concentration of all solutions 3×10^{-6} M. MM·T equals 0·36 for formaldehyde. MM·T equals meter multiplier × transmittance.

J. N,N-Dimethyl-p-phenylenediamine

This diamine has been used for the determination of furfural and other unsaturated aldehydes. [79, 80] The stannous chloride double salt of this reagent is stable and easy to prepare. Furfural and its derivatives give a band at 495 nm. The procedure has been described in the cinnamaldehyde section. The type of spectra obtained for furfural and other aldehydes is shown in Fig. 6. [79]

K. 2,4-Dinitrophenylhydrazine

2,4-Dinitrophenylhydrazine (DNPH) can be used to determine furfural. Essentially 1 ml of an acetic acid test solution is treated with 0·1 % DNPH in acetic acid containing 0·5% by volume of conc HCl. [81] After 1 h the absorbance is read at 412 nm. A millimolar absorptivity of 12·3 is obtained. Other aldehydes react about as well. Ketones react but only to about 10% of the extent.

In a series of publications the analysis of furfural with diphenylamine and its derivatives has been discussed. [121]

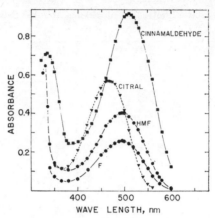

FIG. 6. Absorption spectra obtained in determination of aldehydes (10 µg ml^{-1}) with N,N-dimethyl-p-phenylenediamine. F = furfural; HMF = 5-hydroxymethylfurfural.[79]

The reaction of furfural with 4-hexylresorcinol to give a weak band at 650 nm[122] might be capable of optimization into a worthwhile analytical method.

L. Orcinol

Orcinol is another reagent for furfural as seen in the following procedure.

Orcinol determination of furfural. (a) To 1 ml of aq test solution add 4 ml of reagent (99 ml 0·1 % orcinol in conc HCl–glacial acetic acid, 1:2, and 1 ml of 1 M FeCl$_3$) and heat at 100° for 30 min. Read the absorbance at 598 nm.
   (b) To 2 ml of aq test solution add 2 ml of reagent (1 % orcinol in conc HCl containing 0·1 % FeCl$_3$) and heat at 100° for 20 min. Cool for 10 min, and extract with 4 ml of isoamyl alcohol. Read the absorbance at 668 nm. A millimolar absorptivity of 3·3 is obtained.

M. *m*-Phenylenediamine

A highly selective method for furfural involves its determination with m-phenylenediamine.[79] Thus, aldehydes such as butanal, glyoxal, croton-aldehyde, benzaldehyde, vanillin, cinnamaldehyde, citral, alkyl-furfurals and carbohydrates give colourless to yellow colours with the reagent while furfural gives a violet colour. The following procedure has been recommended.

m-Phenylenediamine determination of furfural.[79] Add 5 ml of 2 % m-phenylene-diamine in 70 % ethanol to 2 ml of 70 % alcoholic test solution containing

2 to 100 µg furfural per ml. Stopper the test tube, shake well, and heat for 30 min at 65°. After cooling in ice water for 1 min, read the absorbance within 10 min at 558 nm.

N. Phloroglucinol

Phloroglucinol gives a fairly insensitive reaction for furfural. Thus, if 2 ml of an aq test solution containing furfural is reacted with 2 ml of a saturated solution of phloroglucinol in conc hydrochloric acid at room temp a band is obtained at 620 nm with an mε of about 2·7.

In alkaline media in the presence of ammonia, phloroglucinol forms 5-aminoresorcinol which reacts with furfural in the presence of H_2O_2 to give an orange-yellow product which is believed to be a derivative of 2-hydroxyglutaconaldehyde.[86] A λ_{max} was obtained at 410 to 415 nm.

O. Pyrogallol

Pyrogallol gives a somewhat more sensitive reaction for furfural; a wavelength maximum was obtained at 496 nm with an mε of 30 by the following method.

Pyrogallol determination of furfural. Heat for 20 min at 100° 1 ml of aq test solution and 4 ml of reagent (99 ml of 0·6% pyrogallol in conc HCl–glacial acetic acid, 2:1, and 1 ml 0·1 M $FeCl_3$). Read the absorbance at 496 nm.

REFERENCES

1. W. Nakahara and K. Mori, *Gann* 35, 208 (1941).
2. V. J. Feron, *Cancer Res.* 32, 28 (1972).
3. P. Grammaticakis, *Bull. Soc. Chim. France* 20, 821 (1953).
4. E. R. Blout and M. Fields. *J. Am. Chem. Soc.* 70, 189 (1948).
5. H. Wehrli *et al. Helv. Chim. Acta* 46, 2705 (1963).
6. C. H. Schmidt. *Chem. Ber.* 90, 1352 (1957).
7. R. Andrisano and G. Pappalardo. *Gazz. Chim. Ital.* 85, 1430 (1955).
8. B. Singh, G. R. Dean and S. M. Cantor. *J. Am. Chem. Soc.* 70, 517 (1948).
9. D. F. Root, J. F. Saeman, J. F. Harris and W. K. Neill, *Forest Products J.* 9, 158 (1959).
10. G. MacKinney and O. Temmer, *J. Am. Chem. Soc.* 70, 3586 (1948).
11. M. L. Wolfrom, R. D. Schuetz and L. F. Cavalieri. *J. Am. Chem. Soc.* 71, 3518 (1949).
12. H. E. Paul, F. L. Austin, M. F. Paul and V. R. Ells. *J. Biol. Chem.* 180, 345 (1949).
13. B. Low. *Acta Chem. Scand.* 4, 294 (1950).
14. R. Andrisano and R. Passerini. *Gazz. Chim. Ital.* 80, 730 (1950).
15. R. F. Raffauf. *J. Am. Chem. Soc.* 72, 753 (1950).

16. L. Fuchs. *Monatsh. Chem.* **81**, 70 (1950).
17. T. Psarras, J. W. Tefteller and H. K. Zimmerman. *Rec. Trav. Chim.* **80**, 232 (1961).
18. G. Holzman, R. V. MacAllister and C. Niemann. *J. Biol. Chem.* **171**, 27 (1947).
19. R. M. Love. *Biochem. J.* **55**, 126 (1953).
20. R. W. Scott, W. E. Moore, M. J. Effland and M. A. Millett. *Anal. Biochem.* **21**, 68 (1967).
21. F. Bandow. *Biochem.* **294**, 124 (1937).
22. F. Bandow. *Z. Physikal. Chem.* **B45**, 156 (1939).
23. D. A. Isăcescu and I. Rebedea. *Studii Cerc. Chim.* **14**, 221 (1965).
24. M. J. Gnagy. *J. Ass. Offic. Agric. Chem.* **38**, 189 (1955).
25. G. N. Soltovets and V. G. Kul'nevich. *Zh. prikl. Khim., Leningr.* **41**, 435 (1968).
26. L. Šutý, O. Červinka and K. Kaštiel. *Papir a Celulosa.* **17**, 262 (1962).
27. A. P. Mathers and J. E. Beck. *J. Ass. Offic. Agric. Chem.* **37**, 861 (1954).
28. R. L. Schoeneman. *J. Ass. Offic. Agric. Chem.* **43**, 657 (1960).
29. P. O. Bethge. *Svensk Papperstid.* **63**, 813 (1960).
30. M. da Cunha Ramos and L. Guedes. *Anais Inst. Vinho Porto* 45 (1967–1968).
31. E. Lindemann. *Die Stärke* **7**, 280 (1955).
32. S. Gibbard and R. Schoental. *J. Chromatog.* **44**, 396 (1969).
33. E. Tassara, R. Ciurlo and L. Biino. *Rass. Chim.* **18**, 118 (1966).
34. E. Tassara and R. Ciurlo. *Rass. Chim.* **15**, 274 (1963).
35. E. Tassara, R. Ciurlo and L. Biino. *Ann. Falsif. Expert. Chim.* **59**, 405 (1966).
36. T. I. Takhonova, L. Y. Gertsberg and P. V. Zubritskii. *Z. Anal. Khim.* **17**, 245 (1962).
37. R. Jacquemain and M.-C. Rémy. *Bull. Soc. Chim., France* 1207 (1964).
38. T. E. Friedemann, P. K. Keegan and N. F. Witt. *Anal. Biochem.* **8**, 300 (1964).
39. J. McDougall, J. D. Shada and P. E. Dakin. *Proc. Am. Soc. Brew. Chem.* 48 (1963).
40. F. G. Angell. *Analyst* **72**, 178 (1947).
41. E. S. Marchetti and G. B. Saracco. *Riv. Combust.* **18**, 280 (1964).
42. A. A. Belyakov and V. G. Smirnova. *Anal. Abstr.* **12**, 3570 (1963).
43. Y. Y. Lur'e and V. A. Panova. *Zavod. Lab.* **28**, 281 (1962).
44. L. Vajta, I. Szebényi, M. Horváth and E. Vermes. *Periodica polytech.* **10**, 309 (1966).
45. O. L. Milner and D. Liederman. *Anal. Chem.* **27**, 1822 (1955).
46. G. Youngblood and G. Pucher. *J. Biol. Chem.* **61**, 741 (1924).
47. D. A. Isăcescu, S. Biller and M. Macavei-Bestelei. *Stud. Cercet. Chim.* Bucharest **6**, 247 (1958), through *Anal. Abstr.* **6**, No. 3613 (1959).
48. G. N. Nazyrov and K. Y. Vengerskova. *Lab. Delo* **6**, 35 (1960).
49. E. W. Rice. *Anal. Chem.* **23**, 1501 (1951).
50. R. B. Harrison, J. F. Palframan and B. A. Rose. *Analyst* **86**, 561 (1961).
51. R. B. Harrison. *Analyst* **88**, 644 (1963).
52. R. A. Stillings and B. L. Browning. *Ind. Eng. Chem., Anal. Ed.* **12**, 499 (1940).
53. I. J. Duncan. *Ind. Eng. Chem., Anal. Ed.* **15**, 162 (1943).
54. I. M. Korenman, F. S. Frum and A. A. Russkilsh. *Zavodskaya Lab.* **16**, 3 (1950).
55. G. A. Adams and A. E. Castagne. *Can. J. Res.* **26B**, 314 (1948).
56. E. Haupt, T. Kleinert and E. Stach. *Mitt. Chem. Forsch- Inst. Ind. Osterr.* **1**, 97 (1947).
57. L. Barta. *Biochem. Z.* **274**, 212 (1934).
58. L. H. Lampitt, E. B. Hughes and L. H. Trace. *Analyst* **52**, 260 (1927).
59. G. Pellerin. *Bull. Sci. Pharmacol.* **34**, 78 (1927).
60. A. N. Ponomarev. *Zavodskaja Lab.* **22**, 289 (1956).

61. L. M. Tolman and T. C. Trescott. *J. Am. Chem. Soc.* **28**, 1619 (1906).
62. F. Aeschlimann, P. O. Bettige and J. H. Eggers. *Z. Anal. Chem.* **161**, 324 (1958).
63. W. M. Foley, Jr., G. E. Samford and H. McKennis, Jr. *J. Am. Chem. Soc.* **74**, 5489 (1952).
64. R. Sawamura and T. Koyama. *Yakugaku Zasshi.* **81**, 1689 (1961).
65. L. Sattler and F. W. Zerban. *J. Am. Chem. Soc.* **72**, 3814 (1950).
66. R. Sawamura and T. Koyama. *Yakugaku Zasshi* **84**, 82 (1964).
67. E. Sawicki, R. A. Carnes and R. Schumacher. *Mikrochim. Acta* 929 (1967).
68. R. Sawamura and T. Koyama. *Chem. Pharm. Bull.* **12**, 706 (1964).
69. S. Hunig and J. Utermann. *Chem. Ber.* **88**, 423 (1955).
70. E. Sawicki and C. R. Engel. *Anal. Chim. Acta* **32**, 315 (1967).
71. L. Levi and P. M. Laughton. *J. Agric. Food Chem.* **7**, 850 (1959).
72. L. L. Gent, R. C. Pomatti and H. Levin. *Anal. Chem.* **26**, 413 (1954).
73. K. Christofferson. *Anal. Chim. Acta* **31**, 233 (1964).
74. J. F. Harris and L. L. Zoch. *Anal. Chem.* **34**, 201 (1962).
75. E. W. Rice and J. H. Roe. *J. Biol. Chem.* **188**, 463 (1951).
76. K. Nomura, Y. Sakai and T. Kobayashi. *J. Ferm. Tech.* **43**, 115 (1965).
77. A. S. Maslennikov and G. N. Porývaeva. *Trudy Komiss. Anal. Khim., Akad. Nauk SSSR* **13**, 98 (1963).
78. E. Sawicki and R. A. Carnes. *Mikrochim. Acta* 148 (1968).
79. P. Linko. *Anal. Chem.* **33**, 1400 (1961).
80. S. Hunig, J. Utermann and G. Erlemann. *Ber. Chem.* **88**, 708 (1955).
81. M. Pesez. *J. Pharm. Pharmacol.* **11**, 475 (1959).
82. K. T. H. Farrar. *Aust. Chem. Inst. J. and Proc.* **11**, 186 (1944).
83. T. G. Brady and A. McEvoy-Bowe. *Congr. Intern. Biochim., Resumes Communs., 2° Congr., Paris* 198 (1952).
84. J. Adamiak. *Medycyna Pr.* **18**, 92 (1967).
85. J. G. Reynold and M. Irwin. *Chem. Ind.* 419 (1948).
86. A. A. Ratovskaya and L. A. Kuz'menko. *Zavod. Lab.* **30**, 286 (1964), through *Anal. Abstr.* **12**, # 2884 (1964).
87. R. I. Veksler. *Zhur. Anal. Khim.* **4**, 14 (1949).
88. M. Keeney and R. Bassette. *J. Dairy Sci.* **42**, 945 (1959).
89. A. A. Belyakov and V. G. Smirnova. *Hyg. Sanit.* **30**, 390 (1965).
90. G. I. Benzina. *Hyg. Sanit.* **31**, 383 (1966).
91. A. Wahbab. *Pakistan J. Sci. Res.* **4**, 111, 121 (1952).
92. J. Kelus and K. Wawienia. *Roczniki Panstwowego Zakladu Hig.* **23**, 1 (1972).
93. Official Methods of Analysis of the Association of Official Agricultural Chemists, Tenth Edition, p. 140, Association of Official Agricultural Chemists, Washington, D.C. (1965).
94. T. Fernandez, J. M. Rocha and N. Rufino. *Quimica* **68**, 1173 (1972).
95. S. Nagy and V. Randall. *J. Agric. Food Chem.* **21**, 272 (1973).
96. H. L. Dinsmore and S. Nagy. *J. Food Sci.* **37**, 768 (1972).
97. S. Nagy, V. Randall and H. L. Dinsmore. *Proc. Florida State Hort. Soc.* **85**, 222 (1972).
98. S. Dunstan and A. E. Gillam. *J. Chem. Soc.* 140 (1949).
99. P. O. Bethge. *Svensk Papperstidning* **59**, 372 (1956).
100. H. L. Jones. *Tappi* **44**, 745 (1961).
101. J. Stenhouse. *Ann.* **156**, 197 (1870).
102. H. Schiff. *Ber.* **20**, 540 (1887).
103. G. DeChalmot. *Ann.* **271**, 12 (1892).

B

104. W. Dieckmann and L. Beck. *Ber.* **38**, 4122 (1905).
105. T. Zincke and G. Muehlhausen. *Ber.* **38**, 3824 (1905).
106. C. V. Brouilette, W. M. Foley and H. McKennis. *J. Am. Chem. Soc.* **76**, 4617 (1954).
107. R. W. Drisko and H. McKennis. *J. Am. Chem. Soc.* **74**, 2626 (1952).
108. C. F. Koelsch and J. J. Carney. *J. Am. Chem. Soc.* **72**, 2285 (1950).
109. J. C. McGowan. *Anal. Chem.* **26**, 1645 (1954).
110. J. Rombaut and G. Smets. *Bull. Soc. Chim. Belges* **58**, 421 (1949).
111. W. Borsche, H. Leditschke and K. Lange. *Ber.* **71**, 957 (1938).
112. W. Konig. *J. Prakt. Chem.* **72**, 555 (1905).
113. H. Leditschke. *Chem. Ber.* **85**, 483 (1952).
114. W. Konig. *J. Prakt. Chem.* **88**, 193 (1913).
115. W. Konig, K. Hey, F. Schulze, E. Silberkweit and K. Trautmann. *Ber.* **67**, 1274 (1934).
116. H. L. Dinsmore and S. Nagy. *JAOAC* **57**. In press (1974).
117. W. C. Scott and M. K. Veldhuis. *JAOAC* **49**, 628 (1966).
118. H. Hirayama, K. Hiraki and Y. Nishikawa. *Japan Analyst* **20**, 1435 (1971).
119. F. Bohlmann, P. Herbst and I. Dohrmann. *Chem. Ber.* **96**, 226 (1963).
120. E. C. Kirby and D. H. Reid. *J. Chem. Soc.* 494 (1960).
121. C. Izard-Verchere, P. Rumpf and C. Viel. *Bull. Soc. Chim. France* 2118, 2122, 2134 (1971).
122. I. R. Cohen and A. P. Altshuller. *Anal. Chem.* **33**, 726 (1961).

27. GLUTACONALDEHYDE (5-FORMYLBUTENE-2-AL)

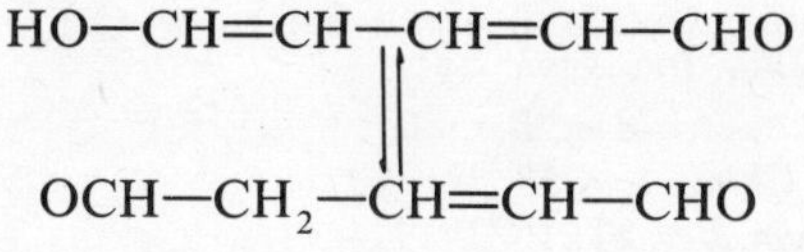

$$HO-CH=CH-CH=CH-CHO$$

$$OCH-CH_2-CH=CH-CHO$$

I

I. PHYSICAL AND SPECTRAL PROPERTIES

The free aldehyde, **I**, is unstable in aq solution. The sodium salt is somewhat stable at room temp. In aq solution this salt absorbs at λ 228, 365 nm and mε 2·5, 50, respectively.[1] The potassium salt dissolved in dimethylformamide containing 3% Et_3N absorbs at λ 362·5 nm, mε 56·2.[2] The aldehyde has been reported as absorbing at 363 nm in alkaline solution and at 307 nm in acid solution.[3] An alcoholic solution of the aldehyde acidified carefully with sulphuric acid gives the red–violet cationic resonance structure[4]

$$(HO{=}CH{=}CH{=}CH{=}CH{=}CH{=}OH)^+$$

Glutaconaldehyde reacts with mercaptans containing the structure, RCH_2SH, in sulphuric acid solution, e.g. thioglycolic acid, thiolactic acid, thioglycerin, homocysteine, glutathione and cysteine.[5] The chromogen formed from cysteine absorbs at 490 nm (with a weaker band near 420 nm) in 82% sulphuric acid. The pure pentamethine, **II**, obtained from the interaction of cysteine and glutaconaldehyde in alcoholic H_2SO_4 absorbs at 530 nm (and weaker band at about 420 nm) in water at pH 1·6.

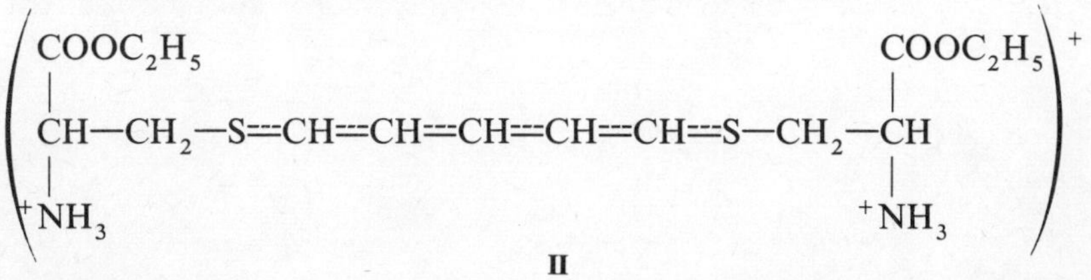

$$\left(\begin{array}{c} COOC_2H_5 \\ | \\ CH-CH_2-S{=}CH{=}CH{=}CH{=}CH{=}CH{=}S-CH_2-CH \\ | \\ {}^+NH_3 \end{array} \right. \left. \begin{array}{c} COOC_2H_5 \\ | \\ \\ | \\ {}^+NH_3 \end{array} \right)^+$$

II

Glutaconaldehyde has been shown to react with MBTH giving a chromogen absorbing at 392 nm. Benzoylation of glutaconaldehyde gives 4-benzoyloxy-1-formyl-1,3-butadiene which reacts with MBTH to give a chromogen absorbing at 392 nm. Glutaconaldehyde[6] and its benzoyl derivative[3] are readily prepared.

REFERENCES

1. G. Scheibe, D. Bruck and F. Dorr. *Chem. Ber.* **85**, 867 (1952).
2. S. S. Malhotra and M. C. Whiting. *J. Chem. Soc.* 3812 (1960).
3. M. A. Paz, O. O. Blumenfeld, M. Rojkind, E. Henson, C. Furfine and P. M. Gallop. *Arch. Biochem. Biophys.* **109**, 548 (1965).
4. F. Klages and H. Träger, *Chem. Ber.* **86**, 1327 (1953).
5. G. Kunovits. *Anal. Chim. Acta* **55**, 221 (1971).
6. P. Baumgarten. *Chem. Ber.* **57**, 1622 (1924).

28. GLUTARALDEHYDE

$$OHC-CH_2-CH_2-CH_2-CHO$$

I. INTRODUCTION

Pure glutaraldehyde exhibits an absorption maximum at 280 nm; absorbance at this wavelength conforms to Beer's law.[1] A second maximum found in commercial samples of glutaraldehyde at 235 nm indicates the presence of impurities, probably α,β-unsaturated aldehydes of polymeric origin.

Purification of glutaraldehyde has been achieved by saturation of its aq solution with sodium chloride, extraction with ether and distillation.[2] Effective purification is achieved by repeated treatment with charcoal of high surface area (Norit Ex) or by vacuum distillation in an all-glass, multiple-plate column at low temperature followed by treatment of the distillate with the high surface active carbon and then reaction with antacid to remove the last traces of glutaric acid, Fig. 7.

In the preparation of standard pure glutaraldehyde the distilled glutaraldehyde is diluted with demineralized, distilled water to a concentration of 8%. The aldehyde is then packaged in neutral, glass ampoules and stored under nitrogen or freon at refrigerator or freezer temperatures.[1] Purification, quantitation and stability of this aldehyde have been discussed.[3, 4]

On dissolution in water pure glutaraldehyde undergoes very rapid hydration. The almost complete hydration of glutaraldehyde in aq solution is very different from the much lesser degree of hydration observed for mono-functional aldehydes.[5−7] This is probably due to the ease with which the two ends of the glutaraldehyde molecule can approach one another to form the cyclic monohydrate. The following equilibrium is postulated, Fig. 8.[2]

The hydration phenomenon is further complicated by polymerization. Distilled glutaraldehyde, alone or dissolved in chloroform or benzene, undergoes rapid polymerization, apparently catalysed by traces of water, to a glassy solid with an acetal-like structure, **I**.[2, 8]

23

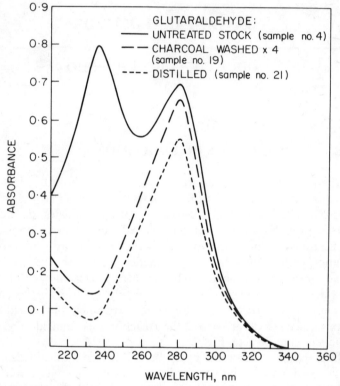

Fig. 7. Spectral absorption curves of untreated, charcoal-washed and distilled glutaraldehyde. The maximum at 280 nm is produced by the dialdehyde and absorption at 235 nm is progressively reduced by purification.

This polymer, unlike that formed in alkaline solution, reverts to the monomer on heating.

It is postulated that in acidic solution glutaraldehyde rapidly polymerizes to trimeric forms, **II**.

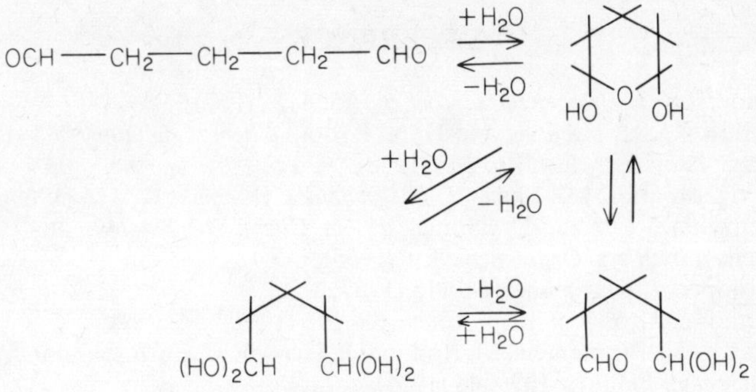

FIG. 8. Glutaraldehyde equilibrium.

Glutaraldehyde can be determined through its 280 nm absorption band[1] or by reaction with MBTH[9] or 2,4-dinitrophenylhydrazine.[2, 10] With MBTH it forms the azine absorbing at 305 nm and gradually changing to 350 nm or the formazan cation with mε 20 at λ_{max} 670 nm. The analytical procedure is given in the aliphatic aldehydes section.

A. 2,4-Dinitrophenylhydrazine

With 2,4-dinitrophenylhydrazine, glutaraldehyde forms a bis-dinitrophenylhydrazone which absorbs at λ 355 nm, mε 45·2 in chloroform and λ 435, 523s nm, mε 43·4, 25·9 in alcoholic sodium hydroxide.

DNPH analysis for glutaraldehyde in tanning liquor.[2] Weigh an aliquot of test solution containing about 5 mg of glutaraldehyde into a 25 × 120 mm tube and add 10 ml of ethanol followed by 5 ml of reagent. (Dissolve 0·5 g 2,4-dinitrophenylhydrazine in 2 ml conc H_2SO_4 and add 3 ml water. Cool and dilute to 15 ml with methanol. Prepare before use.) Allow to stand for 1 h with occasional stirring. Add about 0·5 g of analytical grade Celite. Filter the precipitated dinitrophenylhydrazone through a fritted glass funnel with suction. Wash tube and precipitate three times with 5 ml portions of methanol. Discard filtrate, and collect the filtrate obtained from washing with five 10-ml portions of hot ethylene dichloride. Transfer the filtrate to a 100 ml volumetric flask, cool and dilute to the mark with additional ethylene chloride. For analysis dilute a 1 ml aliquot of this solution to 50 ml with ethylene dichloride and measure the absorbance at 360 nm.

REFERENCES

1. P. J. Anderson. *J. Histochem. Cytochem.* **15**, 652 (1967).
2. P. M. Hardy, A. C. Nicholls and H. N. Rydon. *Chem. Communs.* 565 (1969).
3. G. Hesse. *Acta Histochem.* **46**, 253 (1973).
4. N. A. Frigerio and M. J. Shaw. *J. Histochem. Cytochem.* **17**, 176 (1969).
5. P. Greenzaid, Z. Luz and D. Samuel. *J. Am. Chem. Soc.* **89**, 749 (1967).
6. R. P. Bell. *Adv. Phys. Org. Chem.* **4**, 1 (1966).
7. D. L. Hooper. *J. Chem. Soc. (B)*, 115 (1967).
8. A. Aso and Y. Aito. *Makromol. Chem.* **58**, 195 (1962).
9. M. A. Paz, O. O. Blumenfeld, M. Rojkind, E. Henson, C. Furfine and P. M. Gallop. *Arch. Biochem. Biophys.* **109**, 548 (1965).
10. L. A. Jones and C. K. Hancock, *J. Am. Chem. Soc.* **82**, 105 (1960).

29. GLYCERALDEHYDE

$$HOCH_2—CHOH—CHO$$

I. INTRODUCTION

The optically active forms of the free aldehyde polymerize much more readily than the inactive form. Solid DL-glyceraldehyde is a dimer which is gradually converted to the monomeric form in aq solution. The presence of the monomer in aq solution is shown by the weak band (derived from an $n \rightarrow \pi^*$ transition) at 294 nm.[1]

Glyceraldehyde can be assayed by enzymatic,[2-6] colorimetric[7-11] and fluorimetric[12-15] methods. In many of these methods dihydroxyacetone and pyruvaldehyde react also since under the conditions of the procedures glyceraldehyde and dihydroxyacetone are pyruvaldehyde precursors.

II. SPECTROPHOTOMETRIC METHODS

A. Nicotinamide adenine dinucleotide

One enzymatic method for measuring changes in the dihydroxyacetone or glyceraldehyde content of blood or tissue homogenate depends on the formation of the chromogen absorbing at 340 nm when α-hydroxycarbonyl compounds are warmed at pH 10 with NAD^+.[2] Beer's law is obeyed over the range of 2 to 50 µg. Glucose does not interfere, while pyruvate, glyceraldehyde and dihydroxyacetone react. Pyruvic acid (lithium salt) at the concentration of 1 mg ml^{-1} gave the equivalent of 0·04 mg ml^{-1} of dihydroxyacetone in the following procedure.

NAD$^+$ determination of glyceraldehyde.[2] Pipette 0·1 ml test solution into 3·5 ml distilled water in a 5-ml centrifuge tube. Add with mixing 0·2 ml of 0·3 N carbon dioxide-free barium hydroxide followed by 0·2 ml of 0·3 N zinc sulphate. Centrifuge immediately for 10 min at 375 g. Prepare a single reagent blank and samples, baseline blanks and standard solutions in duplicate. Pipette 3 ml of the supernatant into 0·2 ml of NAD^+ (prepare 0·03 M solution of nicotinamide adenine dinucleotide by dissolving 200 mg of NAD^+

27

in several ml of water, adding approx 1·5 ml of N/10 NaOH to bring the pH
to 6 and finally diluting to 10 ml) in 5 ml centrifuge tubes. Add 0·1 ml of
buffer. (Add 36·3 g of tris-(hydroxymethyl)aminomethane in 100 ml water
and sufficient 1 N HCl to adjust pH to 10). Cover tubes with tin foil and heat
at 56° for one hour. If a precipitate forms, centrifuge solutions at 375 g for
5 minutes. Read absorbance at 340 nm against the reagent blank.

Glyceraldehyde and dihydroxyacetone can be assayed following their
quantitative reduction to glycerol with sodium borohydride.[5] Mixtures
of glycerol with either one of the trioses can be differentiated by this method
provided that the triose-to-glycerol ratio does not exceed about 3:1. The
method was applied to a yeast strain growing on these substrates. In the
following procedure glyceraldehyde or dihydroxyacetone are reduced quantitatively. Beer's law is obeyed from 0·01 to 0·16 μmol of glycerol or glyceraldehyde.

Reductive assay of glyceraldehyde (and dihydroxyacetone).[5] *Reagents.*
Glycerol kinase. Dilute 0·1 ml of a commercial preparation (425 units of
activity or 5 mg protein/ml of 2·2 M ammonium sulphate) to 1 ml with 2·2 M
ammonium sulphate solution, giving a final concentration of 0·5 μg protein/μl.

Pyruvate kinase. Dilute 0·2 ml of commercial preparation (1250 units of
activity or 10 mg protein/ml of 2·2 M ammonium sulphate solution) to 1 ml
with 2·2 M ammonium sulphate solution.

Lactic dehydrogenase. Dilute 0·2 ml of a commercial preparation (1800 units
of activity or 5 mg protein/ml of 2·2 M ammonium sulphate solution) to 2 ml
with ammonium sulphate solution.

NADH. 2·5 mg ml^{-1} water.

Buffer. 0·1 M triethanolamine HCl which is 6 mM in $MgSO_4$ and 2 mM in KCl.
Adjust pH to 7·6 with 1 N NaOH. Store at 4°.
Phosphoenolpyruvate tricyclohexylammonium salt. 3·5 mM in buffer. Store
at 4° for at most 1 week.

ATP. Adjust a 75 mM aq solution to pH 7 with 1 N NaOH. Store up to 6
weeks in 0·25 to 0·5 ml lots.
Substrate mixture. Ten milliliters phosphoenolpyruvate in buffer, 0·25 ml
ATP, 1 ml NADH, 0·1 ml pyruvate kinase, and 0·1 ml lactic dehydrogenase.

Procedure. Reduce a test solution containing 2 to 50 μg of glyceraldehyde (or
dihydroxyacetone) by adding 1·5 ml of 0·9 N NaBH$_4$ in 1 N NaOH. Let

stand for 30 min at room temp. Add 0·3 ml of 5 N H_2SO_4 and shake well to decompose the borohydride. Dilute 1:50 to 1:2000, as necessary. Place 1 ml of the substrate mixture in a cuvette followed by a 1 ml aliquot of the reduced test solution. Measure absorbance with cuvette chamber maintained at 32°. After establishing a steady baseline reading (about 0·7 to 0·8 absorbance) add 8 µg of glycerol kinase and follow reaction for 4 minutes. Analyse a standard glyceraldehyde solution (0·07 µM ml^{-1}) with each set of determinations.

The assay is based upon the following reactions, Fig. 9, and is followed by recording the decrease in NADH absorbance at 340 nm.

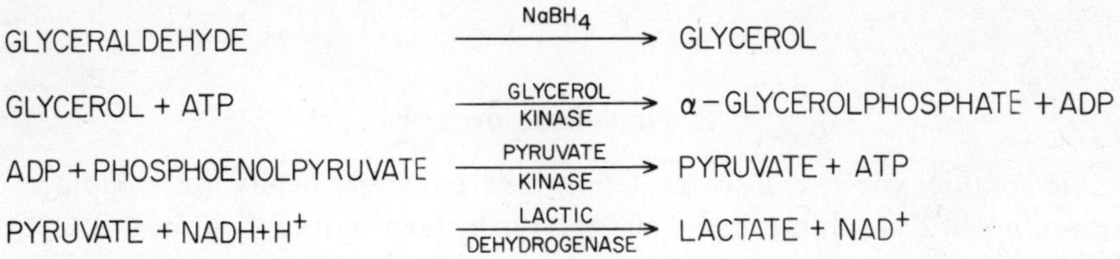

GLYCERALDEHYDE $\xrightarrow{\text{NaBH}_4}$ GLYCEROL

GLYCEROL + ATP $\xrightarrow[\text{KINASE}]{\text{GLYCEROL}}$ α-GLYCEROLPHOSPHATE + ADP

ADP + PHOSPHOENOLPYRUVATE $\xrightarrow[\text{KINASE}]{\text{PYRUVATE}}$ PYRUVATE + ATP

PYRUVATE + NADH+H$^+$ $\xrightarrow[\text{DEHYDROGENASE}]{\text{LACTIC}}$ LACTATE + NAD$^+$

FIG. 9. Assay of glyceraldehyde. ATP = adenosine triphosphate, ADP = adenosine diphosphate, NAD$^+$ = nicotinamide–adenine dinucleotide, NADH = reduced nicotinamide–adenine dinucleotide.[5]

Since the previous method does not distinguish between D-glyceraldehyde and dihydroxyacetone and would suffer interference from large amounts of glycerol, a method was developed which is reported not to have these objectionable features.[3] However, the method is still not a direct assay for glyceraldehyde but D-glyceraldehyde could be determined in the mammalian lens by assaying simultaneously dihydroxyacetone with glycerol kinase (16) and dihydroxyacetone plus D-glyceraldehyde with triokinase (EC 2.7.1.28), Fig. 10. Although this procedure was applied successfully to the assay of

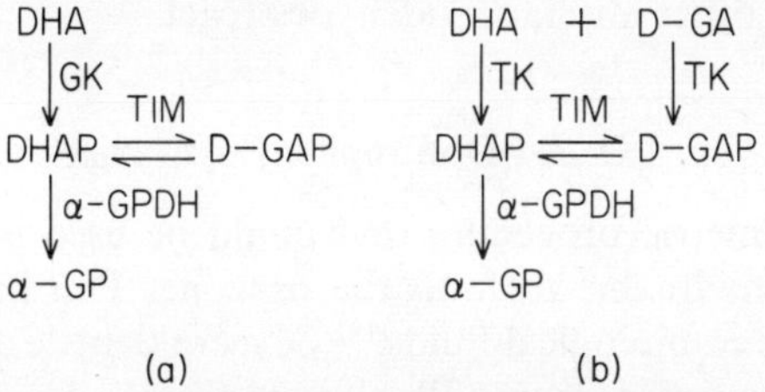

FIG. 10. Assay of triose phosphates, dihydroxyacetone and D-glyceraldehyde.[3] Assay mixture contains NADH and ATP. To both (a) and (b) add α-glycerophosphate dehydrogenase: triose phosphate isomerase. The amount of NADH oxidized is equivalent to the amount of triose phosphate (i.e. phosphates of dihydroxyacetone or DHA and D-glyceraldehyde or D-GA) present. Then to (a) add glycerol kinase or GK and to (b) add triokinase or TK. The amount of NADH oxidized in (a) is equivalent to the amount of DHA present, and that in (b) to the sum of DHA and D-GA. The amount of D-GA is obtained by difference.

D-glyceraldehyde in perchloric acid extracts of eye lens, interference was observed from perchloric extracts of liver and kidney.[3, 4] These difficulties have been overcome by using tungstic acid, rather than perchloric acid, for deproteinization.[4] Thus, the use of tungstic acid in place of perchloric acid permits the accurate estimation of D-glyceraldehyde and dihydroxyacetone in liver homogenates.

Glyceraldehyde and many other aliphatic aldehydes could be determined by the non-specific reaction[6]

$$\text{Glyceraldehyde} + \text{NADH} + \text{H}^+ \xrightarrow[\text{dehydrogenase}]{\text{alcohol}} \text{Glycerol} + \text{NAD}^+$$

B. Naphthoresorcinol

Glyceraldehyde can also be determined colorimetrically with naphtho-resorcinol in 27 N sulphuric acid at λ 660 nm by heating for 20 min at 100°C.[11] Hydroxypyruvate and glycolaldehyde and its precursors react also. With N,N-dimethyl-p-phenylenediamine glyceraldehyde gives a band at 410 nm with mε 8·2.[10] Other aldehydes and ketosteroids react.

C. 3-Methyl-2-benzothiazolinone hydrazone

With MBTH, glyceraldehyde and other aliphatic aldehydes can be determined either through azine or formazan cation formation.[7] The procedures are given in the aliphatic aldehydes section. In the azine procedure λ_{max} 312 nm, mε 22 is obtained at pH 4 and λ_{max} 296 nm, mε 21 at pH 1. At 100° for 10 min, a peak of the glyceraldehyde "osazine", λ_{max} 400, is obtained. The formazan cation procedure is more sensitive; at the λ_{max} 670, mε is 60. This is one of the more sensitive procedures for glyceraldehyde but it must be remembered that other aliphatic aldehydes react.

D. 2,4-Dinitrophenylhydrazine

Another colorimetric procedure that could be used is the reaction with 2,4-dinitrophenylhydrazine to form the osazone. This has been done with dihydroxyacetone in biological fluids.[9] Glyceraldehyde and pyruvaldehyde cannot be distinguished from dihydroxyacetone. The procedure would proceed as follows. Following reaction with the reagent, excess reagent is removed by reaction with pyruvic acid followed by partition between benzene and sodium bicarbonate solution. The benzene layer containing the 2,4-dinitrophenylosazone of pyruvaldehyde is evaporated and the coloured anion, I, formed after the addition of alcoholic sodium hydroxide is measured.

$$O_2N-\!\!\bigcirc\!\!-N-N=\overset{\overset{\displaystyle CH_3}{|}}{C}-C=N-N-\!\!\bigcirc\!\!-NO_2$$

I

λ_{max} 586 nm

Blood, urine and tissue homogenates were analysed. Beer's law was obeyed. Monosaccharides gave a colour similar to that obtained with glyceraldehyde, but they are removed by alkali treatment. Dihydroxyacetone is easily destroyed by strong alkali.

E. Other phenylhydrazines

Phenylhydrazine could also be used. Glyceraldehyde gives the osazone, absorbing at 395 nm, mε 20·6.[8] p-Nitrophenylhydrazine could also be used,[17] dependent on the basicity of the solvent, wavelength maxima could be obtained ranging around 700 nm and mε about 100.

III. FLUORIMETRIC METHODS

Of the fluorimetric procedures for the determination of glyceraldehyde the o-phenylenediamine,[12] anthrone[13] and 5-hydroxy-1-tetralone[14, 15] procedures are worth mentioning.

Glyceraldehyde and dihydroxyacetone reacted with o-phenylenediamine gave compounds fluorescing at $F335/435$. Hexoses, and especially pentoses, gave fluorescent derivatives also.

Glyceraldehyde, as well as dihydroxyacetone, pyruvaldehyde and pentoses, react with anthrone to give fluorogens. The following procedure can be used. Anthrone estimation of glyceraldehyde, dihydroxyacetone and pyruvaldehyde shows that pyruvaldehyde gives twice the intensity as obtained by the other two compounds.

Anthrone determination of glyceraldehyde. To 2 ml of aq test solution add 0·5 ml of 0·3 % anthrone in acetic acid. Mix and cool in an ice bath while adding 3 ml conc H_2SO_4. Heat at 100° for 7 minutes. Cool and read at $F463/505$.

Glyceraldehyde can also be determined with 5-hydroxy-1-tetralone.[14] Hexoses and other glyceraldehyde precursors react also. A greenish-yellow fluorescence is obtained. Microgram amounts of glyceraldehyde can be determined. This reaction is discussed in the glyceraldehyde precursors section.

REFERENCES

1. W. Berndt. *Monatsh. Chem.* **85**, 387 (1954).
2. M. U. Tsao and E. L. Schwartz. *Anal. Biochem.* **3**, 448 (1962).
3. J. M. Charlton and R. van Heyningen. *Anal. Biochem.* **30**, 313 (1969).
4. D. J. Walton and L. M. Gauchie. *Anal. Biochem.* **46**, 352 (1972).
5. J. K. Pinter, J. A. Hayashi and J. A. Watson. *Arch. Biochem. Biophys.* **121**, 404 (1967).
6. H. Holzer and H. W. Goedde in H. U. Bergmeyer, Ed. "Methods of Enzymatic Analysis," Academic Press, New York, 1963, p. 297.
7. M. A. Paz, O. O. Blumenfeld, M. Rojkind, E. Henson, C. Furfine and P. M. Gallop. *Arch. Biochem.* **109**, 548 (1965).
8. J. C. P. Schwarz and M. Finnegan. *J. Chem. Soc.* 3979 (1956).
9. M. U. Tsao and E. L. Schwartz. *Anal. Biochem.* **2**, 107 (1961).
10. M. Pesez and J. Bartos. *Talanta* **10**, 69 (1963).
11. D. F. Dickens and D. H. Williamson. *Biochem. J.* **68**, 84 (1958).
12. J. C. Towne and J. E. Spikner. *Anal. Chem.* **35**, 211 (1963).
13. R. Sawamura and T. Koyama. *Chem. Pharm. Bull.* (*Tokyo*) **12**, 706 (1964).
14. T. Momose and Y. Ohkura. *Pharm. Bull.* **4**, 209 (1956).
15. T. Momose and Y. Ohkura. *Chem. Pharm. Bull.*, (*Tokyo*) **6**, 412 (1958).
16. O. Wieland, in H. U. Bergmeyer, Ed. "Methods of Enzymatic Analysis," Academic Press, New York, 1963, p. 244.
17. E. Sawicki, T. R. Hauser and R. Wilson. *Anal. Chem.* **34**, 505 (1962).

30. GLYCERALDEHYDE-3-PHOSPHATE

$$OHC—CH—CH_2—O—PO_3H_2$$
$$|$$
$$OH$$

I. PHYSICAL PROPERTIES

$pK_1 = 1.42$; $pK_2 = 6.45$. Hydrolysis constant (1 N HCl, 100°) $k = 37 \times 10^3$, $t_{\frac{1}{2}} = 8.1$ min.

II. INTRODUCTION

In acid solution phosphate is slowly split off at room temp and rapidly at elevated temperatures. Glyceraldehyde-3-phosphate is unstable in alkaline solution. A suitable storage precursor is 1-bromopropane-1,2,3-triol-3-phosphate; on solution and adjustment of pH to 7 it forms glyceraldehyde phosphate.

Glyceraldehyde-3-phosphate prepared[1] and partially purified by solvent precipitation[2] is contaminated with considerable amounts of inorganic phosphate. The two phosphates are readily separated on bisulphite ion-exchange columns.[3] Glyceraldehyde-3-phosphate is recovered as a bi-sulphite complex by precipitation with alcohol.

MBTH could be used for the colorimetric determination of glyceraldehyde phosphate. Nitro blue tetrazolium has been used in histochemical studies to demonstrate the presence of glyceraldehyde phosphate in tissue sections.[4]

III. ENZYMATIC METHODS

The L- form can be determined in the following manner:[5]
(a) L-Glyceraldehyde-3-phosphate + D-fructose-6-phosphate

$$\downarrow \text{transaldolase}$$

D-Glyceraldehyde-3-phosphate + L-sorbose-6-phosphate

(b) D-Glyceraldehyde-3-phosphate + NAD$^+$ + H$_2$O

$$\text{arsenate} \quad\Bigg\downarrow\quad \substack{\text{D-glyceraldehyde-3-phosphate} \\ \text{dehydrogenase}}$$

3-Phosphoglycerate + 2H$^+$ + NADH

With excess fructose-6-phosphate both actions proceed until all the test substance is used up. The increase of absorbance at 340 nm due to the formation of NADH is a measure of the test substance since 1 μmol of NADH is formed for each μmol of L-glyceraldehyde-3-phosphate. Standard solutions of L-glyceraldehyde-3-phosphate are obtained from DL-glyceraldehyde-3-phosphate by removing the D-glyceraldehyde-3-phosphate enzymatically.[6] DL-Glyceraldehyde-3-phosphate can be prepared from the diethyl acetal monobarium salt.[7] It should be used at once.

Another enzymatic reaction that could be used for the estimation of glyceraldehyde-3-phosphate is the following.[8–10]

D-Glyceraldehyde-3-phosphate + Pi + NADP$^+$
$$\downarrow$$
1,3-Diphospho-D-glycerate + NADPH

The reaction is catalysed by glyceraldehyde phosphate dehydrogenase. The increase of absorbance at 340 nm due to the formation of NADPH would be a measure of the test substance.

Another, and more involved, method consists of the coupled determination of dihydroxyacetone phosphate, glyceraldehyde-3-phosphate and its precursor fructose-1,6-diphosphate. This can be done spectrophotometrically at 340 nm[11] or fluorimetrically at $F$350/460 or with appropriate filters.[12] These metabolites are assayed by coupling them sequentially to the NADH oxidizing step involving α-glycerophosphate dehydrogenase (αGPD) according to the following reactions:

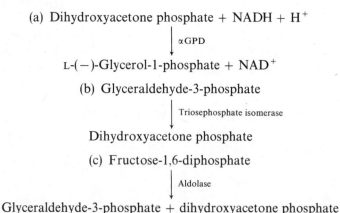

(a) Dihydroxyacetone phosphate + NADH + H$^+$
$$\Bigg\downarrow \quad \alpha\text{GPD}$$
L-(−)-Glycerol-1-phosphate + NAD$^+$

(b) Glyceraldehyde-3-phosphate
$$\Bigg\downarrow \quad \text{Triosephosphate isomerase}$$
Dihydroxyacetone phosphate

(c) Fructose-1,6-diphosphate
$$\Bigg\downarrow \quad \text{Aldolase}$$
Glyceraldehyde-3-phosphate + dihydroxyacetone phosphate

Essentially glyceraldehyde-3-phosphate is determined by coupling reactions (a) and (b). The balanced equation is:

$$Glyceraldehyde\text{-}3\text{-}phosphate + NADH + H^+$$
$$\Updownarrow$$
$$Glycerol\text{-}1\text{-}phosphate + NAD^+$$

The decrease in absorbance at 340 nm due to the oxidation of NADH is a measure of the concentration of the aldehyde.

REFERENCES

1. P. Oesper, Arch. *Biochem. Biophys.* **95**, 237 (1961).
2. O. Meyerhof. *Bull. Soc. Chim. Biol.* **20**, 1033, 1345 (1938).
3. B. Koser and P. Oesper. *Anal. Biochem.* **17**, 119 (1966).
4. S. R. Himmelhoch and M. J. Karnovsky. *J. Biophys. Biochem. Cytol.* **9**, 573 (1961).
5. E. Racker in H. U. Bergmeyer, "Methods of Enzymatic Analysis," Academic Press, New York, 1963, p. 241.
6. R. Venkataraman and E. Racker. *J. Biol. Chem.* **236**, 1876 (1961).
7. J. M. Charlton and R. van Heyningen. *Anal. Biochem.* **30**, 313 (1969).
8. M. Gibbs. *Methods in Enzymology* **1**, 411 (1955).
9. L. L. Rosenberg and D. I. Arnon. *J. Biol. Chem.* **217**, 361 (1955).
10. F. N. Brenneman and W. A. Volk. *J. Biol. Chem.* **234**, 2443 (1959).
11. T. Bucher and H. Hohurst, in H. U. Bergmeyer, Ed., "Methods of Enzymatic Analysis," Academic Press, New York, 1963, p. 246.
12. P. K. Maitra and R. W. Estabrook. *Anal. Biochem.* **7**, 472 (1964).

31. GLYCIDAL (EPIHYDRINALDEHYDE)

$$\underset{CH_2-CH-CHO}{\overset{O}{\triangle}}$$

I. PHYSICAL AND SPECTRAL PROPERTIES

This aldehyde has been reported to be carcinogenic for mice and rats.[1,2] In the gaseous state, it absorbs at 295 nm with mε 0·017.[3] In acid solution it forms glyceraldehyde.[4] Because of its weak absorbance colorimetric methods have been used in the analysis of the aldehyde. Thiobarbituric acid,[4] phloroglucinol,[5,6] azulene and MBTH could be used in its assay.

Using the malonaldehyde procedure glycidaldehyde gives a band at λ 590 with mε 11·6 with azulene. With proper adjustment of conditions the sensitivity of this procedure could be considerably improved.

Other aliphatic aldehyde reagents could be used, especially MBTH.

REFERENCES

1. B. L. Van Duuren, L. Langseth, L. Orris, M. Baden and M. Kuschner. *J. Natl. Cancer Inst.* **39**, 1213 (1967).
2. B. L. Van Duuren, L. Langseth, B. M. Goldschmidt and L. Orris, *J. Natl. Cancer Inst.* **39**, 1217 (1967).
3. F. C. Goodspeed and F. E. Blacet. *J. Phys. Chem.* **67**, 2501 (1963).
4. S. Patton. *Food Research* **25**, 554 (1960).
5. N. Drozdov and N. Materanskaya. *Myasnaya Ind. SSSR.* **22**, No. 2, 30 (1951); through *Chem. Abstr.* **45**, 6541 (1951).
6. M. A. Pyke. *Analyst* **60**, 515 (1935).

32. GLYCOLALDEHYDE (HYDROXYETHANAL)

$$HOCH_2\!-\!CHO$$

I. INTRODUCTION

The pure diethylacetal of this aldehyde is prepared in 95% yield from chloro-acetal[1] and in about 50% yield from bromoacetal[2] after reaction with alcoholic potassium hydroxide solution. Acid hydrolysis of the warm solution of the acetal forms the aldehyde.

In the solid state glycolaldehyde exists as a dimer which reverts gradually to the monomer in aq solution.

II. REAGENTS

Some of the reagents which have been used for the determination of glycolaldehyde include 2,4-dinitrophenylhydrazine (DNPH),[3–6] diphenyl-amine,[7] MBTH;[8] naphthoresorcinol,[9] pyrogallol or chromotropic acid,[10] resorcinol[11, 12] and NADH.[13]

A. 2,4-Dinitrophenylhydrazine

The DNPH methods consist of the oxidation of glycolaldehyde to glyoxal, formation of the bis-dinitrophenylhydrazone and measurement of the absorbance of the dianion, Fig. 11. Other monocarbonyl compounds do not

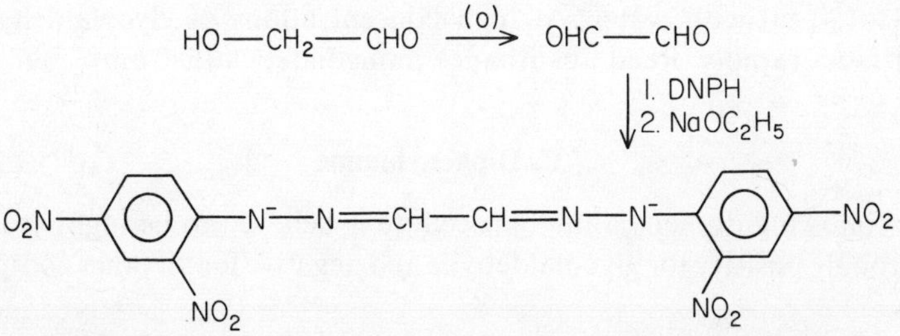

FIG. 11. Reaction of glycolaldehyde with 2,4-dinitrophenylhydrazine.

37

interfere since their dinitrophenylhydrazones absorb at much shorter wavelengths.

In the following method the chromogen has bands at 560, mε 41·2 litres per millimole per centimetre and near 350 nm. Beer's law is obeyed. The temperature dependency of the molar absorptivity is small; no difference was found between the absorbances at 20° and 30°. The blue colour is stable for at least 60 minutes. The dihydrazone is very slightly soluble in carbon tetrachloride but can be quantitatively extracted with benzene. Some of the excess reagent is extracted into benzene but this does not interfere. If this were a problem the colour due to excess DNPH can be eliminated by treating the reaction mixture with 2,4-pentanedione to form a colourless pyrazole.[14]

DNPH determination of glycolaldehyde.[3] Add 5 ml of 0·05% DNPH in 45% perchloric acid (stable for several weeks) to 1 ml of the aq test solution containing between 0·5 and 5 μg of the aldehyde. Dilute to 20 ml with water and heat in a stoppered flask on a boiling water bath for one hour. Cool and transfer contents to a separatory funnel. Extract dihydrazone with 20 ml of benzene and with 5 ml of benzene. Combine extracts, add 5 ml sodium ethoxide (1·0 g sodium in 100 ml ethanol) and dilute to 50 ml with ethanol. After 5 min, read absorbance at 560 nm.

The following DNPH procedure makes use of the oxidizing properties of a hot solution of excess reagent. The resulting glyoxal bis-dinitrophenyl-hydrazone dianion absorbs at 580 nm with an mε of 52·4. The reagent itself in alkaline methanol had a long wavelength band at 425 nm with an mε of about 0·8 to 1·5 dependent on the concentration of the reagent. In contrast a monocarbonyl anion, such as the acetone 2,4-dinitrophenylhydrazone anion has a long wavelength band at 530 nm with mε 9·8 in alkaline methanol.

DNPH determination of glycolaldehyde.[6] Reflux for 50 min at 75° a mixture of 2 ml of aq test solution and 2 ml of 0·1 % DNPH in carbonyl-free methanol, 3 M in HCl. After the heating period, wash down the reflux condenser with 2 ml of carbonyl-free methanol, add 10 ml of 10% methanolic KOH and dilute to 20 ml with water. At high concentrations of glycolaldehyde the colour fades rapidly. Read absorbance immediately at 580 nm.

B. Diphenylamine

The following diphenylamine procedure is believed to be highly selective. It is strongly positive for glycolaldehyde and negative for all other compounds tested.

Diphenylamine determination of glycolaldehyde.[7] Heat 1 ml of aq test solution and 2 ml of reagent (0·8 g of diphenylamine in 80 ml of acetic acid and 0·55 ml of H_2SO_4) for 30 min at 100°. A grass green colour is obtained. Read the absorbance at 580 nm minus the absorbance at 660 nm.

C. 3-Methyl-2-benzothiazolinone hydrazone

Glycolaldehyde, like most other aliphatic aldehydes, can be determined with MBTH. By a procedure described in the aliphatic aldehyde section, an mɛ of 60 is obtained at λ 670 nm.[8]

D. Naphthoresorcinol

Naphthoresorcinol has been used for the determination of glycolaldehyde and its precursors. For example, in the following procedure glycolaldehyde and hydroxypyruvate can be determined.[9] Beer's law is obeyed from 0·1 to 1 µmol of glycolaldehyde or hydroxypyruvate.

Naphthoresorcinol estimation of glycolaldehyde (and hydroxypyruvate).[9] In the absence of glycolaldehyde precursors, such as hydroxypyruvate, use the following procedure. Mix 1 ml of aq test solution containing 0·1 to 1 µmol of glycolaldehyde with 0·1 ml of 0·5% ethanolic naphthoresorcinol in a glass-stoppered tube. Slowly add 6 ml of 27 N H_2SO_4 and shake the tubes. Heat in a boiling water bath for 20 minutes. Cool in running water and read the absorbance at 660 nm.

If hydroxypyruvate is present, then total glycolaldehyde (free and precursor) is obtained.

Where glycolaldehyde and hydroxypyruvate are present in a mixture the following procedure can be used to determine glycolaldehyde. The formation of a green colour immediately on mixing with the sulphuric acid solution indicates the possible presence of free glycolaldehyde.

Naphthoresorcinol estimation of glycolaldehyde.[9] Shake 5 ml of the acidic test solution containing 0·5 to 10 µmoles of the aldehyde in a stoppered test tube with 9 g of Bio-Deminrolit G resin (The Permutit Co.) until the pH of the liquid reaches approximately 4. Filter off the resin. React the hydroxypyruvic acid-free filtrate in the previously described naphthoresorcinol procedure. The resin quantitatively absorbs over 95% of the hydroxypyruvic acid. The recovery of glycolaldehyde is about 80%.

E. Nicotinamide adenine dinucleotide

Glycolaldehyde can also be determined enzymatically[13] by the decrease in absorbance at the 340 nm maximum of NADH.

$$\text{HOCH}_2\text{—CHO} + \text{NADH} \xrightarrow[\text{dehydrogenase}]{\text{alcohol}} \text{HO—CH}_2\text{—CH}_2\text{OH} + \text{NAD}^+$$

Other aliphatic aldehydes react also.

F. Pyrogallol

Glycolaldehyde forms a deep violet chromogen with pyrogallol in sulphuric acid and forms this chromogen more rapidly than its precursors.[10] In the following procedure copper (II) and iron (III) in relatively low concentrations inhibited colour development. The chromogen is stable only in conc acid; addition of an equal volume of water to the final solution changes the colour from violet to brown.

Pyrogallol determination of glycolaldehyde.[10] To 0·5 ml of aq test solution containing 0·05 to 0·7 μmol of the aldehyde add 6 ml of conc H_2SO_4 rapidly and shake. Cool and add 1 ml of reagent (prepare fresh a mixture of 1 ml 10 mM aq calcium glycerate and 100 ml of 0·3% pyrogallol in conc H_2SO_4). Mix by shaking. Heat at 100° for 30 min and cool. Read absorbance at 570 nm.

The pyrogallol and chromotropic acid methods were compared for the determination of glycolaldehyde and its precursors. Assay for glycolaldehyde with chromotropic acid gave a band at 695 nm with mε ∼ 8. The details of these methods will be discussed more fully in the section on glycolaldehyde precursors.

Table 8. The sugars tested and their R_f values.[15] Adsorbent and solvent system as described in the text

	$R_f \times 100$
Glycolaldehyde	70; 45
Glyceraldehyde	59
Dihydroxyacetone	60; 50
Erythrose	45
Arabinose	39
Xylose	47
Lyxose	45
Rhamnose	51
Glucose	34
Mannose	36
Galactose	30
Fructose	32
Sorbose	32
Lactose	14
Saccharose	24

G. Resorcinol

Glycolaldehyde gives a purple colour with resorcinol–hydrochloric acid.[11, 12] Ketohexoses, adenosine-5-phosphate and heptuloses produce similar colours. Ketopentoses produce yellow to green colours while aldehexoses give weak purple colours.

In addition, glycolaldehyde could be determined by some of the glyoxal procedures since it is a glyoxal precursor.

H. Fluorescent 2-aminobiphenyl procedure

The detection of glycolaldehyde through its fluorescent reaction with 2-aminobiphenyl[15] could be used for its assay. Essentially a mixture of monosaccharides formed from the aldol condensation of formaldehyde is separated on a Kieselgel G plate saturated with 0·03 M boric acid with ethyl acetate–isopropanol–acetic acid–water (4:2:1:1). The plate was sprayed with a 1:1 (v/v) mixture of 0·1% 2-aminobiphenyl in ethanol and 20% H_2SO_4, heated in an oven at 105–110° for 15 min and examined under UV light at 365 nm. Glycolaldehyde was found at R_f 0·70 with an intense bluish-white fluorescence; its dimer was found at R_f 0·45, but it did not react in this reaction, Table 8. Only glyceraldehyde and dihydroxyacetone showed positive reactions, but their intensities were relatively much weaker.

REFERENCES

1. F. Beyerstedt and S. M. McElvain. *J. Am. Chem. Soc.* **58**, 530 (1936).
2. W. H. Hartung and H. Adkins. *J. Am. Chem. Soc.* **49**, 2520 (1927).
3. R. A. Basson and T. A. du Plessis. *Analyst, Lond.* **92**, 463 (1967).
4. T. Banks, C. Vaughn and L. M. Marshall. *Anal. Chem.* **27**, 1348 (1955).
5. C. Neuberg and E. Strauss. *Arch. Biochem.* **7**, 211 (1945); *Ibid.* **11**, 457 (1946).
6. C. F. Wells. *Tetrahedron*, **22**, 2685 (1966).
7. Z. Dische and E. Borenfreund. *J. Biol. Chem.* **180**, 1297 (1949).
8. M. A. Paz, O. O. Blumenfeld, M. Rojkind, E. Henson, C. Furfine and P. M. Gallop. *Arch. Biochem. Biophys.* **109**, 548 (1965).
9. D. F. Dickens and D. H. Williamson. *Biochem. J.* **68**, 84 (1958).
10. E. L. Coe. *Anal. Biochem.* **10**, 236 (1965).
11. J. H. Roe. *J. Biol. Chem.* **107**, 15 (1934).
12. J. H. Roe, J. H. Epstein and N. P. Goldstein. *J. Biol. Chem.* **178**, 839 (1949).
13. H. Holzer and H. W. Goedde in H. U. Bergmayer, Ed., Methods in Enzymatic Analysis, Academic Press, New York, 1963, p. 297.
14. D. P. Johnson, F. E. Critchfield and J. E. Ruch. *Anal. Chem.* **34**, 1389 (1962).
15. T. Nakai, H. Demura and M. Koyama. *J. Chromatog.* **66**, 87 (1972).

33. GLYOXAL

OHC—CHO

I. INTRODUCTION

M.p. 15°, b.p. 51°, D_4^{20} 1·14, n_D^{20} 1·3826. Polymerizes on standing or in the presence of a trace of water. The monomer predominates at glyoxal concentrations below 1 M.[1] At higher glyoxal concentrations, the monomer remains at 1 M due to dimerization and higher order oligomerization, the predominant species between 1 and 10 M being **I**.

In alkaline solution glyoxal forms glycolic acid. Glyoxal sodium bisulphite can be readily prepared and purified.[2] It is useful as a standard source of glyoxal.

In water glyoxal absorbs at 267·5 nm, mε 0·00575.[3] Obviously this band cannot be used to determine trace amounts of glyoxal. We will describe a variety of photometric methods that can be used for this purpose. Some of the reagents to be described for the determination of glyoxal are shown in Table 9.

II. REAGENTS

A. o-Aminophenol

In connection with the first reagent described in this Table the analogous o-aminophenol can be reacted with glyoxal to give the dianil which can chelate with various metals to give coloured chromogens, e.g. **II** with nickel or cadmium acetate and **III** with uranyl acetate.[20]

Table 9. Reagents useful and potentially useful in the determination of glyoxal

Reagent	$F_{exc/em}$ or λ_{max}	mε	Ref.
2-Aminobenzenethiol	600	2·4	4
Azulene	618	100·0[a]	5, 6
2,3-Diaminophenazine	600	23	4, 7
1,2-Dianilinoethane	555	1·9[b]	4
Dimedone	F395/460		9
Dimedone plus alkali	F465/520		9
2,3-Dimethyl-1H-indolizinium perchlorate	612	30[a, c]	5
2,4-Dinitrophenylhydrazine	608	65[d]	4
2-Hydrazinobenzothiazole	F470/520		12[e]
2-Hydroxy-1-naphthalhydrazone	Red fluor. + colour		13[e]
3-Hydroxythianaphthene	Red colour		14[f]
3-Methyl-2-benzothiazolinone hydrazone	407[g]	46	15
3-Methyl-2-benzothiazolinone hydrazone	670	23	16
2-Methylindole	505	—	17
4-Nitrophenylhydrazine	702	97	4
Phthalaldehyde	Violet colour		18[f]
Resorcinol	488	60	19
Salicylalhydrazone	Yellow fluor.		13[e]
4,6,8-Trimethylazulene	660	47[a]	5[h], 6

[a] mε value for pure dye. Only a simple organic synthetic procedure is available; this could be readily modified and made analytically useful.

[b] Value for a 10^{-3} M solution; λ_{max} 550 nm, mε 2·4 has been obtained in original procedure.[8]

[c] Other bands at longer wavelength are λ 1010, 895 nm with mε 13·5 and 11·0, respectively.

[d] λ_{max} 580, mε 35·4 has been obtained by a different procedure.[10] The pure dye gave λ_{max} 575, mε 66·4 in alcoholic sodium hydroxide solution.[11]

[e] Only the qualitative test described in this paper.

[f] Potential use. Only the synthesis described in the paper.

[g] Solvent and other effects discussed in body of paper.

[h] Long wavelength band also present at λ 920 nm, mε 13·5.

M	λ_{max}	mε
Ni	563	19·6
Cd	635	10·7

II

λ_{max}	mε
606	12·7

III

o-Aminothiophenol could probably be used similarly. But as presently used[4] it has too low a sensitivity for trace analysis.

B. Azulenes

Azulene could be used to determine glyoxal.[5, 6] On the basis of the following reaction, Fig. 12, a theoretical millimolar absorptivity of 200 is possible if the reaction took place quantitatively and if the formaldehyde formed as a byproduct formed a quantitative yield of the same chromogen.

4,6,8-Trimethylazulene can also be used to determine glyoxal but the reaction that takes place is entirely different[5, 6] as shown in Fig. 13. Analysis could be accomplished with either the mono-cationic or di-cationic structures.

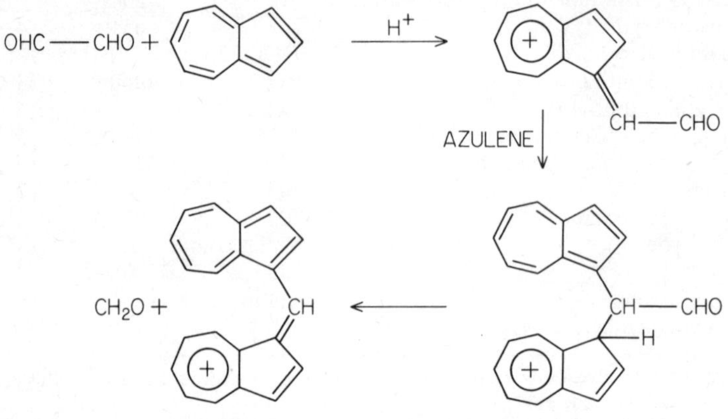

FIG. 12. Reaction of glyoxal with azulene.[5, 6]

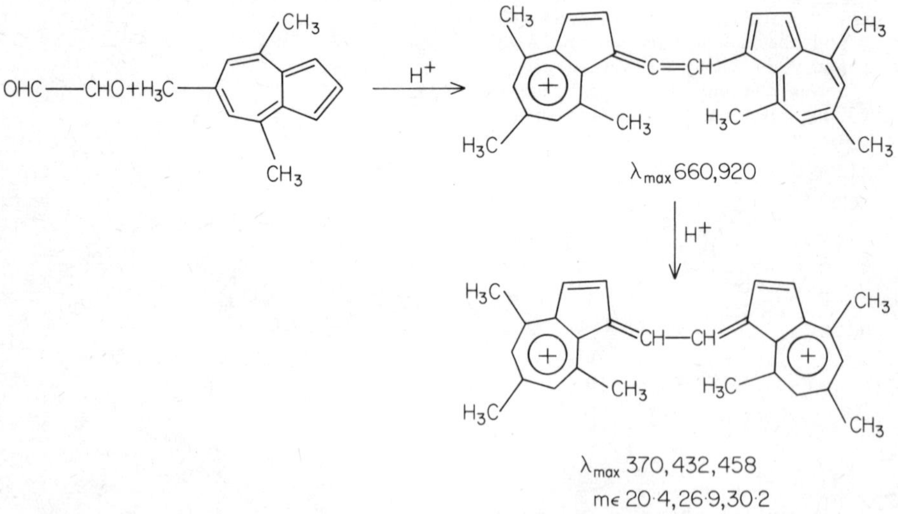

λ_{max} 660,920

λ_{max} 370,432,458

mϵ 20·4,26·9,30·2

FIG. 13. Reaction of glyoxal with 4,6,8-trimethylazulene.[5, 6]

C. Chromotropic acid

Glyoxal reacted with chromotropic acid in strong sulphuric acid solution shows the presence of the 575 and 480 bands derived from formaldehyde and a weaker band at 750 nm with a shoulder at 700 nm. The last two bands are probably due to impurities with the 700 nm band possibly derived from glycolaldehyde.

D. 2,3-Diaminophenazine

This reagent is easily prepared from o-phenylenediamine[4] and can also be used to determine glyoxal.[7] A yellow pyrazino[2,3-b]-phenazine, IV, is formed which forms a blue salt in acidic solution.

IV

In both of the procedures to be described Beer's law is obeyed from about 0·02 to 0·2 μM. The chromogens obtained from glyoxal, pyruvaldehyde and 2,3-butanedione in procedure A are shown in Fig. 14. Only large amounts of pyruvaldehyde, 2,3-butanedione and other α-diketo compounds would interfere. The following compounds did not interfere: glyoxylic acid and other α-keto acids, glycolic acid, succinic acid, formic acid, formaldehyde, acetaldehyde, benzil and 1,2-naphthoquinone. Glycolaldehyde gives the glyoxal reaction. The following procedures are probably two of the more highly selective methods described in Table 9.

2,3-Diaminophenazine determination of glyoxal. Procedure A.[7] To 1 ml of aq test solution add 0·7 ml of 0·021% diaminophenazine in 10 N H_2SO_4 (stable for 5 d at 4°) and 0·5 ml conc H_2SO_4. Mix, heat at 100° for 1 h and cool in an ice-water bath. Add 1 ml of cold 0·02% aq potassium nitrite and shake vigorously. Add 1 ml of 50% hypophosphorous acid, shake and heat at 100° for one hour. Cool and read the absorbance at 600 nm. Colour is stable for at least 24 hours.

The nitrite–hypophosphorous acid treatment was necessary to convert the excess interfering reagent (red brown in acid solution) to the straw yellow phenazine.

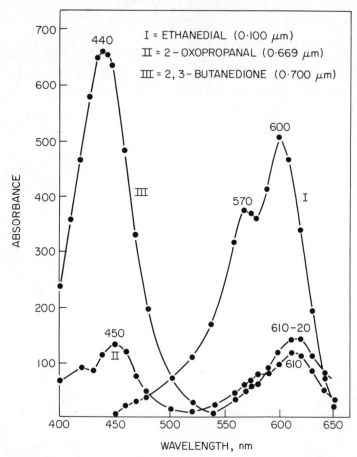

Fig. 14. Absorption spectra of reaction products of glyoxal, pyruvaldehyde and 2,3-butanedione with 2,3-diaminophenazine in sulphuric acid solution.[4]

Procedure B is suitable for the analysis of glyoxal in biological materials which contain glyoxal and pyruvaldehyde precursors. The appearance of an absorption maximum at 715 nm indicates the presence of pyruvaldehyde. The small contribution of this aldehyde to the absorbance of the glyoxal reaction product at 600 nm can be corrected by subtracting the amount of pyruvaldehyde which is determined at 715 nm.

2,3-Diaminophenazine determination of glyoxal. Procedure B.[7] To 1 ml of the aq test solution (not exceeding 0·15 μM ml^{-1}) in a calibrated tube add 1 ml of 0·021 % of the diaminophenazine. Heat at 100° for exactly 10 minutes.

Cool and add 1 ml of 0·02 % aq potassium nitrite followed by 0·5 ml of 50% hypophosphorous acid. Heat the tubes again at 100° for 20 minutes. Cool and dilute to 4 ml by the addition of 0·5 ml glacial acetic acid. Read the absorbance at 600 nm.

E. 1,2-Dianilinoethane

This reagent is probably the least sensitive of those listed in Table 9. In the original procedure λ_{max} 550 nm, mε 2·4 was obtained.[8] The hydrolysate of periodate-oxidized starch was assayed with the method. The violet chromogen in the procedure is reported to be a free radical cation obtained as shown in Fig. 15.[21]

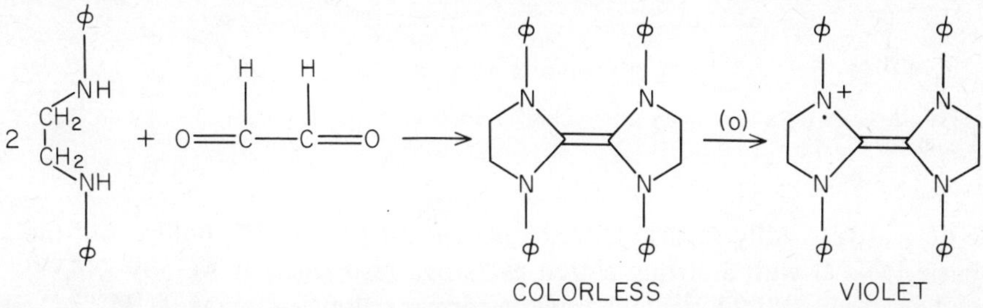

FIG. 15. Reaction of 1,2-dianilinoethane with glyoxal.[21]

F. Dimedone

Dimedone can also be used to assay for glyoxal.[8] Other aliphatic aldehydes would react, especially formaldehyde.

G. 2,4-Dinitrophenylhydrazine

2,4-Dinitrophenylhydrazine, DNPH, has been used to determine glyoxal without[4, 10] and with separation[22–26] of the osazone. Paper,[22] thin layer[23–26] and column[26] chromatography have been used in separating glyoxal DNPH from other carbonyl dinitrophenylhydrazones. A column chromatographic separation is shown in Fig. 16.

Glyoxal and its precursors gave the same dinitrophenylosazone when these compounds were allowed to react overnight with DNPH.[27] This osazone absorbs in chloroform at λ 391, 438 with mε 14·8, 26·9, respectively.

Sometimes excess reagent interferes with the analysis. Separation of the reagent from the desired product may be difficult, especially since the reagent is usually present in several hundredfold excess. Some of the methods of separating the chromogen from reagent are chromatography on adsorbents,[28, 29] oxidation of excess DNPH with Benedict's reagent,[30, 31] reaction with pyruvic acid or some other carbonyl compound which yields

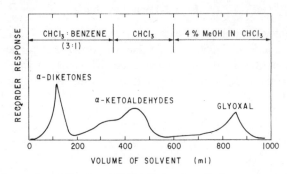

FIG. 16. Class separation of dicarbonyl bis(2,4-dinitrophenylhydrazones) on a MgO–Celite column.[26]

a derivative readily separable from the desired product,[31] pulling out the basic DNPH with a strong cation exchange resin such as AG50W-X4,[32] and reaction with 2,4-pentanedione to form a colourless pyrazole, **V**.[10]

V

DNPH can be substituted for *p*-nitrophenylhydrazine in the procedure described with that reagent.[4] The glyoxal dinitrophenylosazone has been prepared for a colorimetric determination of glyoxal as an enzymatic oxidation product of carbohydrates.[33]

In the following procedure compounds such as 2,4-pentanedione, 3-keto-butyraldehyde, adipaldehyde and glutaraldehyde do not interfere. Glyoxal is readily determined in the presence of monocarbonyl compounds. Positive results are obtained with 1,4-benzoquinone, pyruvaldehyde and 2,3-butane-dione. The colour is stable for at least 30 minutes. An mε of 35·4 was obtained at 580 nm for glyoxal. Beer's law was obeyed. A colourless blank is obtained through the decolorization reaction of condensing excess reagent with 2,4-pentanedione.

2,4-Dinitrophenylhydrazine determination of glyoxal.[10] To 3 ml of aq test solution add 1 ml of 10% (v/v) sulphuric acid followed by 1 ml of reagent. (Dissolve 0·1 g DNPH in 50 ml methanol and add 4 ml of conc HCl. Dilute to 100 ml with water and mix). Heat at 98° for 30 minutes. Add 2 drops of 2,4-pentanedione, mix and let stand for 2 minutes. Cool to room temp and dilute to 15 ml with water. Add 5 ml of methylene chloride and shake well. Let the phases separate and pipette 3 ml of lower layer into a test tube. Evaporate methylene chloride under vacuum at room temperature. To the residue, add 10 ml of 2% diethanolamine in pyridine (v/v). Read absorbance at 580 nm.

Glyoxal has also been determined in beer with the help of 2,4-dinitrophenylhydrazine.[34] Thin layer chromatography is necessary to separate the osazone family from other substances on silical gel G plates with a solvent system of butyl acetate–dioxane–decalin–formamide (30:30:40:4). Glyoxal 2,4-dinitrophenylosazone was separated from the osazones of pyruvaldehyde, 2,3-butanedione and 2,3-pentanedione on silica gel with toluene. The glyoxyl osazone was eluted with ethyl acetate, the solvent was evaporated, the residue dissolved in pyridine containing 2·5% diethanolamine, and the absorbance read at 587 nm.

H. 2-Hydrazinobenzothiazole

Glyoxal can also be determined fluorimetrically with 2-hydrazinobenzothiazole.[12] The postulated mechanism is shown in Fig. 17. Optimum conditions have not been established in the following procedure. Beer's law is not obeyed. Glyoxal, pyruvaldehyde and 1,3-dihydroxyacetone give relative fluorescence intensities of 100, 16 and 9 respectively at $F470/510$. Anywhere from about 0·01 to 6 µg of glyoxal can be determined. The sensitivity can be improved further.

2-Hydrazinobenzothiazole, HBT, determination of glyoxal. To 1 ml of aq test solution add 1 ml of reagent (0·1% HBT in 0·1% aq H_2SO_4) and heat for 10 min at 100°. Cool and add 1 ml of 10% alcoholic tetraethylammonium hydroxide. Dilute to 10 ml with dimethylformamide. Read at $F470/510$.

I. 2-Hydroxy-1-naphthalhydrazone

2-Hydroxy-1-naphthalhydrazone has only been used as a fluorescence spot test for glyoxal.[13] The postulated reaction is shown in Fig. 18. The vivid red fluorescence of the di-anion could be used for the determination of

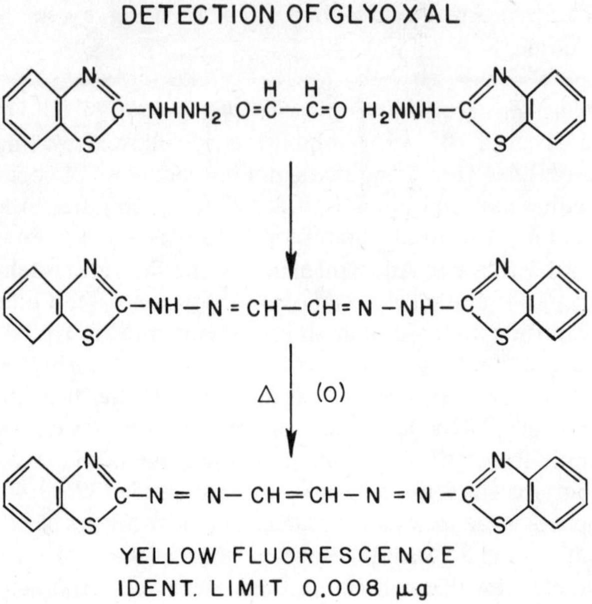

DETECTION OF GLYOXAL

YELLOW FLUORESCENCE
IDENT. LIMIT 0.008 μg

FIG. 17. Postulated reaction of 2-hydrazinobenzothiazole with glyoxal.[12]

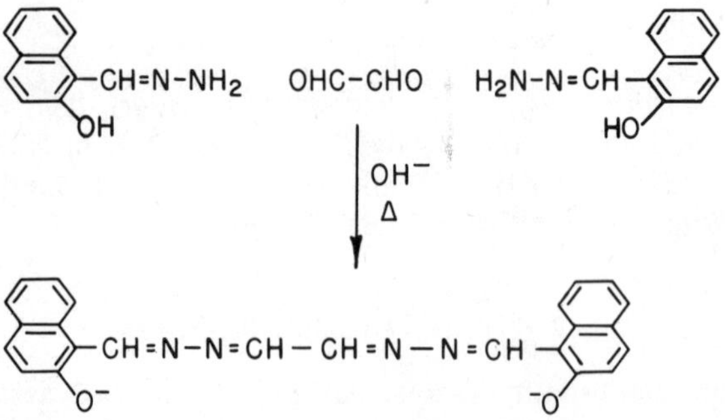

FIG. 18. Reaction of 2-hydroxy-1-naphthalhydrazone with glyoxal.

glyoxal. It is possible that excess reagent would have to be eliminated by one of the methods described in this section.

J. 3-Hydroxythianaphthene

3-Hydroxythianaphthene could probably also be used for the determination of glyoxal with the procedure based on the determination of bis-2-thianaphthene-ethylene indigo, Fig. 19. This vinylog of thioindigo absorbs at λ 508 nm.[35]

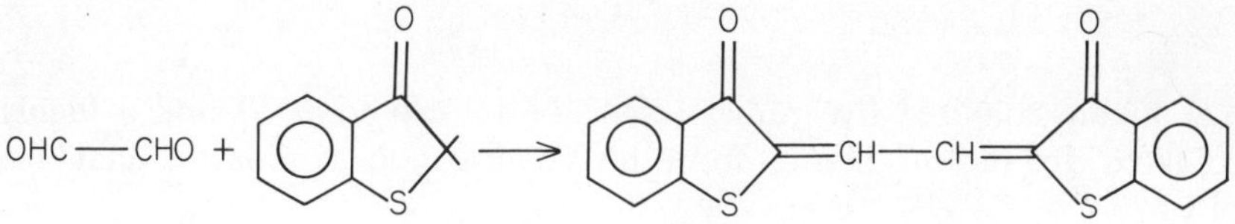

FIG. 19. Reaction of 3-hydroxythianaphthene with glyoxal.

K. 3-Methyl-2-benzothiazolinone hydrazone

Glyoxal can be determined with MBTH by two different types of procedure, one involving azine formation[15, 16, 36, 37] and the other involving formazan cation formation.[16, 38] Both procedures are given in the aliphatic aldehyde section. The azine procedure is much more highly selective and will be discussed in this section.

The following procedure is considered to be highly selective since aliphatic aldehydes and ketones form colourless azines with MBTH. Excessively large amounts could interfere by consuming the reagent. Pyruvaldehyde and 2,3-butanedione could be expected to interfere. Glyoxal precursors, such as glyoxal in glycosidic attachment and glycolaldehyde and its glycosides, do not interfere unless heat or long standing are utilized in the analysis.

The spectral characteristics of the bisazine, **VI**, as reported in the literature appear to be contradictory but are probably due to some extent to solvent effects. Thus, a single peak has been reported at 405 nm in 50% acetic acid,[37] at 406 to 410 nm with mε 45·9 $\pm$ 0·5 in 50 to 94% acetic acid,[15] at concentrations of acetic acid greater than 97% a doublet at 397 and 414 nm with mε about 55,[15] and in 10% aqueous ethanol a triplet at 391, 410 and 445 nm with mε 40, 40 and 24, respectively. In the analytical procedure described in the aliphatic aldehyde section mε values of 33, 35 and 32 were obtained at 391, 410 and 445 nm, respectively. A doublet in 96% ethanol at 398 and 417 nm[36] is also obtained in absolute ethanol, and in 80% ethanol the

C'

doublet is still as pronounced but not as distinct.[15] A singlet peak at 410 nm was observed in 33 and in 50% ethanol.[15] Some of this data is probably due to impurities just as some of the formazan colour in the MBTH procedure is derived from aliphatic aldehyde impurities in glyoxal.

VI

A highly coloured free radical could be formed from **VI** and a highly coloured free radical dianion from the 2-hydrazinobenzothiazole analogue of **VI**.

In the following procedure glyoxal is determined in the presence of glycol-aldehyde and triethanolamine.

MBTH determination of glyoxal.[15] To 1·0 g of the triethanolamine test sample in a 50 ml volumetric flask add 6·7 ml of 1 N H_2SO_4 followed by 2·5 ml of 0·4% MBTH.HCl in 80% acetic acid (prepared daily) and dilution to volume with 80% acetic acid. Shake well, and allow to stand at room temp for at least 2·5 hours. Concurrently prepare a blank, by diluting 6·7 ml of water and 2·5 ml of 0·4% MBTH to 50 ml with 80% acetic acid. Read the absorbance at 407 nm. Calculate the glyoxal content by using the value of 125 μg glyoxal per 100 ml per 1·0 absorbance unit.

For an aq test solution without much basic material the volume of 1 N H_2SO_4 necessary to neutralize the basic material can be omitted.

L. 2-Methylindole

2-Methylindole can also be used for glyoxal but pyruvaldehyde and malon-aldehyde react also.[17] A wavelength maximum is obtained at 505 nm. The procedure is given in the malonaldehyde section.

M. 4-Nitrophenylhydrazine

Probably the most sensitive colorimetric method for glyoxal is the 4-nitrophenylhydrazine procedure.[4] The following mechanism is postulated, Fig. 20. The solvent and pH effects on this osazone are worth noting for any future attempts at further improvement.

The spectrum of pure glyoxal bis-4-nitrophenylhydrazine in dimethyl-formamide containing 10% of 10% aq tetraethylammonium hydroxide solution and 10% additional water contained a band at a maximum wavelength of 702 nm with mε of 106. In the determination of glyoxal by the recommended 4-nitrophenylhydrazine procedure, a band was also obtained at 702 nm with mε of 97, representing a 92% yield of the final chromogen.

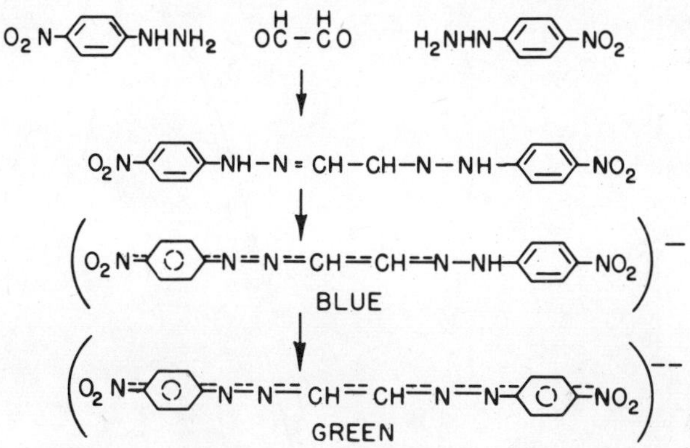

FIG. 20. Equations for *p*-nitrophenylhydrazine determination of glyoxal.[4]

Further valuable data and evidence for the reaction sequence can be obtained from an examination of the absorption spectra of the pure bis-4-nitrophenylhydrazone in solvents of varying basicity, Fig. 21. In weakly acidic dimethylformamide, the absorption spectrum of the neutral compound is obtained (λ_{max} 456 nm, mε 72). In a fairly strong basic solvent, such as alkaline methanol, the absorption spectrum indicates a large proportion of mono-anion (λ_{max} 595 nm, mε 50) and a small amount of the di-anion (shoulders at 675 and 725 nm). In the more strongly basic methyl cellosolve and dimethylformamide solutions, the di-anion is almost exclusively present. The di-anion absorbs at longer wavelength and with greater intensity in alkaline dimethylformamide (λ_{max} 702 nm, mε 106) than in alkaline methyl cellosolve (λ_{max} 692 nm, mε 93). This is because conjugated anions usually absorb at longer wavelengths and with greater intensity in the more basic solvent.[7] In a more weakly alkaline methyl cellosolve solution containing 10% of a 10% aq tetraethylammonium hydroxide solution and an additional 10% water, the wavelength maximum was shifted to 637 nm. This absorption at shorter wavelengths is apparently derived from the mono-anion.

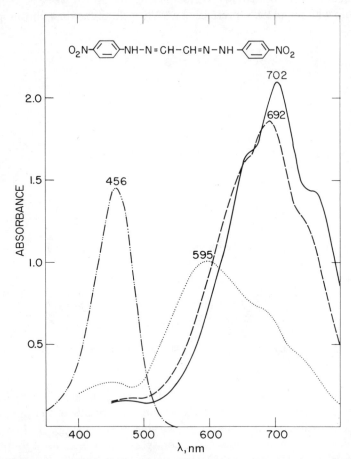

FIG. 21. Visible absorption spectrum of glyoxal bis-4-nitrophenylhydrazone (2×10^{-5} M) in dimethylformamide containing a drop of conc hydrochloric acid (—··—··); methanol containing 10% of dimethylformamide and 10% of 29% methanolic tetraethylammonium hydroxide (········); methyl cellosolve containing 10% of dimethylformamide and 10% of 29% methanolic tetraethylammonium hydroxide (————); and dimethylformamide containing 10% and 29% methanolic tetraethylammonium hydroxide (———).[4]

The di-anion can also be obtained in both methanol and methyl cellosolve solution by increasing the amount of alkali in the standard analytical procedure. For example, a mixture of 1 ml of aq test solution and 1 ml of the

0·1 % reagent solution was heated for 10 min at 100°, cooled, treated with 3 ml of 10 % aq tetraethylammonium hydroxide and enough solvent to dilute to 10 ml. With methyl cellosolve and methyl alcohol, the following wavelength maxima and molar absorptivities were obtained: 692 nm, mε 80 and 688 nm, mε 67, respectively.

When dimethylformamide was used as the test solvent and 29 % methanolic tetraethylammonium hydroxide as the base, dilution with dimethylformamide gave a solution absorbing at 702 nm, mε 102; dilution with methyl cellosolve gave λ_{max} 692 nm and with methanol, λ_{max} 595 nm. These spectra, identical with that obtained from pure glyoxal bis-p-nitrophenylhydrazone, indicate clearly that they are all derived from the bis-4-nitrophenylhydrazone and not from glyoxal 4-nitrophenylhydrazone.

In the following procedure dimethylformamide could be substituted for water as the test solvent with very little change in absorption maximum and intensity. The colour was stable for about 30 minutes. From an initial absorbance of 0·95 at λ_{max} 702 nm, the absorbance had decreased to 0·94 in 35 min and to 0·31 in 18 hours. By this time the band at 702 nm had changed into a shoulder, and a new band had appeared at 612 nm. Numerous tests over a period of a month with varying concentrations of glyoxal gave millimolar absorptivity values of 97 ± 2. Twenty replicate determinations were made on a test solution containing 10 μg of glyoxal, and the standard deviation was 1·05 %. Beer's law was obeyed from 0·7 (for $A = 0·1$) to 14·5 μg of glyoxal per 10 ml of final solution. The absorptivity obtained for glyoxal in the procedure was 1·67 μg^{-1} ml cm^{-1}.

The test was not specific for glyoxal, because pyruvaldehyde, glycolaldehyde, dihydroxyacetone, and biacetyl also reacted (Table 10). Glycolaldehyde reacts to some extent because it forms a little glyoxal under test conditions.[1] Larger aliphatic α,β-diketones (e.g. 2,3-octanedione) reacted only slightly. Other diketone-type compounds reacted in the procedure to give bands around 580 to 610 nm. Other diketones such as benzil that form chromogens near 600 nm offer little interference in the procedure unless present in large amounts.

4-Nitrophenylhydrazine determination of glyoxal.[4] Heat a mixture of 1 ml of aq test solution and 1 ml of 0·1 % of 4-nitrophenylhydrazine in dimethylformamide containing 1 % conc H_2SO_4 at 100° for 10 minutes. Cool to room temp. Add 1 ml of 10 % aq tetraethylammonium hydroxide and dilute to 10 ml with dimethylformamide. Read absorbance at 702 nm within 40 min after final dilution. Results are given in Table 10.

An alternative procedure consists of substituting a reagent containing 0·05 % 4-nitrophenylhydrazine and 0·5 % H_2SO_4 in dimethylformamide for the recommended reagent and 29 % methanolic tetraethylammonium

Table 10. Determination of glyoxal and other compounds with
4-nitrophenylhydrazine[4]

Compound	λ_{max} (nm)	$m\varepsilon$
Glyoxal	702	97
Pyruvaldehyde	695	78
Biacetyl	647	25
	684	25
Glycolaldehyde	702	16
1,3-Dihydroxyacetone	690	18
DL-Glyceraldehyde	685	3
2,3-Octanedione	698	2
Benzil	578	4
α-Furil	580	7
α-Pyridil	575	24
6,6'-Dimethyl-2,2'-dipyridyl	570	50
1-Phenyl-1,2-propanedione	580	12
1,4'-Nitrophenyl-1,2-propanedione	605	6
1,4-Diacetylbenzene	593	25
1,4-Diphenyl-2-butene-1,4-dione	648	8
Acenaphthenequinone	570	28
Phenanthraquinone	565	70
Isatin	610	25
1,4-Benzoquinone	575	6

hydroxide for the other alkali and finally diluting to 5 ml with dimethyl-formamide. Glyoxal gives the same results in this procedure.

A third procedure utilizes the following steps.[39] To 0·5 ml of the alcoholic test solution add 0·5 ml of 0·04% alcoholic p-nitrophenylhydrazine containing 0·1% conc HCl. Heat at 70° for 20 to 30 min, cool to room temp and add 9 ml of 0·4% benzyltrimethylammonium hydroxide in dimethylformamide (base prepared freshly from 40% methanolic benzyltrimethylammonium hydroxide). Read the absorbance at 690 nm. Glyoxal gives an $m\varepsilon$ of 58 at this wavelength.

N. Phenylhydrazines

Phenylhydrazine can react with glyoxal to form the bisphenylhydrazone. This compound in strongly alkaline solution in the presence of oxygen forms the radical di-anion, VII.[40]

VII

Glyoxal bis(phenylhydrazone) absorbs at λ 382 nm, mϵ ~49 in dimethyl-sulphoxide; in alkaline solution and in the presence of air it gives a deep violet-purple unstable solution exhibiting bands at λ_{max} 455 and 562 nm.

1,1-Diphenylhydrazine could also be used to determine glyoxal. The osazone, $(C_6H_5)_2N—N{=}CH—CH{=}N—N(C_6H_5)_2$, absorbs at 372 nm in 2-methoxy-ethanol, at 428 nm in strong perchloric acid solution and at 540, 1018 and 1152 nm in strong acid solution containing a small amount of nitrate.[41] These latter spectral bands are postulated to be derived from a free radical cation. Glyoxal could be analysed at any of these wavelengths.

A reaction utilized for aliphatic aldehydes can also be used for glyoxal. This is the determination with phenylhydrazine and 3-phenyl-5-nitrosamino-1,2,4-thiadiazole to form a formazan anion.[42] With glyoxal a band is obtained at 490 nm with mϵ about 7. Other aliphatic aldehydes give bands at or near 490 nm.

O. o-Phthalaldehyde

A solution of o-phthalaldehyde in the presence of glyoxal, potassium cyanide and sodium bicarbonate and air rapidly acquires a violet colour due to the formation of the isonaphthazarin, anion, **VIII**.[18] Analysis could be either at the anion or neutral stages.

VIII

P. Resorcinol

Glyoxal can be determined with resorcinol.[19] An mϵ of 59·5 is obtained at 487·5 nm. Monochloroacetaldehyde, dichloroacetaldehyde and some glyoxal precursors give positive results. Large amounts of other aldehydes could interfere by using up reagent. The procedure is given in the dichloro-acetaldehyde section.

Q. Salicylalhydrazone

In the fluorescent detection of glyoxal a yellow fluorescence at the detection limit of 10 ng is obtained.[13] The fluorogen, **IX**, is formed. This method could be quantitated for the fluorimetric determination of glyoxal or pyruvaldehyde.

IX

REFERENCES

1. E. B. Whipple. *J. Am. Chem. Soc.* **92**, 7183 (1970).
2. A. R. Ronzio and T. D. Waugh. *Org. Synth.* **24**, 61 (1944).
3. G. Mackinney and O. Temmer. *J. Am. Chem. Soc.* **70**, 3586 (1948).
4. E. Sawicki, T. R. Hauser and R. Wilson. *Anal. Chem.* **34**, 505 (1962).
5. M. Fraser and D. H. Reid. *J. Chem. Soc.* 1421 (1963).
6. E. C. Kirby and D. H. Reid. *J. Chem. Soc.* 3579 (1961).
7. J. M. Dechary, E. Kun and H. C. Pitot. *Anal. Chem.* **26**, 449 (1954).
8. C. S. Wise, C. L. Mehltretter and J. W. Van Cleve. *Anal. Chem.* **31**, 1241 (1959).
9. E. Sawicki and R. A. Carnes. *Mikrochim. Acta* **148** (1968).
10. D. P. Johnson, F. E. Critchfield and J. E. Ruch. *Anal. Chem.* **34**, 1389 (1962).
11. L. A. Jones and C. K. Hancock. *J. Am. Chem. Soc.* **82**, 105 (1960).
12. E. Sawicki and W. C. Elbert. *Talanta* **5**, 63 (1960).
13. E. Sawicki and T. W. Stanley. *Chemist-Analyst* **49**, 107 (1960).
14. S. K. Guha and J. N. Chatterjea. *J. Indian Chem. Soc.* **30**, 379 (1953).
15. F. W. Neumann. *Anal. Chem.* **41**, 2077 (1969).
16. M. A. Paz, O. O. Blumenfeld, M. Rojkind, E. Henson, C. Furfine and P. M. Gallop. *Arch. Biochem.* **109**, 548 (1965).
17. H. Scherz, G. Stehlik, E. Bancher and K. Kaindl. *Mikrochim. Acta* 915 (1967).
18. F. Weygand. *Ber.* **75**, 625 (1942).
19. W. Buchler and W. Heizler. *Z. Anal. Chem.* **194**, 422 (1963).
20. E. Bayer. *Chem. Ber.* **90**, 2325 (1957).
21. D. M. Lemal and K. I. Kawano. *J. Am. Chem. Soc.* **84**, 1761 (1962).
22. I. Martin. *Chem. Ind. London* 1439 (1958).
23. W. Y. Cobb. *J. Chromatog.* **14**, 512 (1964).
24. D. P. Schwartz, M. Keeney and O. W. Parks. *Microchem. J.* **8**, 176 (1964).
25. P. Ronkainen and H. Suomalainen. *Acta Chem. Fenn.* **39**, 280 (1966).
26. D. P. Schwartz, J. Shamey, C. R. Brewington and O. W. Parks. *Microchem. J.* **13**, 407 (1968).
27. P. Ronkainen, D. Kaempagen and H. Suomalainen. *Z. Anal. Chem.* **201**, 14 (1964).
28. F. P. Veitch, Jr. and H. S. Milone. *J. Biol. Chem.* **158**, 61 (1945).
29. P. E. Hilmer and W. C. Hess. *Anal. Chem.* **21**, 822 (1949).
30. H. Reich, S. J. Sanfilippo and K. R. Crane. *J. Biol. Chem.* **198**, 713 (1952).
31. H. Reich, K. F. Crane and S. J. Sanfilippo. *J. Org. Chem.* **18**, 822 (1953).
32. D. P. Schwartz, A. R. Johnson and O. W. Parks. *Michrochem. J.* **6**, 37 (1962).
33. T. Banks, C. Vaughn and L. M. Marshall. *Anal. Chem.* **27**, 1348 (1955).

34. S. R. Palamand, G. D. Nelson and W. A. Hardwick. *Am. Soc. Brewing Chemists Proc.* 186 (1972).
35. E. B. Knott. *J. Soc. Dyers Colourists* **67**, 302 (1951).
36. G. Henske, G. Hanische and H. Fischer. *Ann.* **643**, 161 (1961).
37. O. O. Blumenfeld, M. A. Paz, P. M. Gallop and S. Seifter. *J. Biol. Chem.* **238**, 3855 (1963).
38. E. Sawicki, T. R. Hauser, T. W. Stanley and W. Elbert. *Anal. Chem.* **33**, 93 (1961).
39. M. Pesez and J. Bartos. *Talanta* **5**, 216 (1960).
40. A. J. Fatiadi. Organic Chemistry Section, NBS Technical Note 587, p. 102, National Bureau of Standards, August, 1972.
41. E. Sawicki, T. W. Stanley, J. Pfaff and H. Johnson. *Anal. Chem.* **35**, 2183 (1963).
42. M. Pesez, J. Bartos and J. F. Burtin. *Talanta* **5**, 213 (1960).

34. GLYOXALS

R—CO—CHO

A. 2,4-Dinitrophenylhydrazine

The 2,4-dinitrophenylosazones of α-ketoaldehydes are readily separated from other carbonyl dinitrophenylhydrazones and then assayed as the di-anions. The stability of these compounds adsorbed on a strong anion-exchange resin has been demonstrated.[1, 2] They have been separated on Celite impregnated with ethanolamine and with benzene saturated with ethanolamine as the mobile phase.[3] The ethanolamine is then removed by adsorption onto Amberlite IR 120 (H⁺), 16–50 mesh, 8–10% cross linked. The glyoxal derivative has to be separated with a special column composed of 7·5 g of Celite, 1·5 ml water and 3.5 ml of ethanolamine. A separation is shown in Table 11 and Fig. 22. Each osazone is present as a blue zone.

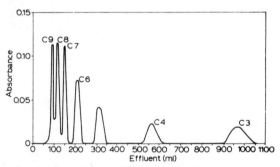

FIG. 22. Plot of absorptivity v. volume of effluent for chromatogram of α-keto-aldehyde 2,4-dinitrophenylosazones. Approx 0·05 μm each; flow rate = 133 ml h⁻¹; fractions read at 390 nm.[2]

Dinitrophenylhydrazones of α-ketoaldehydes, α-diketones and glyoxal can be separated by thin layer chromatography into these classes.[3, 4] An ethyl acetate solution of the osazones is spotted on a thin layer plate (MgO– Analytical Grade Celite, 3:7) and the plate is developed with chloroform–

Table 11. Separation of α-ketoaldehyde
2,4-dinitrophenylosazones.[3]

$$O_2N-\text{(ring)}-NH-N=\underset{\underset{R}{|}}{C}-CH=N-NH-\text{(ring)}-NO_2$$

with NO₂ and O₂N substituents on the rings

R	$100\,R_{Pyr}$ [a]	Recovery, %
$CH_3(CH_2)_6$	9	98
$CH_3(CH_2)_5$	11	95
$CH_3(CH_2)_4$	15	102
$CH_3(CH_2)_3$	22	98
$CH_3(CH_2)_2$	31	97
CH_3CH_2	57	97
CH_3	100	96
H	390	99

[a]Pyr = pyruvaldehyde

$$R = \frac{\text{volume of effluent to peak of compound}}{\text{volume of effluent to peak of standard}}$$

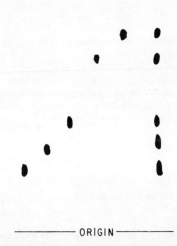

——— ORIGIN ———

Fig. 23. Separation of dicarbonyl bis(2,4-dinitrophenylhydrazones) into classes. Support: MgO–Celite (3:7); solvent: $CHCl_3 : CH_3OH$ (95:5). Diagonally from top to bottom; 2,3-octanedione, 2,3-butanedione, α-ketononanal, α-ketopropanal, and glyoxal. Column on right is a mixture of all compounds.[3]

methanol (95:5) for about 90 min as shown in Fig. 23.[3] This procedure can detect 9×10^{-5} μ moles of an osazone.

These same classes can be separated by column adsorption chromatography on MgO–Celite 545 (1:9) with the help of benzene as a slurrying and test solution solvent and development with the solvents shown in Fig. 16 of the glyoxal section (Chapter 33). Recoveries are nearly quantitative.

A homologous series of α-keto aldehyde bis(2,4-dinitrophenylhydrazones) can be separated by partition thin layer chromatography. The coating for the plates is made by shaking vigorously 12·5 ml of polyethylene glycol 400 in 70 ml of absolute ethanol with 15 g of sieved Microcel T-38. Plates are prepared, air-dried for 10 min and then heated at 100° for 5 minutes. The ethyl acetate test solution is spotted and the plate is developed with benzene–hexane (3:2) saturated with the stationary phase. The separation is shown in Fig. 24. Exposure of the spots to diethylamine vapour gives a violet colour that is visible for 4×10^{-5} μmoles of the osazone.

FIG. 24. Separation of a series of α-ketoaldehyde bis DNPHs by thin-layer partition chromatography. Support: Microcel T-38; stationary phase: polyethylene glycol 400; mobile phase: benzene–hexane (3:2) saturated with stationary phase. Diagonally from top to bottom C_9 through C_3. Column on left is a mixture of the 7 members.[3]

These various bands or spots can be eluted and then determined spectrally as the neutral compound or as the di-anion.

B. 3-Methyl-2-benzothiazolinone hydrazone

The steroid glyoxals can be determined with MBTH, Table 27 and procedure[5] in the aliphatic aldehydes section. The chromogen formed from 4-pregnen-11β,17α-diol-3,20-dione-21-al is the osazone, **I**.

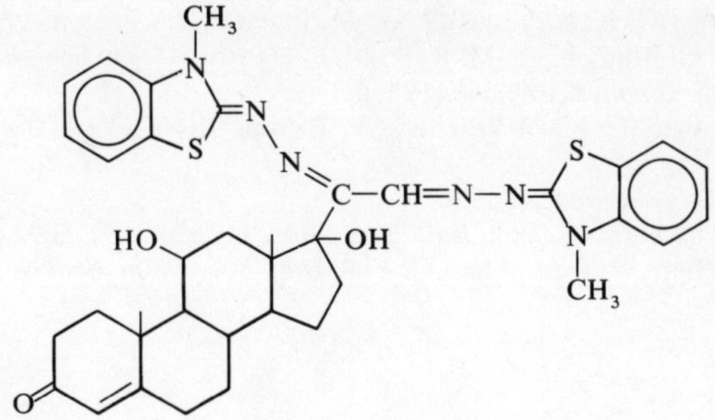

I

C. Diphenylamine

Diphenylamine can be used to determine glyoxals[6] by the Dische procedure for 2-deoxyribose[7] or its modification utilizing N-methyldiphenylamine or 2,4-dimethyldiphenylamine.[8, 9] The chromogen is believed to have the structure **II**.[6]

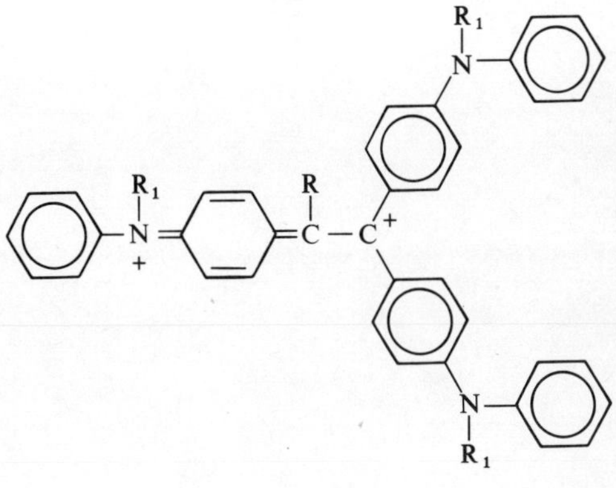

II

Analysis is in the neighbourhood of 600 to 650 nm. Pyruvaldehyde, propylglyoxal and phenylglyoxal have given positive results.

REFERENCES

1. D. P. Schwartz, A. R. Johnson and O. W. Parks. *Microchem. J.* **6**, 37 (1962).
2. D. P. Schwartz. *J. Chromatog.* **9**, 187 (1962).
3. D. P. Schwartz, J. Shamey, C. R. Brewington and O. W. Parks. *Microchem. J.* **13**, 407 (1968).

4. D. P. Schwartz, M. Keeney and O. W. Parks. *Microchem. J.* **8**, 176 (1964).
5. M. A. Paz, O. O. Blumenfeld, M. Rojkind, E. Henson, C. Furfine and P. M. Gallop. *Arch. Biochem. Biophys.* **109**, 548 (1965).
6. C. Rioux-Lacoste, C. Izard-Verchere, P. Rumpf and C. Viel. *Compt. Rend.* **274**, 1621 (1972).
7. Z. Dische. *Mikrochemie* **8**, 4 (1930).
8. C. Izard-Verchere and C. Viel. *Bull. Soc. Chim. France* 2122, 3092 (1971).
9. C. Izard-Verchere, P. Rumpf and C. Viel. *Bull. Soc. Chim. France* 2134 (1971).

35. GLYOXYLIC ACID

OCH—COOH

I. INTRODUCTION

M.p. 98°. Very soluble in cold water and sparingly soluble in ethanol, ether and benzene.

Glyoxylic acid plays an important role in the metabolism of organic acids, e.g. as a key intermediate of the glyoxylate cycle.[1, 2]. It is converted into tartronic semialdehyde by glyoxylate carboligase (tartronate-semialdehyde synthase, EC 4.1.1.47) and condenses with acetyl–Coenzyme A in the presence of malate synthase (EC 4.1.3.2) to yield malate. Its interconversion with glycolate appears to be of some physiological importance to plants and microorganisms. It is also involved in enzymatic transamination reactions with some amino acids.[3]

Examination of the ultraviolet absorption spectra of glyoxylic acid in neutral, acid or weakly alkaline aq solution disclosed no maxima.[4, 5] In aq solution the compound is apparently present as the hydrate, dihydroxy-acetic acid.

Some of the reagents which have been used for the analysis of glyoxylate are shown in Table 12. A few other reagents which have seen little use for the analysis of glyoxylate will also be mentioned.

II. REAGENTS

A. o-Aminobenzaldehyde

o-Aminobenzaldehyde with methylamine can be used for the determination of glyoxylate.[37] This reaction has been discussed in the alipatic aldehydes section. It has been applied to the analysis of glyoxylate with o-amino-benzaldehyde and glycine as reagents.[6] It makes possible the selective determination of the aldehyde acid in the presence of common α-keto acids. The absorption spectra of o-aminobenzaldehyde (λ_{max} 365 nm) and the chromogen (λ_{max} 440 nm) derived from glyoxylate under the standard

Table 12. Reagents useful in the analysis of glyoxylic acid

Reagent	λ_{max}	mε	Ref.
o-Aminobenzaldehyde + glycine	440		6
2,7-Dihydroxynaphthalene	530		7
2,4-Dinitrophenylhydrazine	365[a]	24·0	8–12
2,4-Dinitrophenylhydrazine	406	11·2	·13
4'-Hydrazino-2-stilbazole[b]	410/550		14
Indole	Red		15
Indol-3-ylbutyric acid	550		16
Lysergic acid	590		16
MBTH	670	54·0	17
2-Methylindole	490		18
NADH	340		19[c], 22
p-Nitrophenylhydrazine[d]	390	24·6	23
o-Phenylenediamine	338/518		24
Phenylhydrazine	340[e]	18·7	25, 26
Phenylhydrazine	537[f]	49·3	28
Phenylhydrazine	520		33
Pyrogallol	600	10·1	34
Resorcinol	550	—	35
Resorcinol	490[g]/530		36

[a]Spectrum of pure derivative at pH 7·4.[10] In 1 N NaOH λ_{max} 455? nm, mε 18·2.

[b]Analysed at $F$460/550 and in a strong acid media so as to diminish the weak fluorescence of excess reagent.

[c]See also Refs (20) and (21) wherein pyruvate is determined by a procedure that can be used for glyoxylate.

[d]Spectrum of pure derivative.

[e]Also determined at λ 324 nm, mε 17[27] and at λ 328 nm, mε 17·1.[28]

[f]For the pure chromogen in 4 N HCl in 50% ethanol λ_{max} 520 nm, mε 51 is obtained.[29] The following values have been obtained in analogous analytical procedures: λ_{max} 517, mε 27,[30] λ 520, mε 16·3,[31] and λ 520, mε 17·9.[32]

[g]mε of 1·63 obtained at λ_{max} 490 nm.

conditions are shown in Fig. 25. The reaction sequence is depicted in Fig. 26 wherein a dihydroquinazoline is postulated as the yellow chromogen. Various amines can be used in place of glycine with o-aminobenzaldehyde to determine glyoxylic acid, Table 13. Of these, cadaverine gave the highest colour intensity while the ω-amino acids and methylamine were as effective as glycine. A rectilinear relation was obtained for the absorbances of 0·05 to 1·5 μmol of glyoxylate, 2 to 50 μmol of pyruvate and 5 to 60 μmol of oxalo-acetate. In a series of 15 assays on different samples of glyoxylate the precision range was ±4%. In practice the keto acids hardly interfered with the analysis of glyoxylate. However aliphatic and aromatic aldehydes did inter-fere while acetone, alcohols, amino acids, urea, glucose, sucrose, organic

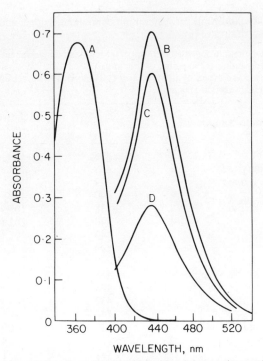

FIG. 25. Absorption spectra of o-aminobenzaldehyde and the reaction products from glyoxylic acid, pyruvic acid and oxaloacetic acid.[6] (A) One mM o-aminobenzaldehyde solution in 0·2 M glycine-KCl buffer, pH 7·8 was used as a control. (B. C and D). The reaction mixtures containing 1·0 μmol of glyoxylic acid (B), 25 μmoles of pyruvic acid (C) and 25 μmol of oxaloacetic acid (D) were incubated under standard conditions.

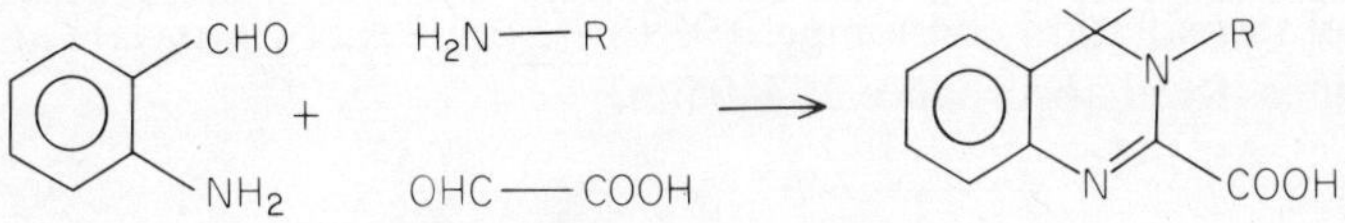

FIG. 26. Reaction of o-aminobenzaldehyde and a primary amine with glyoxylic acid.

acids, copper sulphate, ammonium sulphate and salt did not interfere. The following procedure is applicable in a modified form for the assay of enzymes which catalyse the formation of glyoxylate, e.g. isocitrate lyase (EC 4.1.3.1) and glycollate oxidase (EC 1.3.1.1).

Determination of glyoxylate with o-*aminobenzaldehyde and glycine.*[6]
o-Aminobenzaldehyde, 0·025 M; prepare fresh daily, or store at −20° until used. Buffer, 1 M glycine–KCl, pH 7·8.[6a]

   Procedure. Heat 1 ml of buffer, 1 ml of o-aminobenzaldehyde reagent and

Table 13. Relationship between amino compounds added, and absorption spectra of products.[6]

The reaction mixture consisted of 1·0 ml of 0·1 M potassium phosphate buffer, pH 7·8, containing 0·2 M amino compounds, 1·0 ml of 0·025 M o-aminobenzaldehyde and 1·2 ml of glyoxylic acid (1·0 μmole). The absorbance was read at each absorption maximum.

Amino compounds	λ_{max} (nm)	Relative absorbance
Cadaverine	438	110
γ-Aminobutyrate	438	104
ε-Aminocaproate	440	104
β-Alanine	440	102
δ-Aminovalerate	438	102
Lysine	440	102
Ornithine	440	101
Glycine	440	100
Methylamine	440	98·0
S-(β-Aminoethyl)-cysteine	438	98·0
Taurine	438	91·5
Arginine	437	47·0
Alanine	440	41·5
Phenylalanine	438	41·0
Glutamate	436	35·4
Valine	437	31·5
Ethylenediamine	440	11·4
None	—	0

1·2 ml of test solution containing 0·05 to 1·5 μmoles of glyoxylate at 37° for 15 minutes. Read absorbance at 440 nm.

B. 2,7-Dihydroxynaphthalene

Glyoxylate can be determined after reduction to glycolic acid by the following procedure utilizing 2,7-dihydroxynaphthalene. Since glycolic acid is a formaldehyde precursor in this procedure other appropriate reagents discussed in the formaldehyde precursor section can be substituted here.

2,7-Dihydroxynaphthalene estimation of glyoxylic acid.[7] Add 5 mg of magnesium powder to 0·2 ml of test solution, 2 N in H_2SO_4. Mix and allow to stand at room temp for 1 hour. To 0·2 ml of this solution add 2 ml of 0·01 % 2,7-dihydroxynaphthalene in conc H_2SO_4, keeping the solution ice-cold during the addition. Mix well while cooling and then heat at 100° for 20 minutes.

Allow to cool in an ice bath, dilute with 4 ml of 2 N H_2SO_4, mix, and cool to room temp. Read the absorbance at 530 nm.

Beer's law is obeyed from 5 to 20 µg. Oxalic acid also reacts. Lactic and malic acid interfere since they give a yellow colour with the reagent. Carbohydrates interfere due to caramelization of the sugar by H_2SO_4. More details and other methods can be found in the formaldehyde precursor section where glycolic acid is discussed more fully.

C. 2,4-Dinitrophenylhydrazine

2,4-Dinitrophenylhydrazine can be used for the determination of glyoxylic acid.[38] Other carbonyl compounds, and especially keto acids, would also react; their dinitrophenylhydrazones would have similar spectra. Fig. 27. Glyoxylic acid dinitrophenylhydrazone can be extracted from non-alkaline aq solution with ethyl acetate,[8, 9, 12] ether,[39] chloroform plus ethanol,[40] and even xylene,[8] toluene[41] and ethylbenzene[11] could be used. Glyoxylate DNPH in organic solvent containing the DNPHs of neutral carbonyl

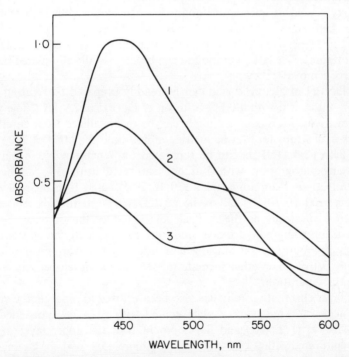

Fig. 27. Absorption spectrum of 2,4-dinitrophenylhydrazone of glyoxylic acid, 1, compared with pyruvic acid, 2, and α-ketoglucaric acid, 3, 0·001 % solution of hydrazones in N NaOH.[8]

compounds and excess DNPH reagent can be extracted with 1 N sodium carbonate[8, 9, 40] or ammonium hydroxide.[31] If ethyl acetate is the organic solvent, petroleum ether has to be added to it before the extraction with 1 N sodium carbonate can be considered complete.[12, 42] The following method has been used. Other keto acids would react and be extracted quantitatively also.

DNPH estimation of glyoxylic acid.[12] To 5 ml of deproteinized test solution containing less than 1·5 μmol of glyoxylate (or total carbonyl compounds) add 1 ml of DNPH reagent. Shake and allow to react for 30 min at 30°. Extract with 8 ml of ethyl acetate and discard the water layer. Evaporate the ethyl acetate solution *in vacuo.*To the dried dinitrophenylhydrazone mixture add 10 ml of benzene and 20 ml of 0·1 N NaHCO$_3$. Stopper and shake vigorously for one minute. Transfer to a separatory funnel and collect the lower layer. Determine the absorbance. The DNPH of glyoxylic acid has λ_{max} 358 nm with mε 24 in 0·1 N NaHCO$_3$. Add an equal volume of 2 N NaOH. The DNPH of glyoxylic acid has λ_{max} 406 nm with mε 11·2. This latter value is quite different from that reported previously.[10]

Glyoxylic acid in microgram quantities can be determined by methods used for keto acids.[8] Other keto acids and 1-hydroxy-6-nitro-1,2,3-benzo-triazole,[12, 43] believed to be formed through the action of alkali on DNPH, would interfere. The latter compound can be successfully eliminated through extractive removal.[12]

The DNPH of glyoxylic acid can be readily prepared by treating an aq solution of the acid with a 0·1 % solution of DNPH in 2 N HCl. The yellow precipitate which forms immediately can be recrystallized from aq ethanol. It exists in cis-trans forms, one melting at 190° and the other at 202°.[44, 45]

The keto acid DNPHs can be separated on Whatman No. 4 paper by paper chromatography with butanol saturated with 3% ammonia,[9] *n*-butanol–ethanol–ammonia 0·5 N (70:10:20),[46] and isopropanol–water–ammonia (200:20:10).[46] Glyoxylic acid DNPH can then be eluted and determined spectrally as the neutral compound or the di-anion. Sodium carbonate or sodium hydroxide solutions can be used for elution. Thin layer chromatography on silica gel G impregnated with propionic acid and with petrol ether–ethyl formate (65:35) as the developer can also be used in the separation.[47]

Thin layer chromatography has also been utilized to separate the various α-keto acids.[13] Thus, with a plate coated with silica gel moistened with 0·1 N Na$_2$CO$_3$ (1:2, w/v) and development with the upper layer of ethyl acetate (saturated with 0·1 N NaHCO$_3$)–methanol (5:1, v/v), the cis and trans forms of glyoxylic acid 2,4-dinitrophenylhydrazone were separated, eluted with methanol containing 1% conc. ammonia, dried *in vacuo*, dissolved in 0·1 N NaHCO$_3$, treated with an equal volume of 2 N NaOH and determined spectrophotometrically.

The DNPH of glyoxylic acid can also be determined through reduction to glycine followed by separation and/or analysis of the glycine by ninhydrin or one of the formaldehyde precursor methods or some other appropriate method. Reduction may be effected by catalytic hydrogenation,[48, 49] by nascent hydrogen obtained from tin or zinc and HCl,[50, 51] or by electrolytic reduction at the mercury cathode,[52] the latter being especially rapid and simple with satisfactory yields. Other keto acids also react.

D. 4′-Hydrazino-2-stilbazole

4′-Hydrazino-2-stilbazole has been used for the fluorimetric determination of α-keto acids in blood[14] and could be used to determine glyoxylic acid after separation or in the absence of other keto acids. The reagent can react with glyoxylic acid to form three main chromogens, Fig. 28. The cation is the one analysed fluorimetrically by exciting at 450 nm so as to decrease the fluorescence contribution of the reagent. The reagent fluoresces much more weakly in strong acid solution than it does in neutral or weakly alkaline solutions while the hydrazone of glyoxylic acid fluoresces much more strongly in strong acid solution than it does in weakly acidic, neutral or weakly

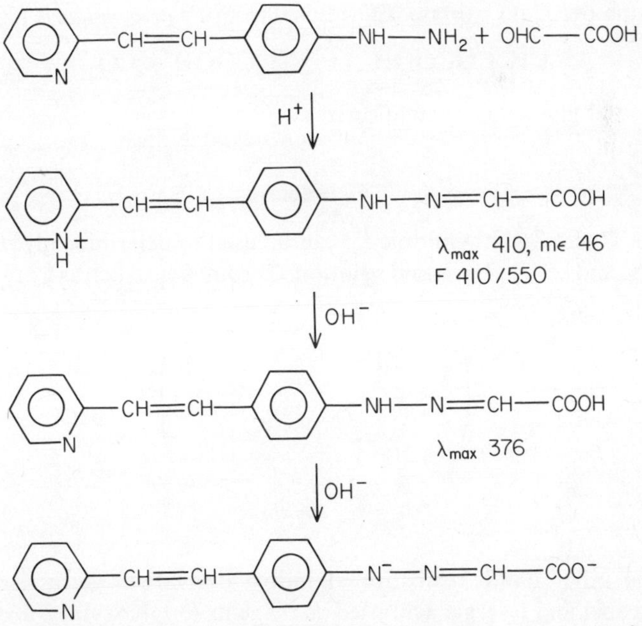

FIG. 28. Reaction sequence for determination of glyoxylic acid with 4-hydrazino-2-stilbazole.

alkaline solutions. The limit of determination of glyoxylic acid is 2×10^{-6} M. A linear relation exists between the concentration and the fluorescence intensity from about 2×10^{-6} M to 8×10^{-5} M. Essentially negative results are given by acetone, acetophenone, acetaldehyde, glucose, glucuronic acid, etc. Formaldehyde and salicylaldehyde give a weak fluorescence. 2,3-Butanedione and glyoxal give about 54 and 24% relative fluorescence intensity, respectively, as compared to glyoxylic acid. It was necessary to stabilize the fluorescence intensity by irradiation with light of 405 nm, presumably to shift the cis, trans equilibrium to the trans form.

The following procedure was used.

Determination of glyoxylic acid with 4'-hydrazino-2-stilbazole.[14] To 1 ml of the aq test solution add 1 ml of buffer (1 N NaOOCH–0·5 N HCl, 2:1, v/v, pH 4) and 1 ml of 0·015% of the aq hydrazine HCl. Let stand for 1 h at 20 to 30° in a dark place. Add 2 ml of 1 N HCl, mix and irradiate with a light of 405 nm for 10 minutes. Read the fluorescence intensity at $F450/550$.

In some of these reactions where the keto acids interfere, enzymatic methods could be used to destroy the keto acids without affecting glyoxylic acid. For example, with 'yeast carboxylase' (EC 4.1.1.1).[53, 54]

$$CH_3COCOOH \rightarrow CH_3CHO + CO_2$$

Or with the pyruvate oxidase (EC 1.2.3.3) from *Proteus vulgaris* (55)

$$CH_3COCOOH \rightarrow CH_3COOH + CO_2.$$

In both cases glyoxylate is unaffected.

E. Indoles

Indole[15] and 2-methylindole[18] can be used to determine glyoxylic acid, aldehydes, and keto acids in acid solution. Chromogens, such as **I**, are probably obtained.

I
λ_{max} 490 nm

On the other hand 3-substituted indole derivatives, such as indole-3-ylbutyric acid and lysergic acid used as reagents for glyoxylates are attacked at the 2-position of indole forming **II** and **III**, respectively. With either of these

2 reagents amounts of glyoxylate as low as $1 \mu g\,ml^{-1}$ can be determined in the following procedure.

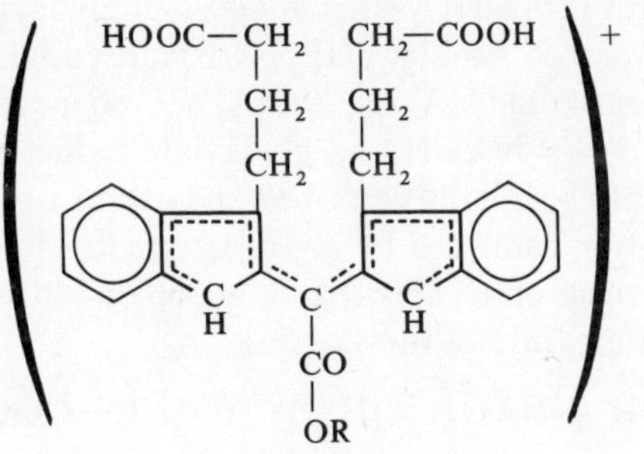

II
λ_{max} 550 nm

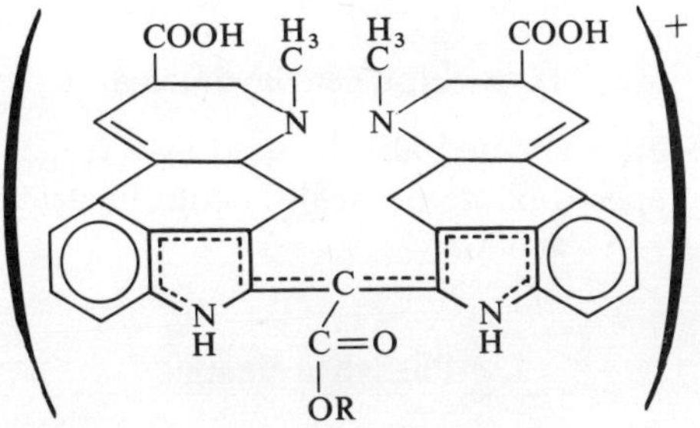

III
λ_{max} 590 nm

Determination of glyoxylate with indole-3-ylbutyric acid or lysergic acid.[16] To 0·1 ml of 0·04% aq indol-3-ylbutyric acid (or lysergic acid) add 0·4 ml of test solution. Add 4 ml of conc H_2SO_4 and set aside for 4 minutes. Measure the absorbance at 550 nm (590 nm for lysergic acid).

It is probable that aldehydes would also react in the procedure.

F. 3-Methyl-2-benzothiazolinone hydrazone

MBTH can be used to determine glyoxylate;[56] at λ 670 nm an mε of 54 is obtained.[17] α-Keto acids tend to decarboxylate to aldehydes when heated under the conditions of this analytical procedure. And aliphatic aldehydes react well in this method, so it is not surprising that pyruvaldehyde gives an mε of 22·8 at 670 nm. This analytical procedure is described in the aliphatic aldehydes section.

G. Enzymatic methods

Enzymatic methods involving nicotinamide-adenine dinucleotide (NAD$^+$) and its reduced form (NADH) for the analysis of glyoxylate are known and others could be developed readily. Thus, glyoxylate could serve as a substrate for lactic dehydrogenase and NADH,[19] NADP$^+$, coenzyme A and glyoxylate dehydrogenase,[57–59] or NADH and glyoxylate reductase (EC 1.1.1.26).[22] The latter method has been fully described and can be used for plant extracts. The following reaction catalysed by glyoxylate reductase proceeds stoichiometrically. The decrease of the absorbance at 366 or 340 nm due to the oxidation of NADH is a measure of the reaction.

$$OHC—COOH + NADH + H^+ \rightarrow HOH_2C—COOH + NAD^+$$

Glyoxylate reductase also reacts with hydroxypyruvate to give D-glycerate, but the enzyme does not react with pyruvate, α-oxoglutarate, oxaloacetate, mesoxalate, phenylglyoxylate or acetaldehyde.

H. p-Nitrophenylhydrazine

p-Nitrophenylhydrazine could also be used as a reagent in the assay for glyoxylate either spectrophotometrically, colorimetrically or probably phosphorimetrically.

I. o-Phenylenediamine

Glyoxylate, like other α-keto acids, could be determined fluorimetrically.[24] The salt of the product, **IV**, can be determined at $F338/518$. The final product

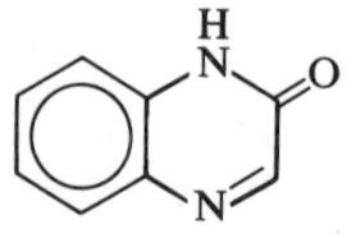

IV

could be determined as the neutral compound, **IV**, or as the cation, di-cation or anion of **IV**. The cationic form present in 50% H_2SO_4 has not been identified. In the following procedure pyruvic acid gives six times greater fluorescence intensity than obtained with glyoxylate. A straight line relationship was obtained (for pyruvic acid and probably for glyoxylic acid) between the fluorescence intensity and the concentration. The fluorescence intensity was stable for at least 2 days. The fluorescence intensity obtained with glyoxylate should be capable of much more enhancement either by optimizing the conditions or by using some other aromatic o-diamine.

o-*Phenylenediamine determination of glyoxylate and other α-keto acids.*[24] To 1 ml of a 2 N H_2SO_4 test solution in a 5 ml volumetric flask add 1 ml of 0·01 % o-phenylenediamine in 2 N H_2SO_4 and 1 ml of 2 N H_2SO_4. Heat in a hot water bath at 90 to 95° for 3 hours. Cool in ice water and add 1·66 ml of cold conc H_2SO_4. Mix carefully with cooling and then dilute to the mark with 50% H_2SO_4 (1:1, w/w). Read the fluorescence intensity at $F338/518$.

It is possible that in many of these methods the glyoxylate determination could be made more selective by destroying or complexing the glyoxylate in one-half the test solution and using this solution as the blank. Thus, glyoxylate–cysteine[60, 61] or tris (hydroxymethyl) aminomethane–glyoxylate[62] complexes could be formed.

J. Phenylhydrazine

A large variety of methods are available for the analysis of glyoxylate with phenylhydrazine either as the phenylhydrazone[25, 27, 28, 63–66] or as N,N′-diphenylformazan or phenylazoformaldehyde phenylhydrazone.[28–32, 67–73]

Although phosphate buffer has been reported to inhibit the formation of the hydrazone,[30, 63] it did not seem to have an adverse effect on the results obtained by others.[28] The following procedure involving the formation of the chromogen, **V**, could probably be further simplified.

$$HOOC—CH=N—NH—\bigcirc$$

V

Determination of glyoxylate as the phenylhydrazone.[25] Warm 2 ml of the acidic (between pH 2 and 6) test solution containing less than 1 μmol of the aldehyde at 38° for 5 min and then add 0·1 ml of 4% phenylhydrazine. Heat again for 2 min at 38°. Cool for 1 min and then dilute to 50 ml with 0·01 N HCl. Read the absorbance at 340 nm. An mε of 18·7 is obtained.

The structure of the principal chromogen formed in the determination of glyoxylic acid with phenylhydrazine and an oxidizing agent has been identified as 1,5-diphenylformazan, as opposed to the structure, 1,5-diphenylformazan-3-carboxylic acid, previously proposed.[29] Some of the evidence is shown in Fig. 29. The postulated mechanism is shown in Fig. 30 and the effect

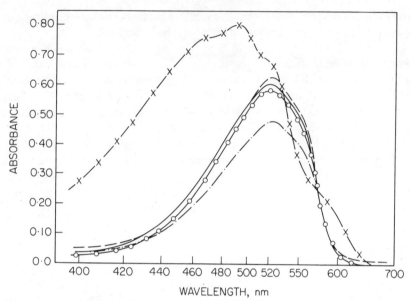

FIG. 29. Absorption spectra: (———) coloured product formed from D-glucaric acid
$(0.69 \times 10^{-5} \text{ M})$ in procedure described in detail elsewhere (1) (in water); (0) coloured product
formed from glyoxylic acid $(2.0 \times 10^{-5} \text{ M})$ in procedure of Kramer et al.[32] (in water):
(- - - - -) 1,5-diphenylformazan $(1.2 \times 10^{-5} \text{ M})$ synthesized by method of von Pechmann[74]
in 4 N hydrochloric acid–50% ethanol (since crystalline 1,5-diphenylformazan and
1,5-diphenylformazan-3-carboxylic acid were practically insoluble in water, their absorption
spectra were taken in the solution mixture indicated here); (-·-) 1,5-diphenylformazan
$(0.96 \times 10^{-5} \text{ M})$ prepared from glyoxylic acid in 4 N hydrochloric acid–50%ethanol; (×)
1,5-diphenylformazan-3-carboxylic acid $(4 \times 10^{-5} \text{ M})$ in 4 N hydrochloric acid–50%
ethanol.[29]

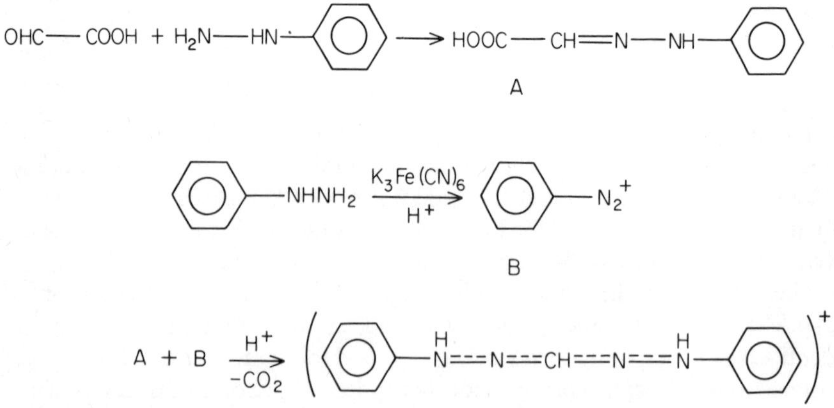

$$\text{OHC} - \text{COOH} + \text{H}_2\text{N} - \text{HN} - \bigcirc \longrightarrow \text{HOOC} - \text{CH} = \text{N} - \text{NH} - \bigcirc$$

A

$$\bigcirc - \text{NHNH}_2 \xrightarrow[\text{H}^+]{\text{K}_3\text{Fe(CN)}_6} \bigcirc - \text{N}_2^+$$

B

$$\text{A} + \text{B} \xrightarrow[-\text{CO}_2]{\text{H}^+} \left(\bigcirc - \overset{\text{H}}{\text{N}} = = = \text{N} = = = \text{CH} = = = \text{N} = = = \overset{\text{H}}{\text{N}} - \bigcirc \right)^+$$

FIG. 30. Reaction sequence for phenylhydrazine determination of glyoxylate.

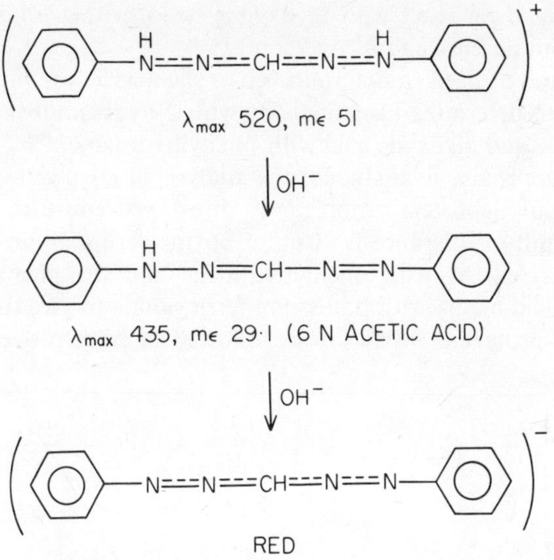

$$\left(\bigcirc-\overset{H}{N}\!\!=\!\!=\!\!N\!\!=\!\!=\!\!CH\!\!=\!\!=\!\!N\!\!=\!\!=\!\!\overset{H}{N}-\bigcirc\right)^{+}$$

λ_{max} 520, mϵ 51

$\downarrow$ OH^{-}

$$\bigcirc-\overset{H}{N}-N\!\!=\!\!CH-N\!\!=\!\!N-\bigcirc$$

λ_{max} 435, mϵ 29·1 (6 N ACETIC ACID)

$\downarrow$ OH^{-}

$$\left(\bigcirc-N\!\!=\!\!=\!\!N\!\!=\!\!=\!\!CH\!\!=\!\!=\!\!N\!\!=\!\!=\!\!N-\bigcirc\right)^{-}$$

RED

FIG. 31. Long wavelength maxima of diphenylformazan in acid, neutral and alkaline solutions.

of pH on the diphenylformazan is shown in Fig. 31. It has also been reported that the diphenylformazan forms a green-blue chromogen in conc H_2SO_4.[29] The spectrum of the neutral diphenylformazan has been reported as having 3 bands at 256 to 260, 296s and 420 to 430 nm in ethanol.[75-79] The long wavelength band has a reputed mϵ ranging from 20·4[78-79] to 28·8.[76] An mϵ of 37 at λ 425 in chloroform has been reported.[28] In the first 15 min after the addition of the ferricyanide the colour intensity changed the most rapidly. After this period the colour diminished by 1% every 6 to 7 minutes. This procedure is probably the most sensitive phenylhydrazine procedure available.

Phenylhydrazine determination of glyoxylate.[28] To 5 ml of aq test solution add 1 ml of 0·4 M Na_2HPO_4–KH_2PO_4 buffer (pH 7·0) and 1 ml of fresh 0·33% aq phenylhydrazine hydrochloride. Allow to stand for 5 min or longer at room temp. Cool to 0° in an ice-water bath and add 5 ml conc HCl precooled to 0° and 1 ml of 1·67% aq potassium ferricyanide. Bring to room temp and then read the absorbance at 535 nm after 15 minutes.

Pyruvic acid does not seem to interfere in this method. In some of the modifications formaldehyde is a strong[30, 32] to weak[31] interference. Glyoxal appears to show some interference.[31, 32] In one modification glyoxal gives an mϵ of 34·8 at λ_{max} 375 nm.[32] Mercaptans are an interference since some of them react with glyoxylate to form thiazolidine derivatives. This latter interference can be overcome.[80]

One method utilized to determine glyoxylic acid in the presence of formaldehyde is to determine formaldehyde with 2-hydrazinobenzothiazole and formaldehyde and glyoxylic acid with phenylhydrazine.[26]

A procedure is also available for the analysis of glyoxylate in protein-rich media without deproteinization.[33] A direct procedure is also described where the limit of tolerance is 40 μg of bovine serum albumin. Essentially, glyoxylate is reacted with phenylhydrazine and the phenylhydrazone is oxidized in acid media with potassium ferricyanide to give the intensely red 1,5-diphenylformazan. Beer's law is followed in both procedures, Fig. 32,

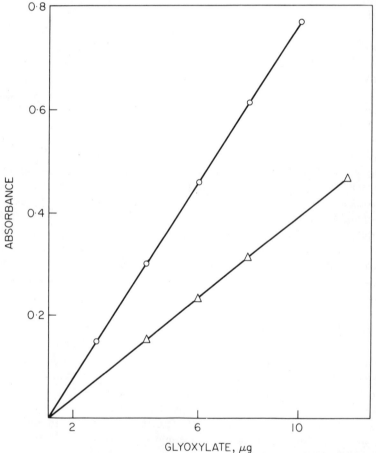

FIG. 32. Beer's law relationship found for direct and solvent extraction methods for glyoxylic acid.[33]

with the chromogen extraction modification almost twice as sensitive. In this latter procedure the colour was stable for 30 min, thereafter it faded at the rate of 2·3% per every 10 minutes. The method is highly reproducible. For 6 µg glyoxylate, the absorbance obtained is 0·46 ± 0·014 (S.D.). Since trichloroacetate inhibits colour formation, it should not be used for deproteinization. The rate of glyoxylate phenylhydrazone formation depends on the tissue extract analysed. Thus, the incubation time in minutes necessary to complete the reaction varies for 5 for bovine serum albumin to 30 for beef liver extract. In these instances use of the direct method resulted in pronounced turbidities concomitantly with colour production. Tissue homogenates analysed by the following procedures included *Neurospora crassa*, Em 5297a; fresh beef liver; fresh leaves of *Pelargonium zonale* and 5 g of *Lathyrus saturis* seeds.

Determination of glyoxylate in biological material.[33] *Reagents.* Buffer: 0·4 M Na_2HPO_4, pH 7·0, containing 10^{-3} M EDTA. Conc HCl, chilled to 0°. Phenylhydrazine HCl, 100 mg in 30 ml water; prepare immediately prior to use. Potassium ferricyanide, 500 mg in 30 ml water; prepared fresh. Glyoxylic acid monohydrate 100 µg per ml of 10^{-4} M EDTA; stored frozen is stable for 7 to 10 d.

Direct analysis. To 3 ml of aqueous test solution containing up to 15 µg of glyoxylic acid hydrate add 1 ml of phosphate buffer (0·4 M, pH 7·0) and 1 ml of the phenylhydrazine solution, mix and incubate for 5 min at room temp. Cool to 0° by immersion in an ice-water bath for 5 min while agitating vigorously. Add 1 ml of conc HCl followed by 1 ml of ferricyanide. Mix and after 15 min read absorbance at 535 nm.

Modified procedure. Run 3 ml of aq test solution through the same procedure as described above up to the stage of ferricyanide addition. Allow to stand at room temp for exactly 10 min, add 7 ml of chloroform–isoamyl alcohol (3:2), mix by vigorous agitation for 1 minute. Draw off lower organic layer, centrifuge briefly at 1000 g to clarify, and read absorbance at 520 nm.

K. Pyrogallol

Pyrogallol reacts with glyoxylic acid in conc H_2SO_4 solution to give a blue chromogen.[15, 34] Beer's law is obeyed from 0·05 to 0·5 µmol of glyoxylate. Glycolaldehyde and its precursors such as the glyceric acids react also but give a band at 570 nm. The spectra of some of these possible interferences are shown in Fig. 33.[34] Five minutes of preheating at 100° in conc H_2SO_4 is sufficient to destroy glyoxylic acid and abolish colour development with pyrogallol. In the following procedure an mε of 10·1 was obtained for glyoxylate at 600 nm.

Pyrogallol determination of glyoxylic acid.[34] To 0·5 ml of aq test solution containing 0·05 to 0·5 µmol of glyoxylic acid add 6 ml of conc H_2SO_4 and 1 ml of 0·3% pyrogallol in conc H_2SO_4 with mixing. Heat for 30 min in a boiling water bath, cool, and then read the absorbance at 600 nm.

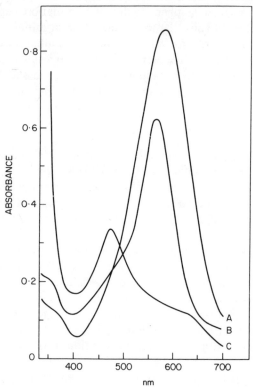

Fig. 33. Absorption spectra of chromogens formed by 3-phosphoglyceric acid, glyoxylic acid, and glucose. Conditions: 0·05 ml water, 3 mg pyrogallol, and 30 min postheating; total volume 7·5 ml; light path 1 cm. Curves: A, 0·5 µmole glyoxylic acid, no preheating; B, 0·50 µmol 3-phosphoglyceric acid, 12 min preheating; C, 1·0 µmol glucose, 12 min preheating.[34]

The pyrogallol procedure should be capable of further improvement through optimization of variables. Pyrogallolcarboxylic acid could also be used since it also gives a blue chromogen with glyoxylic acid.[81] Formaldehyde and acrolein only give orange colours.

L. Resorcinol

Glyoxylic acid has been shown to react with resorcinol to give the lactone

of 2,2',4,4'-tetrahydroxydiphenylacetic acid.[35, 36, 73, 82, 83] From this derivative 2 different compounds could be derived—one a red–violet chromogen
and the other a fluorogen. Both final products have proved useful in the
analysis of glyoxylate. The lactone has been postulated[84] and isolated[82, 83]
and also identified as the product of the condensation of chloral with
resorcinol.[84, 85] It is a colourless compound, insoluble in water and dilute
acids, and soluble in alkali to a blue–violet colour. On contact with air the
alkaline solution becomes red–purple and then orange with a yellow–green
fluorescence,[35] the final visible and fluorescence colours being due to a
quinonic compound.[86] On the basis of this data the following mechanism
can be postulated, Fig. 34.

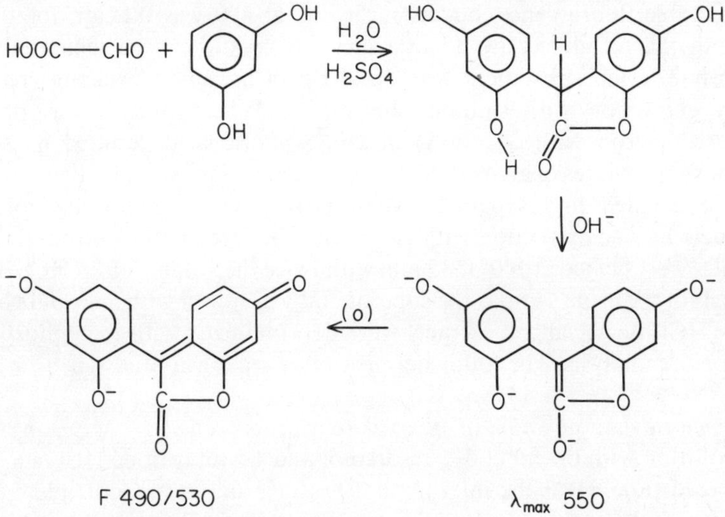

FIG. 34. Reaction sequence for determination of glyoxylate with resorcinol.

The colorimetric determination of glyoxylate has been described by
several investigators.[35, 73, 87, 88] Beer's law is obeyed from 20 to 100 μg of
glyoxylate. The determination is not interfered with by formaldehyde, acetaldehyde, formate, glycolate, oxalate and malonaldehyde.[28] The following
procedure is used.

Resorcinol determination of glyoxylate.[35] To 1 m of an aq test solution add
2 ml of 1 % resorcinol in 30 % H_2SO_4. Heat at 100° for 5 minutes. Cool, add
5 ml water and extract the chromogen with 5 ml ethyl acetate. To 1 ml of the

organic phase add 4 ml ethanol and 0·5 ml of alcoholic 1 N KOH. Read the absorbance within 10 min at 550 nm.

A procedure for the fluorimetric determination of glyoxylic acid in blood, urine and bacterial extracts has been described.[36] Sodium glyoxylate monohydrate was prepared and purified[89] and used as the standard. The criteria for purity of glyoxylic acid and its salts has been discussed.[31] In the procedure an mε of 1·63 was obtained at 490 nm. A linear relation was found for both fluorescence and colour from about 1 to 10 µg of glyoxylate. If a higher and more reasonable mε value could be obtained through optimization of variables, the sensitivity of the fluorimetric procedure could be improved considerably. The fluorescence intensity of the fluorogen is constant for at least 24 h when the concentration of the ascorbic acid is 0·55 M or higher.

As for interferences, glyoxal was the only compound reported to produce a detectable fluorescence, but its mε value at 490 was 0·12 or about one-fifteenth that of glyoxylate. If necessary, glyoxylate can be separated from other interfering substances with the help of an anion exchange resin[90] or by extraction with suitable solvents.[91] Where protein was present, deproteinization with 3% (w/v) metaphosphoric acid resulted in almost complete recoveries of glyoxylate. For serum and urine samples the fluorogen can be isolated and separated quantitatively from interfering coloured products by one extraction with isobutanol. Before analysis serum or urine samples were heated at 100° for 2 min with twice the volume of 1 N HCl. Before analysis of the urine sample, the supernatant was mixed with an equal volume of 1 N HCl. Bacterial cell extracts were deproteinized with metaphosphoric acid before analysis. The following procedure was then followed.

Fluorimetric determination of glyoxylate with resorcinol.[36] Mix 3 ml of the test solution with 0·1 ml of 5% resorcinol and 1·5 ml of conc HCl in a 10 ml stoppered tube. Heat the mixture at 100° for 5 minutes. Cool, add 5 ml of isobutanol, shake the tube for 2 min, and centrifuge. Transfer the isobutanol phase to a 25 ml stoppered tube, add 10 ml of 25% aq potassium carbonate and shake again for 2 minutes. After centrifuging, transfer the aq phase to a 25 ml volumetric flask, add 1 ml of 10% ascorbic acid and dilute to the mark with buffer (200 ml of 0·1 M K_2CO_3 and 800 ml of 0·1 M $KHCO_3$, pH 9·6). Mix and allow to stand for 30 minutes. Read the fluorescence at $F490/530$ within the next 24 hours.

M. Semicarbazide

Semicarbazide could also be used for the determination of glyoxylate; a band is obtained in the ultraviolet at λ 253 nm, mε 12·3.[92] Of course, other α-keto acids such as pyruvate and α-ketoglutarate would interfere.

REFERENCES

1. H. L. Kornberg, in D. M. Greenberg, Ed. "Metabolic Pathways," Vol. 1, 3rd ed., Academic Press, New York, 1967, p. 209.
2. D. M. Greenberg, in D. M. Greenberg, Ed., "Metabolic Pathways," Vol. 3, 3rd ed., Academic Press, New York, 1969, p. 112.
3. A. Meister. "Biochemistry of the Amino Acid," 2nd ed., Academic Press, New York, 1965, p. 354.
4. P. S. Cammarata and P. P. Cohen. *J. Biol. Chem.* **193**, 45 (1951).
5. M. Becker and H. Strehlow. *Z. Elektrochem.* **64**, 813 (1960).
6. K. Soda, S. Toyama, H. Misono, T. Hirasawa and K. Asada. *Agric. Biol. Chem.* **37**, 1393 (1973).
6a. T. Yorifuji and K. Soda. *J. Biol. Chem.* **246**, 5085 (1971).
7. V. P. Calkins. *Anal. Chem.* **15**, 762 (1943).
8. T. E. Friedemann and G. E. Haugen. *J. Biol. Chem.* **147**, 415 (1943).
9. D. Cavallini, N. Frontali and G. Toschi. *Nature* **163**, 568 (1949).
10. D. Cavallini. *Ricerca Sci.* **20**, 803 (1950).
11. T. E. Friedemann, in S. P. Colowick and N. O. Kaplan, Eds., "Methods in Enzymology," Vol. 3, Academic Press, New York, 1957, p. 414.
12. C. Kawano, H. Katsuki, T. Yoshida and S. Tanaka. *Anal. Biochem.* **3**, 361 (1962).
13. N. Ariga. *Anal. Biochem.* **49**, 436 (1972).
14. S. Mizutani, T. Nakajima, A. Matsumoto and Z. Tamura. *Chem. Pharm. Bull.* (Tokyo), **12**, 850 (1964).
15. W. R. Fearon. *Biochem. J.* **14**, 548 (1920).
16. J. Vachek and B. Kakac. *Cslka Farm.* **18**, 388 (1969).
17. M. A. Paz, O. O. Blumenfeld, M. Rojkind, E. Henson, C. Furfine and P. M. Gallop. *Arch. Biochem.* **109**, 548 (1965).
18. Z. Dische, R. Weil and E. Landsberg. *J. Biol. Chem.* **208**, 23 (1954).
19. M. R. Banner and S. B. Rosalki. *Nature* **213**, 726 (1967).
20. F. Wroblewski and J. S. LaDue. *Proc. Soc. Exptl. Biol. Med.* **91**, 569 (1956).
21. K. S. Henley and H. M. Pollard. *J. Lab. Clin. Med.* **46**, 785 (1955).
22. H. Klotzsch and H. U. Bergmeyer in H. U. Bergmeyer, Ed. "Methods of Enzymatic Analysis," Academic Press, New York, 1963, p. 300.
23. E. Juni and G. A. Heym. *Anal. Biochem.* **4**, 143 (1962).
24. J. E. Spikner and J. C. Towne. *Anal. Chem.* **34**, 1469 (1962).
25. G. Durand. *Compt. Rend.* **252**, 3479 (1961).
26. L. Josimovic. *Anal. Chim. Acta* **62**, 210 (1972).
27. G. H. Dixon and H. L. Kornberg. *Biochem. J.* **72**, 3p (1959).
28. G. D. Vogels and C. Van Der Drift. *Anal. Biochem.* **33**, 143 (1970).
29. M. Matsui. M. Okada and M. Ishidate. *Anal. Biochem.* **12**, 143 (1965).
30. N. S. T. Lui and O. A. Roels. *Anal. Biochem.* **38**, 202 (1970).
31. B. A. McFadden and W. V. Howes. *Anal. Biochem.* **1**, 240 (1960).
32. D. N. Kramer, N. Klein and R. A. Baselice. *Anal. Chem.* **31**, 250 (1959).
33. J. Nirmala and K. S. Sastry. *Anal. Biochem.* **47**, 218 (1972).
34. E. L. Coe. *Anal. Biochem.* **10**, 236 (1965).
35. M. Pesez and J. Bartos. *Bull. Soc. Chim. France* 481 (1960).
36. P. M. Zarembski and A. Hodgkinson. *Biochem. J.* **96**, 218 (1965).
37. A. M. Albrecht, W. I. Scher and H. J. Vogel. *Anal. Chem.* **34**, 398 (1962).
38. H. Katsuki, T. Yoshida, C. Tanegashima and S. Tanaka. *Anal. Biochem.* **24**, 112 (1968).

39. D. Cavallini and N. Frontali. *Biochem. Biophys. Acta* **13**, 439 (1954).
40. D. Seligson and B. Shapiro. *Anal. Chem.* **24**, 754 (1952).
41. S. Markees. *Experientia* **11**, 205 (1955).
42. H. Katsuki, C. Kawano, T. Yoshida, H. Kanayuki and S. Tanaka. *Anal. Biochem.* **2**, 433 (1961).
43. G. H. N. Towers and D. C. Mortimer. *Nature* **174**, 1189 (1954).
44. S. Ratner, V. Nocito and D. E. Green. *J. Biol. Chem.* **152**, 119 (1944).
45. C. Neuberg and K. Kobel. *Biochem. Z.* **256**, 475 (1932).
46. M. F. S. El Hawary and R. H. S. Thompson. *Biochem. J.* **53**, 341 (1953).
47. P. Ronkainen. *J. Chromatog.* **11**, 228 (1963).
48. A. Meister and P. A. Abendschein. *Anal. Chem.* **28**, 171 (1956).
49. G. H. N. Towers, F. C. Steward and J. F. J. Thompson. *J. Am. Chem. Soc.* **76**, 2392 (1954).
50. M. Alfthan and A. I. Virtanen. *Acta Chem. Scand.* **9**, 186 (1955).
51. A. I. Virtanen, J. K. Miettinen and H. Kunttu. *Acta Chem. Scand.* **7**, 38 (1953).
52. I. Smith and M. J. Smith in I. Smith, Ed. Chromatographic and Electrophoretic Techniques, Vol. I, Interscience, New York, Third edition, 1969, pp. 41, 340.
53. A. Meister. *J. Biol. Chem.* **197**, 309 (1952).
54. M. F. Utter. *The Enzymes* **5**, 320 (1961).
55. P. K. Stumpf. *J. Biol. Chem.* **159**, 529 (1945).
56. K. Soda. *Agric. Biol. Chem.* **31**, 1054 (1967).
57. J. R. Quayle and G. A. Taylor. *Biochem. J.* **78**, 611 (1961).
58. J. R. Quayle. *Biochem. J.* **87**, 368 (1963).
59. J. R. Quayle. *Methods in Enzymology* **9**, 342 (1966).
60. N. A. N. Rao and T. Ramakrishnan. *Biochem. Biophys. Acta* **58**, 262 (1962).
61. J. S. Thompson and K. E. Richardson. *J. Biol. Chem.* **242**, 3614 (1967).
62. K. E. Richardson and N. E. Tolbert. *J. Biol. Chem.* **236**, 1280 (1961).
63. K. S. Choi, K. W. Lee and A. H. Roush. *Anal. Biochem.* **17**, 413 (1966).
64. K. S. Choi, K. W. Lee, S. C. Yu Hico and A. H. Roush. *Arch. Biochem. Biophys.* **126**, 261 (1968).
65. R. Singh. *Phytochem.* **7**, 1503 (1968).
66. K. W. Lee and A. H. Roush. *Arch. Biochem. Biophys.* **108**, 460 (1964).
67. E. G. Young, C. C. MacPherson, H. P. Wentworth and W. W. Hawkins. *J. Biol. Chem.* **152**, 245 (1944).
68. M. Florkin. *Compt. Rend. Soc. Biol.* **134**, 264 (1940).
69. D. E. Metzler and E. E. Snell. *J. Am. Chem. Soc.* **74**, 979 (1952).
70. R. Fosse and A. Hieulle. *Compt. Rend.* **179**, 636 (1924).
71. M. Tanenbaum and C. E. Bricker. *Anal. Chem.* **23**, 354 (1951).
72. D. N. Kramer, N. Klein and R. A. Baselice. *Anal. Chem.* **30**, 520 (1958).
73. L. Josimovic and O. Gal. *Anal. Chim. Acta* **36**, 12 (1966).
74. H. von Pechmann. *Ber.* **25**, 3175 (1892).
75. P. Grammaticakis. *Compt. Rend.* **225**, 684 (1947).
76. B. Hirsch. *Ann.* **637**, 189 (1960).
77. L. Hausser, D. Jerchel and R. Kuhn. *Chem. Ber.* **82**, 515 (1949).
78. M. T. LeBris. *Ann. Chim.* (*Paris*) **11**, 328 (1956).
79. M. T. LeBris and H. Wahl. *Compt. Rend.* **241**, 1143 (1955).
80. I. R. Kennedy and M. J. Dilworth. *Biochim. Biophys. Acta* **67**, 226 (1963).
81. E. Eegriwe. *Z. Anal. Chem.* **100**, 34 (1935).
82. R. Badre. *Bull. Soc. Chim. France* **10**, 46 (1943).
83. P. Vieles and R. Badre. *Bull. Soc. Chim. France* **14**, 247 (1947).

84. J. T. Hewitt and F. G. Pope. *J. Chem. Soc.* **71**, 1084 (1897).
85. J. T. Hewitt and F. G. Pope. *J. Chem. Soc.* **69**, 1265 (1896).
86. M. Pesez. *Ann. Pharm. France* **9**, 187 (1951).
87. M. Pesez. *Bull. Soc. Chim. France* **3**, 676, 2072 (1936).
88. M. Pesez. *J. Pharm. Chim.* **2**, 325 (1942).
89. N. S. Radin and D. E. Metzler. *Biochem. Prep.* **4**, 60 (1955).
90. I. Zelitch. *J. Biol. Chem.* **233**, 1299 (1958).
91. R. M. Buckle. *Clin. Sci.* **25**, 207 (1963).
92. J. A. Olson. *Arch. Biochem. Biophys.* **85**, 225 (1959).

36. 2,4-HEXADIENAL (SORBALDEHYDE)

$$CH_3-CH=CH-CH=CH-CHO$$

I. PHYSICAL AND SPECTRAL PROPERTIES

B.p. 173–174/754 mm, 76°/30 mm, 64 to 66°/11 mm. D_4^{22} 0·9087, n_D^{20} 1·5372.

The ultraviolet absorption spectra of this aldehyde in water, alcohol and hexane and its MBTH azine are compared with the analogous spectra of acetaldehyde and crotonaldehyde, Table 14.

Table 14. Spectral data (λ_{max}, mɛ) for 2,4-hexadienal and its homologues and their MBTH azines

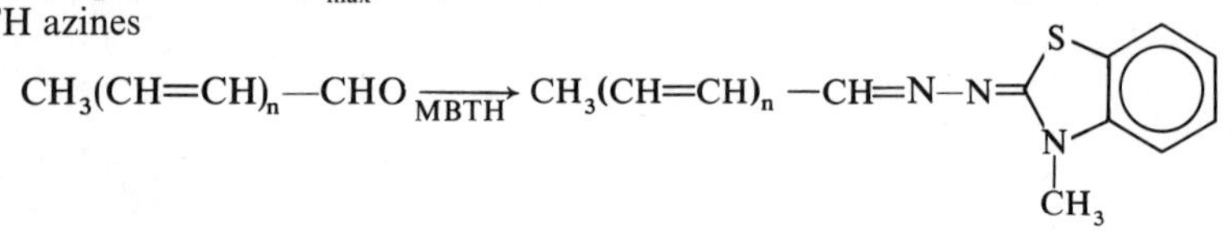

$$CH_3(CH=CH)_n-CHO \xrightarrow{MBTH} CH_3(CH=CH)_n-CH=N-N=$$

	Free aldehyde			
n	Water	Ethanol	Heptane	Azine[a][1]
0	277, 0·008[2,3]		290, 0·017[4]	306, 22
1	305, 0·042[5]	318, 0·03[6]	327, 0·023[7]	330, 30
2[c]	280, 29·5[8]	271, 30·9[9]	260[b], 28·8[8]	362, 33

[a] In 10% aq ethanol.
[b] In isooctane.
[c] See also Refs. 10–12.

This aldehyde can be characterized and analysed through its absorption spectra or through its MBTH azine. The procedure using MBTH[1] has been described in the aliphatic aldehydes section.

REFERENCES

1. M. A. Paz, O. O. Blumenfeld, M. Rojkind, E. Henson, C. Furfine and P. M. Gallop. *Arch. Biochem. Biophys.* **109**, 548 (1965).

2. A.P.I. Research Project No. 44, I, 326 (1949).
3. G. Mackinney and O. Temmer. *J. Am. Chem. Soc.* **70**, 3586 (1948).
4. G. W. Meadows and B. deB. Darwent. *Can. J. Chem.* **30**, 501 (1952).
5. A.P.I. Research Project No. 4, I, 332 (1949).
6. A.P.I. Research Project No. 44, I, 330 (1949).
7. N. S. Bayliss and E. G. McRae. *J. Phys. Chem.* **58**, 1006 (1954).
8. E. M. Kosower and T. S. Sorenson. *J. Org. Chem.* **28**, 692 (1963).
9. E. L. Pippen and M. Nonaka. *J. Org. Chem.* **23**, 1580 (1958).
10. J. A. Barltrop and J. E. Saxton. *J. Chem. Soc.* 1038 (1952).
11. E. R. Blout and M. Fields. *J. Am. Chem. Soc.* **70**, 189 (1948).
12. P. Y. Blanc. *Helv. Chim. Acta* **44**, 607 (1961).

37. 4-HYDROXYBENZALDEHYDE

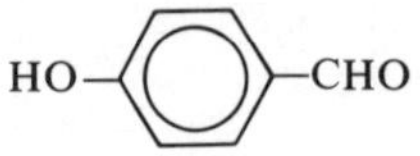

$$HO-\bigcirc-CHO$$

I. PHYSICAL PROPERTIES

M.p. 116–117°. Difficultly soluble in cold water.

II. pH EFFECTS

The absorption spectrum of this aldehyde changes with the pH, Table 15. Addition of alkali to the neutral compound results in the formation of the anion, which absorbs at longer wavelength and greater intensity than the neutral molecule. In conc H_2SO_4 the cation is formed; this chromogen absorbs at even longer wavelength and with greater intensity.

The addition of a drop of conc H_2SO_4 to a methanolic solution of the compound results in the formation of the acetal, which is iso-pi-electronic to m-cresol.[11] This step could be useful in characterization or blank-formation. Unlike the original aldehyde, the acetal is fluorescent and could be assayed at $F281/312$.[12] In this fashion p-hydroxybenzaldehyde could be analysed fluorimetrically.

In studies on grass lignins it has been shown that p-hydroxybenzaldehyde, vanillin and syringaldehyde can be separated by TLC and quantitated.[12, 13] In the following procedure $100 \pm 1.4\%$ recoveries of p-hydroxybenzaldehyde were obtained. Beer's law is obeyed.

TLC determination of p-*hydroxybenzaldehyde, vanillin and syringaldehyde.*[12] To remove iron treat silica gel G with ethanol–conc HCl (9:1) for 30 min, wash with ethanol, and dry at 110°. Spread this silica gel on glass plates to give layers of 0·3 to 0·4 mm thickness. Activate plates at 110° for 30 minutes. Spot and develop with n-hexane–isoamyl alcohol–acetic acid (100:16:0·25). After development, determine the positions of the aldehydes on one of the plates or

Table 15. Ultraviolet absorption spectra of 4-hydroxybenzaldehyde

Solvent	λ_{max}	mε	Ref.
Hexane	265–6	19·0	1
	274s	15·5	
	281	12·0	
	288[a]	6·0	
Ethanol	221	13·8	3
	284	17·4	
	332s	0·18	
50% Alcohol–HCl	285	16·6	4
10% Methanol	204	8·7	5
	221	12·3	
	279s	15·5	
	283	15·5	
	289s	13·8	
0·1 N HCl	220	12·0	6–8
	284	15·9	
0·01 M NaOEt–ethanol	330	7·9	9
50% EtOH–NaOH	336	24·6	4
EtOH, KOH	240	7·2	10
	336	29·5	
0·1 N NaOH	238	7·3	6–8
	330	27·5	
95% H_2SO_4	226	5·6	8
	336	30·2	

[a]Also band at 318 nm, mε 0·10.[2]

on part of a plate containing the standards with DNPH (1 g in 300 ml conc HCl diluted to 1 litre with water). Carefully scrape off corresponding zones of the adsorbent containing the unknown. Scrape a zone of adsorbent above the solvent front into a tube to serve as a blank. Add 10 ml ethanol to each tube, shake and centrifuge at 1400 g for 10 minutes. Decant supernatant into another centrifuge tube containing 0·05 ml of 1·25 N KOH and shake. Centrifuge if any precipitate forms. Read the absorbance at 335 nm (p-hydroxy-benzaldehyde), 352 nm (vanillin), and 368 nm (syringaldehyde). Difference spectra can also be utilized in the assay of these compounds.[14]

III. PHOSPHORIMETRY

Phosphorimetry can also be used in the analysis of p-hydroxybenzaldehyde and analogous compounds.[14] The phosphorescence excitation and emission spectra of 4-hydroxybenzaldehyde and its cation are shown in Fig. 35. The anion should also be phosphorescent, as has been shown for *p*-hydroxy-acetophenone and *p*-hydroxybenzophenone.[14] The method is highly sensitive and could be used to assay this aldehyde directly on a chromatogram or a pherogram.

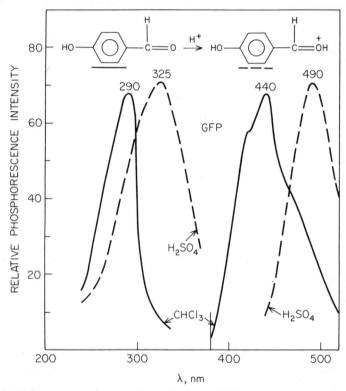

FIG. 35. Phosphorescence excitation and emission spectra of 4-hydroxybenzaldehyde (0·012 μg) on glass fibre paper. In 10 μl of chloroform (———); in 10 μl of conc H_2SO_4 (-----).

We will now discuss some of the colorimetric and fluorimetric procedures which can or could be used for the determination of this aldehyde.

IV. REAGENTS

A. Azulene

Azulene has been used as a sensitive location agent for *p*-hydroxybenzaldehyde.[15] The procedure could be optimized and applied quantitatively. For example, in the following procedure an mε of 15·4 is obtained at λ_{max} 508 nm.

Azulene determination of 4-hydroxybenzaldehyde. To the test substance in 2 ml of dimethylformamide–water (3:1) add 3 ml of 0·1% azulene in acetic acid followed by 3 ml of conc H_2SO_4. Mix and then cool to room temp. Let stand at room temp for 5 minutes. Read the absorbance at 508 nm.

B. Hydrazines and barbituric acid

Another reagent that could be used in the characterization and estimation of 4-hydroxybenzaldehyde is hydrazine. Thus, by spraying a separated spot of the aldehyde on a chromatogram or pherogram with a solution of 1% hydrazine dihydrochloride in water–conc HCl (4:1), a yellow fluorescent spot is obtained.[15] Less than a microgram of the aldehyde can be estimated on paper at $F388/490$.

On the other hand spraying a chromatogram with 1% barbituric acid in conc HCl–water (1:1) and heating at 110° for 5 min brings out a yellow fluorescent spot of **I** which could be used in analysis.

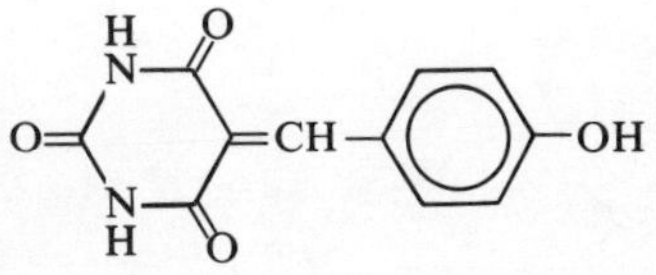

I

4-Hydroxybenzaldehyde could also be analysed fluorimetrically by reaction with 4-nitrophenylhydrazine. The fluorogen would be fluorescent in dioxane and non-fluorescent in alcohol.[16]

Salicyloyl hydrazide can also be used in the fluorimetric analysis of 4-hydroxybenzaldehyde.[17] The reagent fluoresces maximally at 425 nm and is excited maximally at 350 nm while the fluorogen, **II**, excites maximally at 390 nm and fluoresces maximally at 470 nm.

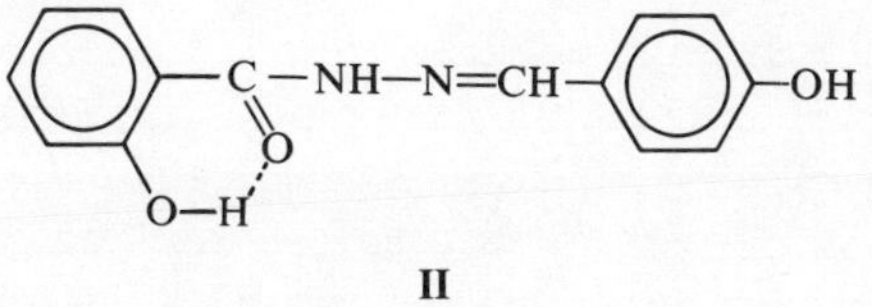

II

D*

REFERENCES

1. J. C. Dearden and W. F. Forbes. *Can. J. Chem.* **37**, 1294 (1959).
2. A. Bertoluzza and A. M. Marinangeli. *Ann. chim.* (Rome) **51**, 981 (1961).
3. N. J. Leonard, R. T. Rapala, H. L. Herzog and E. R. Blout. *J. Am. Chem. Soc.* **71**, 2997 (1949).
4. L. A. Cohen and W. M. Jones. *J. Am. Chem. Soc.* **85**, 3397 (1963).
5. P. Klinke and H. Gibian. *Chem. Ber.* **94**, 26 (1961).
6. L. Doub and J. M. Vandenbelt. *J. Am. Chem. Soc.* **69**, 2714 (1949).
7. K. S. Dodgson and B. Spencer. *Biochem. J.* **53**, 444 (1953).
8. O. Goldschmid. *J. Am. Chem. Soc.* **75**, 3780 (1953).
9. L. A. Cohen. *J. Org. Chem.* **22**, 1333 (1957).
10. H. W. Lemon. *J. Am. Chem. Soc.* **69**, 2998 (1947).
11. E. P. Crowell, W. A. Powell and C. J. Varsel. *Anal. Chem.* **35**, 184 (1963).
12. J. M. Brand. *J. Chromatog.* **21**, 424 (1966).
13. M. J. Reale. *Anal. Biochem.* **13**, 162 (1965).
14. E. Sawicki and J. D. Pfaff. *Anal. Chim. Acta* **32**, 521 (1965).
15. C. R. Engel and E. Sawicki. *Microchem. J.* **13**, 202 (1968).
16. E. Sawicki and J. Pfaff. *Microchem. J.* **12**, 7 (1967).
17. P. S. Chen, Jr. *Anal. Chem.* **31**, 296 (1959).

38. 5-HYDROXYMETHYLFURFURAL

$$HOH_2C-\underset{O}{\boxed{}}-CHO$$

I. PHYSICAL PROPERTIES

B.p. 115–120° at 0·5 mm, m.p. 35°. This aldehyde is much less volatile with steam than furfural and 5-methylfurfural. It is very soluble in water, methanol, ethanol, ether, chloroform, and benzene, difficultly soluble in carbon tetra-chloride, and insoluble in aliphatic hydrocarbons.

The commercial aldehyde can be purified by repeated crystallization from ether/petroleum ether to produce colourless crystals, m.p. 33·5° and a refractive index in the molten state of $1_D{}^{36} = 1·552.$[1] It can be stored in a dark cool place for several weeks without deterioration.

II. SPECTRAL PROPERTIES AND APPLICATIONS

The ultraviolet absorption spectra of 5-hydroxymethylfurfural has been reported in a few solvents, Table 16. The absorbance and wavelength maximum are unaffected by changes in pH over the range 3 to 10 or by a change in buffer.[1, 11, 12] Solutions of the aldehyde tend to deteriorate over the course of several hours.[1] The corresponding acid is formed with an isosbestic point at 264 to 265 nm, Fig. 36.[3] The long wavelength maximum of 5-hydroxymethylfurfural in water shows no change in absorbance from 14° to 31°.[3]

The compound, bis-(5-formyl-2-furfuryl)-ether, m.p. 114°, is obtained as a residue from the distillation of 5-hydroxymethylfurfural. It absorbs at λ 227, mε 5·7 and 281, mε 29·2 in alcohol and λ 230, mε 6·4 and 282, mε 28.4 in water.[3]

The long wavelength maximum of 5-hydroxymethylfurfural shifts to longer wavelength and most likely increases in intensity due to the formation of the mono-cationic salt, I, on the addition of conc sulphuric acid.

Table 16. Ultraviolet absorption spectra of 5-hydroxymethylfurfural

Solvent	λ_{max}	mε	Ref.
Water	228, 282·5	1·9, 16·9	2
	230, 284	3·2, 17	3
	283	16·9	4
	283	14·3	5
	230, 284	3·1, 16·7	6
	285	16·5	7
Phosphate-citrate buffer, pH 3·1–10·4	284	17·9	1
Borate buffer, pH 9·2–10·3	284	17·8	1
Acetic anhydride	278	20	8
28·3 N H_2SO_4	320	22·9	9
82% H_2SO_4	255, 318	5·0, 15·9	10

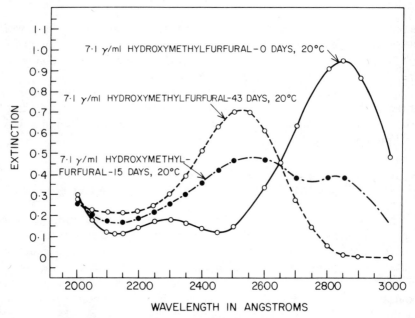

FIG. 36. Autoxidation of 5-(hydroxymethyl)-2-furaldehyde.[3]

I

This aldehyde has been determined through ultraviolet absorption spectral examinations of the decomposition products of caramel,[13] and pentosan mixtures,[14, 15] Tollens distillates,[16] jams,[17] heated sugar solutions,[18] wood and starch hydrolysates,[19] coffee products,[20] foammat orange powders,[21] stored caramel,[13] honey,[22, 23] and wine.[24]

We will describe a few of the methods available for the analysis of 5-hydroxymethylfurfural. Many of the methods in the furfurals and aromatic aldehydes sections could be of value here.

Table 17 lists some of the reagents which have been used in these analyses.

Table 17. Reagents for the determination of 5-hydroxymethylfurfural

Reagent	λ_{max} (mε)	Ref.
Aniline	363, (8·2)[a]	25
Anthrone	630	26–44
Azulene	500 (42)	45
Barbituric acid	550	46–50
Benzidine	400 or 420	51, 52
Carbazole	~600 (5·0)	53
Cysteine	410	54
N,N-Dimethyl-p-phenylenediamine	495	55, 56
Diphenylamine	630, (~28)[b]	53, 57–60
Hydrazine	F405/500[c]	61
5-Hydroxy-1-tetralone	F466/530	
Indole	500 (28.2)[d]	53
MBTH	360[e]	62
MBTH	670 (11·6)	62
N-Methyldiphenylamine	~650 (28)[d]	53
89% H$_2$SO$_4$	321 (25·0)	63
2-Thiobarbituric acid	443	64–66
Thioglycolic acid	550	54
Triphenylamine	~695 (13)[d]	53

[a] See Table 18 for data on long wavelength maximum.
[b] For purified dye.[53] In analytical procedure for 2-deoxypentoses mε 2·7 obtained at λ 645 nm for 5-hydroxymethylfurfural.[58]
[c] $F_{exc/em}$ on paper.　　　　[e] $t_{\frac{1}{2}}$ for reaction at 40° = 3 h.
[d] For purified dye.

III. REAGENTS

A. Aniline

With aniline a Schiff base, II, is formed which can be determined at 363 nm.[6]

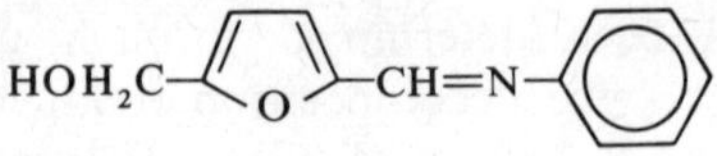

$$HOH_2C \underset{O}{\diagdown\!\!\!\diagup} CH{=}N{-}\bigcirc$$

II

Table 18. Long wavelength absorption maxima of the pure chromogens obtained from reaction of 5-hydroxymethylfurfural and phenylamines[5]

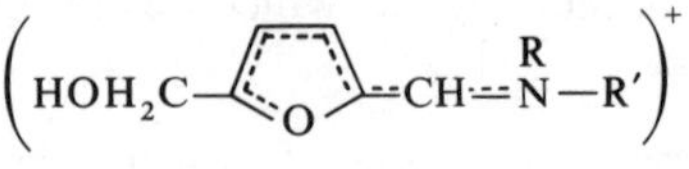

$$\left(HOH_2C \underset{O}{\diagdown\!\!\!\diagup} {=}CH{=\!=}\overset{R}{N}{-}R' \right)^{+}$$

R'RN—	λ_{max}	mε
$C_6H_5NCH_3$—	340	27
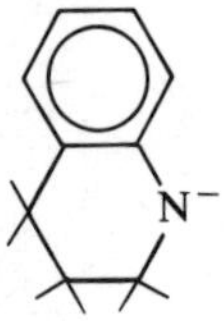 (tetrahydroquinoline N⁻ structure)	358	32
C_6H_5NH—	368	27
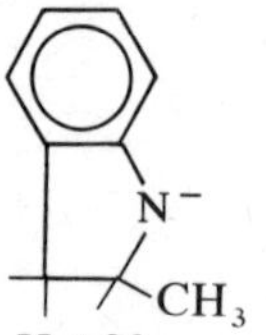 (indoline N⁻ CH₃ structure)	374	32
$(C_6H_5)_2N$—	375	23
$p\text{-}CH_3O\text{-}C_6H_5NH$—	390	24

Double distillation from slightly acidic solution readily separates the readily distillable furfural and 5-methylfurfural from the residual 5-hydroxymethylfurfural. The following procedure can then be used for assay.

Aniline determination of 5-hydroxymethylfurfural.[6] To the slightly acidic sample or distillate (pH > 4) add an equal volume of reagent. (Dilute 10 ml of cold aniline to 100 ml with 2 N HCl) keeping the temp at 25 ± 1°. Continue the incubation for 5 to 8 minutes. Ten min after adding the aniline reagent, read absorbance at 363 nm.

Furfural gave a band at λ 352 nm, mε 7·6 while 5-methylfurfural gave a band at λ 370 nm, mε 11·8, so if 5-hydroxymethylfurfural is not separated from these compounds (or from conjugated aldehydes), their presence would be a serious interference.

B. Azulene

Azulene can also be used for the analysis of 5-hydroxymethylfurfural.[45] An mε of 42 is obtained at λ 500 nm. The chromogen has the structure **III**.

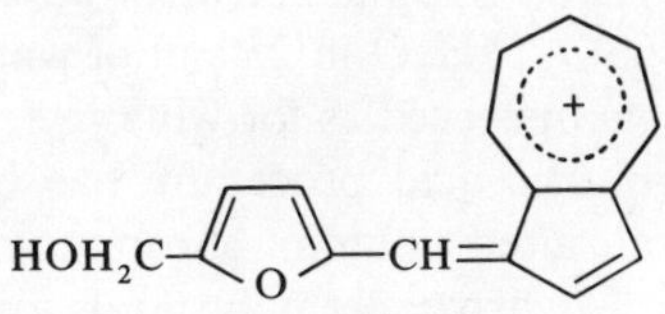

$$HOH_2C-\underset{O}{\overbigcirc}-CH=$$

III

The procedure is given in the furfural section.

C. Barbituric acid

Barbituric acid has been used for the determination of the aldehyde in wine and jam[47] and in tomato concentrate[46] to ascertain the suitability of processing and storage conditions. The following procedures involve the formation of the chromogen, **IV**.

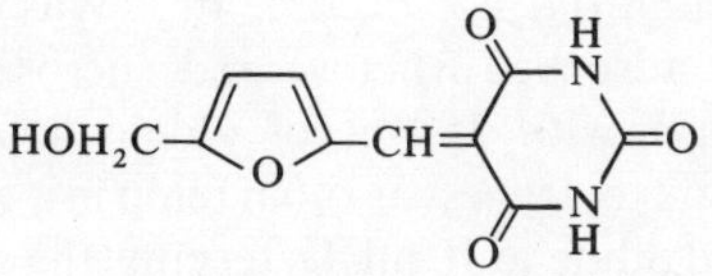

$$HOH_2C-\underset{O}{\overbigcirc}-CH=$$

IV

Barbituric acid determination of 5-hydroxymethylfurfural in tomato concentrate.[46] Mix the tomato concentrate with the appropriate volume of water. To 2 ml of test solution add 1 ml of 15% potassium ferrocyanide and 1 ml of 30% zinc acetate dihydrate solution. Filter. To 2 ml of filtrate add 5 ml of a 10% solution of p-toluidine in isopropanol and 1 ml of 0·5% aq barbituric acid. Measure the absorbance at 550 nm against a blank containing no barbituric acid.

This aldehyde may be present in sugar-containing foods that have been subjected to protracted heating above 70° in acid solutions, as for example in wines, musts and jams.

Barbituric acid determination of 5-hydroxymethylfurfural in jam and wine.[47]
Mix 2 ml of wine with 5 ml of freshly prepared *p*-toluidine reagent (Dissolve
10 g of *p*-toluidine in 50 ml of isopropanol, add 10 ml glacial acetic acid and
dilute to 100 ml with isopropanol) and 1 ml of 0·5% aq barbituric acid.
Read the absorbance at 550 nm against a similar mixture in which water
replaces the barbituric acid solution.

For jam homogenize 25 to 50 g of sample with 30 ml of water and clarify
the mixture with Carrez fluid (boil 180 g of lactic acid in 200 ml of potassium
hydroxide solution of sp. gr. 1·332 and 200 ml of water. Neutralize with dilute
acid. Add 34·65 g of $CuSO_4 . 5H_2O$ in 250 ml of water and dilute to 1 litre).
Dilute to 100 ml, filter and proceed as for wine.

The *p*-toluidine–barbituric acid procedure has been used to determine
5-hydroxymethylfurfural after column chromatography on charcoal.[49]
Recoveries of added 5-hydroxymethylfurfural exceeded 95%. Without
charcoal column cleanup diphenylamine,[57] *p*-toluidine–barbituric acid,[48]
resorcinol[67] and benzidine[52] methods for 5-hydroxymethylfurfural in
honey were unsatisfactory, primarily because fructose, a 5-hydroxymethyl-
furfural precursor, reacted also. In the following method 5-hydroxymethyl-
furfural is separated from fructose before analysis by the *p*-toluidine–barbituric
acid procedure.[48]

Determination of 5-hydroxymethylfurfural in honey.[49] Dissolve 2 g of honey
in 5 ml of water and add the solution to the top of the column (200 mm long
and 11·5 mm wide containing 1 g of water-washed activated charcoal). Add
three 5 ml amounts of water, which is drawn into the column by suction,
ensuring that the column did not become dry. Wash column with 100 ml
water to remove any adsorbed fructose and sucrose. Elute the adsorbed
5-hydroxymethylfurfural with 150 ml of aldehyde-free acetone, filter (if
necessary) and evaporate to dryness at room temp in a current of air. Dissolve
the residue in water and dilute to 10 ml. Determine the quantity of 5-hydroxy-
methylfurfural by the *p*-toluidine–barbituric acid method.

D. Benzidine

Benzidine can be used to determine 5-hydroxymethylfurfural after this
aldehyde has been extracted from glucose solutions with *n*-butanol[51] or
ether.[52] A Schiff base, V, is formed. Other conjugated aldehydes would
interfere.

V

The following procedure can be used. The reagent is unstable and can be stabilized through the addition of about 0·1 % of a reducing agent such as stannous chloride or potassium sulphite.[68]

Benzidine determination of 5-hydroxymethylfurfural in honey.[52] Dissolve 5 g honey (containing less than 0·004% of the aldehyde) in 5 ml water. Extract with ethyl ether (3 × 10 ml). Evaporate the ether from the combined extracts. Dissolve the residue in 10 ml of aldehyde-free *n*-butanol. To 4 ml of this solution add 5 ml of 1·5 % benzidine in acetic acid. Dilute to 10 ml with butanol. After 40 min read the absorbance at 420 nm.

E. Bisulphite and aluminium amalgam

Two other reagents that could be of value in the determination of this aldehyde are sodium bisulphite[14, 16, 69–72] and aluminium amalgam.[20] The bisulphite addition product is quickly formed and could be used to form the blank from the test mixture if other conjugated aldehydes are absent. The absorption due to 5-hydroxymethylfurfural in the 280 nm region is eliminated by treatment with bisulphite if the pH is kept above 3·7[70] due to the formation of **VI** with its decreased conjugation.

$$HOH_2C-\underset{O}{\boxed{}}-\underset{\underset{SO_3Na}{|}}{\overset{\overset{OH}{|}}{CH}}$$

VI

Bisulphite ion exchange chromatographic columns can separate the aldehydes, the 5-hydroxymethylfurfural being then determined at 283 nm with an mε 15·8 for the purified aldehyde.[14, 16, 71, 72] A typical separation is shown in Fig. 37.[71]

Aluminium amalgam reduction of the aldehyde group can also destroy the 283 nm band but 30 min heating at 100° is necessary.

F. N,N-Dimethyl-*p*-phenylenediamine

N,N-Dimethyl-*p*-phenylenediamine has also been used for the determination of the aldehyde.[55, 56, 73] A red chromogen, **VII**, is formed. Other conjugated aldehydes present in a test mixture would interfere.

$$HOH_2C-\underset{O}{\boxed{}}-CH=N-\underset{}{\boxed{}}-N(CH_3)_2$$

VII

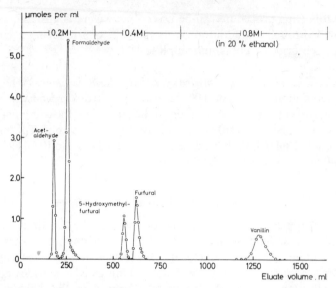

Fig. 37. Chromatography of acetaldehyde, formaldehyde, 5-hydroxymethylfurfural, furfural and vanillin on Dowex 1-X8 in bisulphite form. Column size: 11 × 410 mm; bead size: 150–300 mesh; eluants: 0·2 and 0·4 M NaHSO$_3$, and 0·8 M NaHSO$_3$ in 20% ethanol; flow rates: 0·27, 0·27 and 0·52 ml/cm^2/min.; fraction sizes: 6·5, 6·4 and 25 ml.[71]

The reagent can be used in the determination of the aldehyde in wines. Normal wines do not contain other analogous conjugated aldehydes.[73] Aliphatic aldehydes give a slight yellow colour and carbohydrates do not react. Red wines can also be assayed by the following procedure after clarification with mercuric acetate.

N,N-Dimethyl-p-phenylenediamine determination of 5-hydroxymethyl-2-furfural in sherry and grape concentrate.[73] To 0·5 ml of test solution containing 5 to 200 ppm of the aldehyde add 5 ml benzene and 5 ml of 1% methanolic N,N-dimethyl-*p*-phenylenediamine. Within 30 min read the absorbance at 495 nm.

G. Diphenylamine

Diphenylamine in strong acid solution forms a blue chromogen with 5-hydroxymethylfurfural or its precursors.[53, 57, 58] The chromogen has 2 main bands with maximum absorption at λ 520 and 630 nm. Fig. 38.[53] Several methods are available utilizing this reagent for the determination of 5-hydroxymethylfurfural. The original procedure was used for the furfurals.

Determination of 5-hydroxymethylfurfural.[74] To 10 ml of reagent (1 g of diphenylamine dissolved in 400 ml of anhydrous acetic acid and 11 ml of H_2SO_4) add 5 ml of aq test solution. Heat for 3 min at 100°, cool in tap water and after 2 h read the absorbance at 514 or 648 nm.

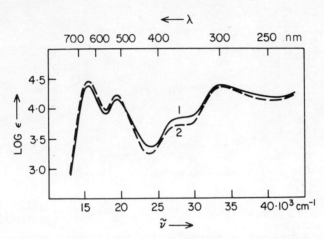

FIG. 38. Absorption spectra of chromogens from fructose or 5-hydroxymethylfurfural and diphenylamine–HCl.[53] Curve 1: Fructose (———). Curve 2: 5-Hydroxymethylfurfural (– – – –).

Reproducible results for 0·25 to 2 mg 5-hydroxymethylfurfural are obtained by measuring the absorbance at 648 nm after 24 h at 25°; under these conditions furfural gave weak and irregular absorbances and glucose, fructose and sorbose did not interfere. Beer's law was obeyed from 0·25 to 2 mg ml^{-1}.

With the Burton modification[75] 5-hydroxymethylfurfural can be determined in alcoholic beverages and fruit juices in the presence of glucose, fructose and sorbose.[57, 58]

Determination of 5-hydroxymethylfurfural in alcoholic beverages and fruit juices.[57, 58, 75] *Reagent.* 6 g Diphenylamine in 400 ml anhydrous acetic acid and 11 ml conc H_2SO_4. Just before use add 2 ml of 1·6% aq acetaldehyde (freshly distilled).

Procedure. To 10 ml of reagent add 5 ml of aq test solution. Read the absorbance at 480 nm after 24 h at room temp.

H. Hydrazine

Hydrazine can be used to locate, characterize and estimate 5-hydroxymethylfurfural separated on a chromatogram through the formation of a yellow fluorogen, Fig. 39. Thus, for example a paper chromatogram sprayed with 1 % hydrazine dihydrochloride in water–conc HCl (4:1, v/v) showed 10 µg of the aldehyde as a bright yellow fluorescent spot, $F405/500$.

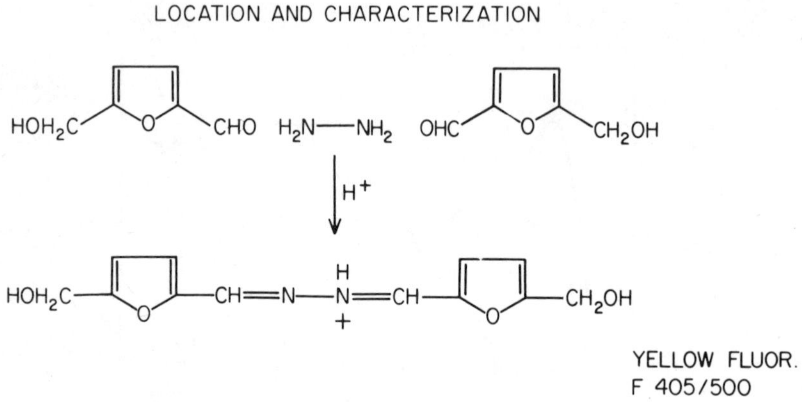

LOCATION AND CHARACTERIZATION

YELLOW FLUOR.
F 405/500

FIG. 39. Reaction of 5-hydroxymethylfurfural with hydrazine in acid solution.

I. 5-Hydroxy-1-tetralone

5-Hydroxy-1-tetralone is another reagent useful for characterizing or determining 5-hydroxymethylfurfural. Since precursors of this aldehyde are plentifully distributed throughout the environment, all equipment, glassware and chemicals used in these analyses must be kept scrupulously clean. In the following procedure a straight line through the origin is obtained for the fluorescence intensity of 0·5 to 7 µg of the aldehyde. The fluorescence intensity is stable for about an hour. Essentially negative results are given by furfural, 5-methylfurfural, furfuryl alcohol, formaldehyde, glyoxal, malonaldehyde, propionaldehyde and cinnamaldehyde. Positive results are given by 5-hydroxymethylfurfural precursors such as dextrose and fructose.

5-Hydroxy-1-tetralone determination of 5-hydroxymethylfurfural. To 0·5 ml of cold aq test solution add 2 ml of freshly prepared 0·02% 5-hydroxy-1-tetralone in conc H_2SO_4 (this reagent should not be over 4 h old) slowly with shaking and cooling. Heat at 100° for 15 minutes. Cool in icebath. Add 7·5 ml water slowly with shaking and cooling. Mix well. Read at $F468/530$ within the hour.

J. 3-Methyl-2-Benzothiazolinone hydrazone

With MBTH, 5-hydroxymethylfurfural can be determined through the azine, **VIII**, or through the formazan cation, **IX**.[62]

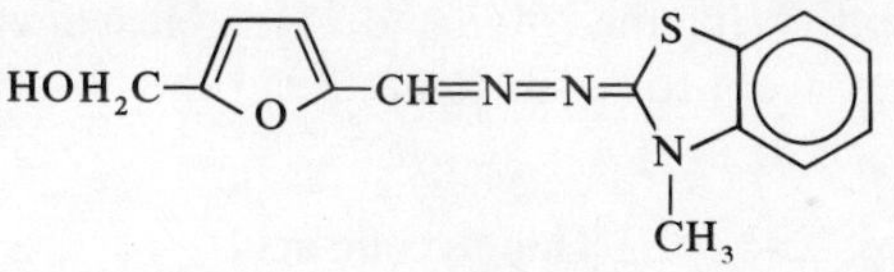

VIII

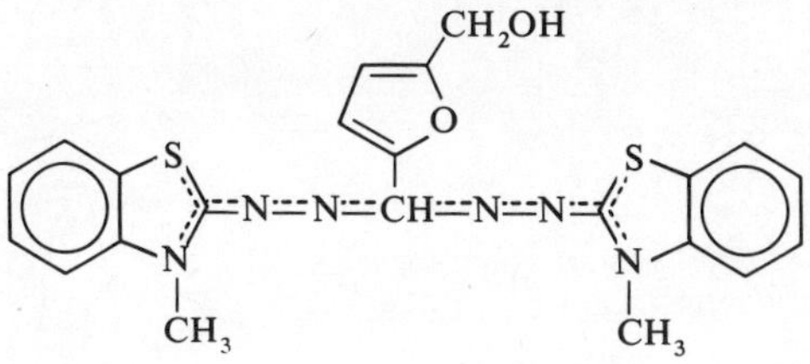

IX

The procedures are given in the aliphatic aldehydes section. The azine absorbs at 360 and 340 nm at pH 4 and 1, respectively, the formazan cation at λ 670 nm, mε 11·6.

K. Thiobarbituric acid

Thiobarbituric acid can be used to determine conjugated aldehydes.[76] Consequently this reagent has been used to determine the aldehyde in mixtures where other conjugated aldehydes are absent or can be separated from the test aldehyde. With the following procedure a relationship has been found to exist between the concentration of 5-hydroxymethylfurfural (a reaction product of the Maillard-type browning) and the degree of browning of spray-processed lactose.[65] Beer's law is obeyed from 10 to 90 μg. The colour is stable for approximately 1 h. The chromogen has the following structure, **X**.

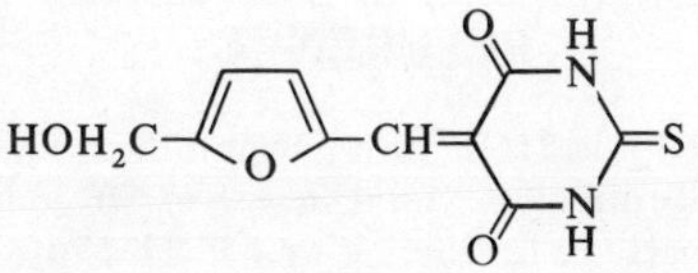

X

TBA determination of 5-hydroxymethylfurfural in lactose.[65] To 10 ml of a test solution containing 500 mg of lactose add 5 ml of 0·3 N oxalic acid. Add 5 ml of 40% trichloroacetic acid, mix and filter through Whatman No. 42 paper. Collect the filtrate in a 25-ml volumetric flask. Add 2·5 ml of freshly prepared (within 6 h) 0·05 M thiobarbituric acid. Wash the filter paper with sufficient pure water to bring the volume to 25 ml. Heat at 40° in a water bath for 30 to 40 minutes. Cool to room temp. Read the absorbance at 443 nm.

L. Thioglycolic acid

In the presence of 90% H_2SO_4, thioglycolic acid is dehydrated to thioglycolid, a molecule which helps to split the ring in 5-hydroxymethylfurfural

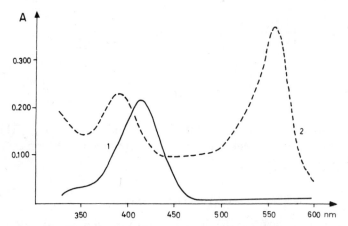

Fig. 40. Absorption spectra. (1) 5-Hydroxymethylfurfural and cysteine in 82% H_2SO_4; (2) 5-Hydroxymethylfurfural and thioglycolic acid in 90% H_2SO_4.[54]

to an open chain derivative which then forms the red-violet polymethine cation, Fig. 40.[54] On the other hand, cysteine reacts with 5-hydroxymethylfurfural without splitting the ring.

REFERENCES

1. T. Psarras, J. W. Tefteller and H. K. Zimmerman. *Rec. Trav. Chim.* **80**, 232 (1961).
2. G. Mackinney and O. Temmer. *J. Am. Chem. Soc.* **70**, 3586 (1948).
3. J. H. Turner, P. A. Rebers, P. L. Barrick and R. H. Cotton. *Anal. Chem.* **25**, 898 (1953).

4. J. F. Harris, J. F. Saeman and L. L. Zoch. *Forest Products Journal.* **10**, 125 (1960).
5. B. L. Scallet and J. H. Gardner. *J. Am. Chem. Soc.* **67**, 1934 (1945).
6. B. Singh, G. R. Dean and S. M. Cantor. *J. Am. Chem. Soc.* **70**, 517 (1948).
7. M. L. Wolfrom, R. D. Schuetz and L. F. Cavalieri. *J. Am. Chem. Soc.* **70**, 514 (1948).
8. G. Kallinich. *Arch. Pharm.* **291**, 274 (1958).
9. R. M. Love. *Biochem. J.* **55**, 126 (1953).
10. B. Mendel, A. Kemp and D. K. Myers. *Biochem. J.* **56**, 639 (1954).
11. J. Bielecki and V. Henri. *Ber.* **47**, 1690 (1914).
12. L. Fuchs. *Monatsh.* **81**, 70 (1950).
13. V. N. Nikiforova and V. B. Evstigneev. *Khlebopekar. i. Konditer. Prom.* **5**, 14 (1961).
14. P. O. Bethge. *Svensk. Papperstid.* **59**, 372 (1956).
15. H. L. Jones. *Tappi* **44**, 745 (1961).
16. P. O. Bethge. *Svensk Papperstid.* **63**, 813 (1960).
17. F. DeFrancesco and G. Margheri. *Boll. Lab. Chim. Provinc. (Bologna)* **12**, 5 (1961).
18. V. B. Erstigneev and V. N. Nikiforova. *Biokhimiya* **15**, 86 (1950).
19. E. Lindemann. *Stärke* **7**, 280 (1955).
20. R. F. Smith. *Analyst* **89**, 146 (1964).
21. R. E. Berry and J. H. Tatum. *J. Agric. Food Chem.* **13**, 588 (1965).
22. A. M. Piette. *Annls. Falsif. Exptl. Chim.* **58**, 40 (1965).
23. J. A. Gautier, J. Renault and M. Julia-Alvarez. *Ann. Falsif.* **54**, 397 (1961).
24. M. da Cunha Ramos and L. G. Gomes. *Anals. Inst. Vinho Porto* **45** (1967–1968).
25. T. E. Friedemann, P. K. Keegan and N. F. Witt. *Anal. Biochem.* **8**, 300 (1964).
26. L. Sattler and F. W. Zerban. *J. Am. Chem. Soc.* **72**, 3814 (1950).
27. R. E. Zipf and A. L. Waldo. *J. Lab. Clin. Med.* **39**, 497 (1952).
28. V. Kapuscinski and B. Zak. *Am. J. Clin. Pathol.* **23**, 784 (1953).
29. R. Dreywood. *Ind. Eng. Chem., Anal. Ed.* **18**, 499 (1946).
30. D. L. Morris. *Science* **107**, 254 (1948).
31. W. L. Brown, M. K. Young and L. G. Seraile. *J. Lab. Clin. Med.* **49**, 630 (1957).
32. W. F. Durham, W. L. Bloom, G. T. Lewis and E. E. Mandel. *Public Health Rept. (U.S.)* **65**, 670 (1950).
33. M. B. Handelsman and M. Sass. *J. Lab. Clin. Med.* **48**, 652 (1956).
34. O. Hansen. *Scand. J. Clin. Lab. Invest.* **12**, 18 (1960).
35. F. A. Loewus. *Anal. Chem.* **24**, 219 (1952).
36. K. Motegi. *J. Japan Biochem. Soc.* **21**, 40 (1949).
37. M. A. Nugent and D. G. Fleming. *Am. J. Med. Technol.* **24**, 8 (1958).
38. S. J. Prokhovnik and J. F. Nelson. *Aust. J. Exptl. Biol. Med.* **31**, 279 (1953).
39. J. H. Roe. *J. Biol. Chem.* **212**, 335 (1955).
40. C. D. Stienecker and M. S. Rheins. *Am. J. Med. Technol.* **25**, 377 (1959).
41. I. Takashita. *Igaku To Seibutsugaku* **34**, 130 (1955).
42. P. J. J. Van Munster. *Ned. Tijdschr. Geneesk.* **96**, 1345 (1952).
43. M. Templeton. *J. Histochem. Cytochem.* **9**, 670 (1961).
44. M. A. Verity and W. J. Brown. *J. Lab. Clin. Med.* **62**, 846 (1963).
45. E. Sawicki and C. R. Engel. *Anal. Chim. Acta* **38**, 315 (1967).
46. E. Trifiro. *Ind. Conserve, Parma* **36**, 314 (1961).
47. F. De Francesco and G. Margheri. *Boll. Lab. Chim. Provinciali* **13**, 466 (1962).
48. O. Winkler. *Z. Lebensm.-Untersuch. Forsch.* **102**, 161 (1955).
49. A. K. Dhar and B. R. Roy. *Analyst* **97**, 981 (1972).
50. W. Postel. *Dt. LebensmittRdsch.* **64**, 318 (1968).
51. Y. Yoshihira and M. Nakamura. *Seizan Kenkyu* **10**, 46 (1958).
52. B. Y. Rao and M. G. Taiwade. *Indian J. Technol.* **4**, 221 (1966).

53. G. Kallinich and H. Thies. *Chem. Ber.* **87**, 759 (1954).
54. G. Kunovits. *Anal. Chim. Acta* **55**, 221 (1971).
55. P. Linko. *Anal. Chem.* **33**, 1400 (1961).
56. S. Hunig, J. Utermann and G. Erlemann. *Ber.* **88**, 708 (1955).
57. A. D. Braun. *Byull. Eksptl. Biol. Med.* (*USSR*) **3**, 454 (1937).
58. R. E. Deriaz, M. Stacey, E. G. Teece and L. F. Wiggins. *J. Chem. Soc.* 1222 (1949).
59. C. Izard-Verchére, P. Rumpf and C. Viel. *Inds. Aliment. Agric.* **89**, 3 (1972).
60. C. Izard-Verchére and C. Viel. *Bull. Soc. Chim. France* 2089 (1972).
61. C. R. Engel and E. Sawicki. *Microchem. J.* **13**, 202 (1968).
62. M. A. Paz, O. O. Blumenfeld, M. Rojkind, E. Henson, C. Furfine and P. M. Gallop. *Arch. Biochem. Biophys.* **109**, 548 (1965).
63. R. W. Scott, W. E. Moore, M. J. Effland and M. A. Millett. *Anal. Biochem.* **21**, 68 (1967).
64. M. Keeney and R. Bassette. *J. Dairy Sci.* **42**, 945 (1959).
65. C. A. Brownley, Jr. and L. Lachman. *J. Pharm. Sci.* **53**, 452 (1964).
66. E. S. Della Monica, J. C. Craig, Jr. and M. J. Calhoun. *J. Dairy Sci.* **51**, 352 (1968).
67. J. E. Schade, G. L. March and J. E. Eckert. *Food Res.* **23**, 446 (1958).
68. J. K. N. Jones and J. B. Pridham. *Biochem. J.* **58**, 288 (1959).
69. H. B. S. Conacher and D. I. Rees. *Analyst* **89**, 806 (1964).
70. P. R. Smith, "The Browning of Confectioners' Glucose Syrups in High Boilings. 1. The Ultraviolet Absorption of Sulphited Glucose and its relation to Hydroxymethylfurfural and Colour Formation", The British Food Manufacturing Industries Research Association, Leatherhead, Technical Circular No. 251, March 1964.
71. K. Christofferson. *Anal. Chim. Acta* **33**, 303 (1965).
72. K. Christofferson. *Svensk Papperstid.* **67**, 540 (1967).
73. E. Meidell and F. Filipello. *Am. J. Enol. Vitic.* **20**, 164 (1969).
74. Z. Dische. *Mikrochemie* **8**, 4 (1930).
75. K. Burton. *Biochemistry* **62**, 315 (1956).
76. A. W. Dox and G. P. Plaisance. *J. Am. Chem. Soc.* **38**, 2164 (1916).

39. 3-HYDROXYPYRUVALDEHYDE (GLYCEROSONE)

$$HOCH_2-CO-CHO$$

I. PHYSICAL AND SPECTRAL PROPERTIES

This compound could be assayed through its anion $(O{=}CH{=}C{=}CH{=}O)^-$.
$$\underset{OH}{|}$$
It can be determined with MBTH giving a strong band at 391 nm[1] with $m\varepsilon$ probably around 30. The reagents used for pyruvaldehyde and glyoxal could be used here.

REFERENCES

1. M. A. Paz, O. O. Blumenfeld, M. Rojkind, E. Henson, C. Furfine and P. M. Gallop. *Arch. Biochem. Biophys.* **109**, 548 (1965).

40. INDOLE-3-ACETALDEHYDE

I. INTRODUCTION

Indole-3-acetaldehyde can be purified through recrystallization of its sodium bisulphite addition product followed by the liberation of the free aldehyde.[1]

Wavelength maxima and mε values have been reported for this aldehyde in ethanolic solution, e.g. λ 222, 280 and 289 nm and mε 32·4, 6·0 and 5·0, respectively.[2]

The determination of this aldehyde has been accomplished by the oxidation of the aldehyde with silver oxide to indole-3-acetic acid which is then determined.[1, 3, 4] Since the reagent used in this procedure contains ferric chloride, it is necessary to remove the silver ions through precipitation with phosphate or to substitute ferric sulphate for the chloride.

In the following procedure 0·015 μmoles of indoleacetaldehyde gives an absorbance of 0·05. Indole-3-aldehyde, indole-3-carboxylic acid, tryptophol and indole-3-acetonitrile show little interference except at very high concentrations. Indol-3-acetic acid would interfere but it could be readily separated from the aldehyde by extraction from alkaline solution or chromatography.

A. Ferric sulphate determination of indole-3-acetaldehyde[4]

Evaporate the ether test solution (containing 2·5 to 25 μg of the aldehyde) to dryness at 50° using a gentle current of dry air. As soon as the ether has evaporated add 1·5 ml of 0·02 M silver sulphate solution. In dim light and within 15 to 20 min add 0·5 ml of 0·12 N NaOH. Shake for 1·5 min and then add 2 ml of a modified Salkowski reagent (0·05 M ferric sulphate in 1·5 N H_2SO_4–water–conc H_2SO_4 (sp. gr. 1·84), 100: 240:160, v/v/v). Read the absorbance at 525 nm after 75 minutes. The colour is stable in the period from 60 to 120 minutes.

The indoleacetic acid formed in this analytical procedure can also be determined fluorimetrically especially around pH 6 and 10.[5-7] This acid can be measured at $F278/348$[6] and can be separated from some interferences by extraction from acidified solution with a non-polar solvent such as benzene and then returned to aq alkali. It can be determined fluorimetrically on paper[8] and on thin layer[9] chromatograms in amounts from about 0·01 to 2 µg. Alternatively, the acid can be determined by a more sensitive fluorimetric method involving reaction of indoleacetic acid with copper sulphate in the presence of approx 30% H_2SO_4.[10] Indoleacetic acid can also be determined phosphorimetrically in ethanol at $P300/40$.[11] The decay time in seconds is 7·1 and the detection limit is 4 ng/ml.

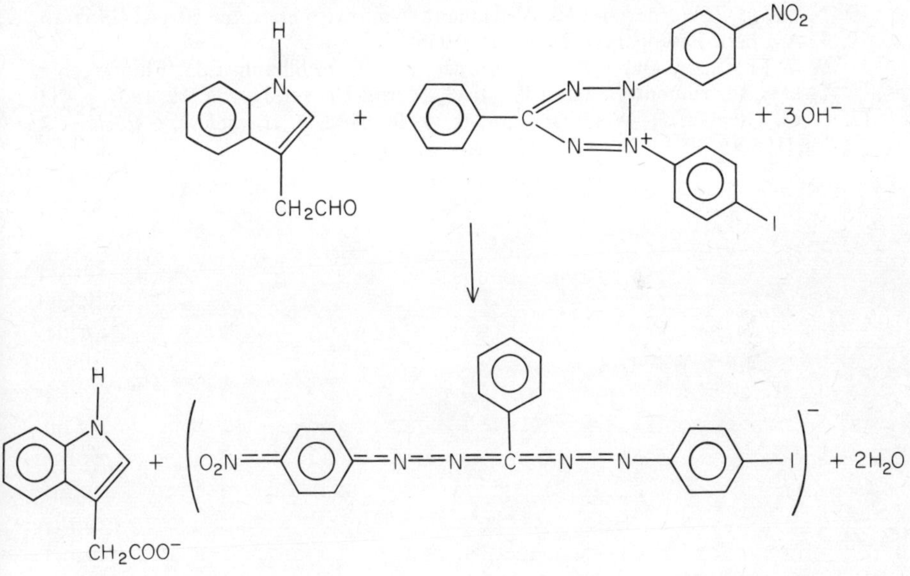

FIG. 41. Reaction of 3-indoleacetaldehyde with 2-(p-iodophenyl)-3-(p-nitrophenyl)-5-phenyltetrazolium chloride.

Indole-3-acetaldehyde could also be determined fluorimetrically or phosphorimetrically in alcoholic and/or acidified alcoholic solutions. It could also be determined through its absorption spectrum in strong alkaline solution or by some of the procedures in the aliphatic aldehydes section. It could also be determined through its reduction of tetrazolium salts[12] as shown by its reaction with 2-(p-iodophenyl)-3-(p-nitrophenyl)-5-phenyltetrazolium chloride, Fig. 41. The neutral chromogen or the chromogen cation could also be used in such an assay.

REFERENCES

1. P. Larsen and S. Klungsöyr. *Physiol. Plant.* **17**, 151 (1964).
2. J. B. Brown, H. B. Henbest and E. R. H. Jones. *J. Chem. Soc.* 3172 (1952).
3. A. J. Clarke and P. J. G. Mann. *Biochem. J.* **65**, 763 (1957).
4. P. Larsen. *Physiol. Plant.* **19**, 780 (1966).
5. H. Weissbach, T. E. Smith and S. Udenfriend. *Biochemistry* **1**, 137 (1962).
6. F. W. J. Teale and G. Weber. *Biochem. J.* **65**, 476 (1957).
7. H. Weissbach, W. King, A. Sjoerdsma and S. Udenfriend. *J. Biol. Chem.* **234**, 81 (1959).
8. R. Mavrodineanu, W. W. Sanford and A. E. Hitchcock. *Contrib. Boyce Thompson Inst.* **18**, 167 (1955).
9. N. Seiler, G. Werner and M. Weichmann. *Naturwissenschaften* **50**, 643 (1963).
10. V. A. Ebert. *Phytopathol. Z.* **24**, 216 (1955).
11. W. J. McCarthy and J. D. Winefordner, in G. C. Guilbault, Ed., "Fluorescence, Theory, Instrumentation and Practice", Marcel Decker, New York, 1967, p. 415.
12. G. G. Glenner, H. Weissbach and B. G. Redfield. *J. Histochem. Cytochem.* **8**, 258 (1960).

41. INDOLE-3-CARBOXALDEHYDE

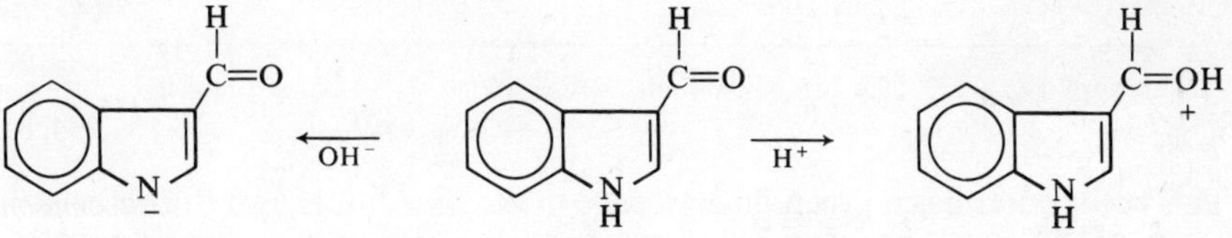

II   I   III

I. PHYSICAL AND SPECTRAL PROPERTIES

M.p. 194°.

With changes of pH, 3-formylindole can be present as the neutral compound I, the anion II, and the cation III. The aldehyde is a weak acid and has a pK_a of 12·36 in aq potassium hydroxide.[1] It is about as strong an acid as benzaldehyde 2,4-dinitrophenylhydrazone, pK_a 12·47[2, 3] or 2,4,6-trinitroaniline, 12·2.[4] Advantage could be taken of the somewhat different spectra of the neutral aldehyde and its anion and cation. In Table 19[5–14] are shown some of this spectral data.

The fluorescence and phosphorescence of the aldehyde and its hemiacetal or acetal derivative could also be useful in analysis. In addition, some of the methods mentioned in the aromatic aldehyde section would be useful here.

Other possibilities in analysis are shown in the properties of indole-3-carboxaldehyde 4-nitrophenylhydrazone, IV.

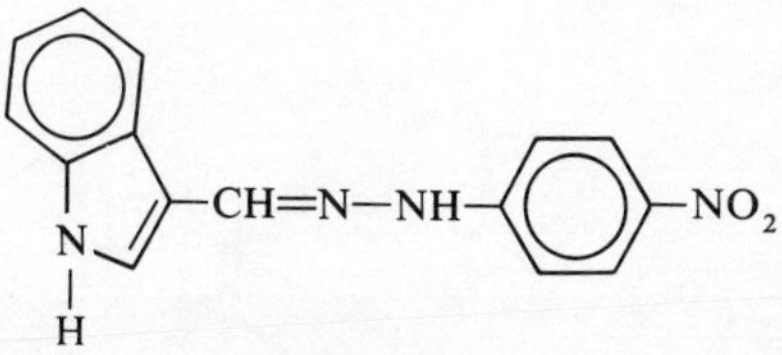

IV

111

Table 19. Ultraviolet absorption spectra of 3-formylindole

Solvent	λ_{max}	mε	Ref.
95% Ethanol	243, 260, 296	13·5, 11·5, 13·2	5–10
Water	210, 245, 262, 302	27·5, 12·6, 11·8, 13·8	11–14
0·02 N NaOH	250, 266, 327	6·3, 17·8, 15·8	11, 12
Water, pH 13	250, 270, 320	~10, ~16, ~13	8
EtOH–NaOH	265, 325	16, 16	9
EtOH–NaOEt	266, 326	20, 20·4	7
Conc H_2SO_4[a]	235, 265, 329	39, 54, 47	7

[a]Also reported λ_{max} 230, 255, 265, 330 and mε ~16, ~16, ~20, ~12·5, respectively.

This compound has a green fluorescence in dioxane but is non-fluorescent in alcohol.[15] In dimethylformamide its long wavelength band is at 440 nm, mε 30 and in dimethylformamide containing 2% of 10% alcoholic tetraethyl-ammonium hydroxide it absorbs at 582 nm, mε 48. The 2-benzothiazolehydra-zone, V, absorbs at shorter wavelengths in the same solvents.

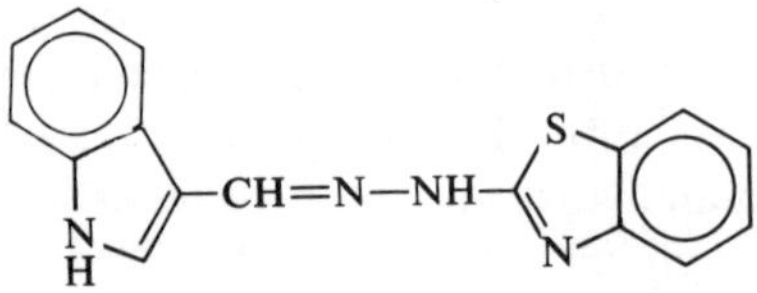

V

λ_{max} (mε)

Dimethylformamide	345 (38)
Alk. dimethylformamide	402 (60)
	478 (10)

3-Formylindole could also be determined with p-nitroaniline by optimizing the procedure used for p-dimethylaminobenzaldehyde and p-dimethyl-aminocinnamaldehyde. The chromogen could form an anion VI, which would absorb at even longer wavelength.

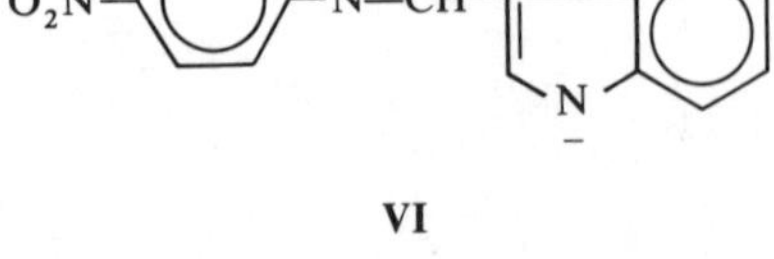

VI

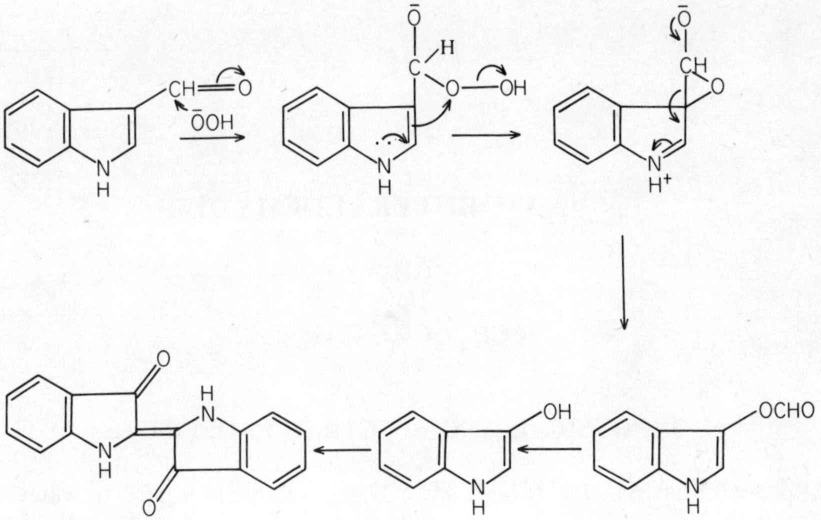

FIG. 42. Postulated mechanism for the formation of indigo from 3-formylindole.[16]

This aldehyde could also be determined by the reaction at room temp of hydrogen peroxide with an alkaline solution of the compound, Fig. 42.[16] Conditions would have to be optimized and the indigo would have to be extracted into an organic solvent before measurement of the absorbance.

REFERENCES

1. G. Yagil. *Tetrahedron* **23**, 2855 (1967).
2. R. Schaal and G. Lambert. *J. Chim. Phys.* **59**, 1151, 1164, 1170 (1962).
3. R. Schaal and C. Gadet. *Bull. Soc. Chim. France* 2154 (1961).
4. K. Bowden. *Chem. Rev.* **66**, 119 (1966).
5. B. Witkop, J. B. Patrick and M. Rosenblum. *J. Am. Chem. Soc.* **73**, 2641 (1951).
6. J. Smuszkovicz and R. C. Thomas. *J. Org. Chem.* **26**, 960 (1961).
7. R. A. Morton and N. I. Fahmy. *Nature* **182**, 939 (1958).
8. G. Berti and A. Da Settimo. *Gazz. Chim. Ital.* **91**, 728 (1961).
9. I. D. Spenser. *J. Chem. Soc.* 3659 (1956).
10. E. Wenkert, N. K. Bhattacharyya, T. L. Reid and T. E. Stevens. *J. Am. Chem. Soc.* **78**, 797 (1956).
11. R. A. Morton and N. I. Fahmy. *Biochem. J.* **72**, 99 (1959).
12. G. F. Smith. *J. Chem. Soc.* 3842 (1954).
13. P. M. Ray and K. V. Thimann. *Arch. Biochem.* **64**, 175 (1956).
14. D. Jerchel and R. Staab-Muller. *Z. Naturforsch.* **9b**, 411 (1954).
15. E. Sawicki and J. Pfaff. *Microchem. J.* **12**, 7 (1967).
16. A. Chatterjee, G. K. Biswas and A. B. Kundu. *J. Indian Chem. Soc.* **46**, 429 (1969).

42. ISOBUTYRALDEHYDE

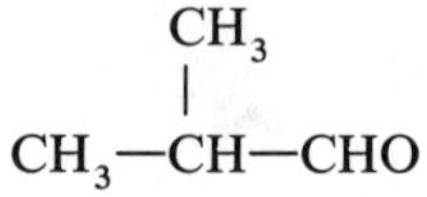

$$CH_3$$
$$|$$
$$CH_3—CH—CHO$$

I. PHYSICAL AND SPECTRAL PROPERTIES

M.p. $-60°$, b.p. $64°$, D_4^{20} 0.7938, n_D^{20} 1.37302. Soluble in 9 parts of water at $20°$.

The compound has a band of low intensity in the ultraviolet, e.g. in n-hexane λ_{max} 290, mε 0.0155.[1]

It can be analysed by many of the methods described in the aliphatic aldehydes section. Isobutyraldehyde in n-butyraldehyde can be determined by reduction with sodium borohydride to the alcohols and assay of isobutanol with a strong sulphuric acid solution of salicylaldehyde.[2] Isobutanol gives an absorbance at λ_{max} 550 nm that is 100 to 150 times more intense than that obtained with an equal quantity of n-butanol.

REFERENCES

1. E. A. Braude and C. J. Timmons. *J. Chem. Soc.* 3131 (1953).
2. G. R. Primavesi. *Analyst* **78**, 647 (1953).

43. MALONALDEHYDE

I. INTRODUCTION

This aldehyde is only known in aqueous solution and is acidic. With ferric chloride it gives an intense red colour. Other reagents useful in its analysis are shown in Table 20.

The diverse possible structures of malonaldehyde in neutral, acid and alkaline solutions are shown in Fig. 43; the structure is affected by solvent composition.[4] It exists predominantly as the thermodynamically stable enolic tautomer in aqueous solution.[2, 4, 9, 24] The main band ($\pi \to \pi^*$) is pH-dependent.[2–4, 25, 26] Dissociation of the enol, pK_a 4·65,[2] starts at pH 2·8 and is complete at pH 6·5 with the band at 245 nm derived from the chelate form, **IV** (stable below pH 2·8), and the band at 267 nm derived from the *sym-trans enolate anion*, **V** (completely dissociated above pH 6·5). The intramolecularly bonded structure of **IV** is supported by the volatility during distillation,[24, 27] disappearance of the $n \to \pi^*$ band at 350 nm[26] and the Sephadex gel elution characteristics of the compound.[28]

II. TECHNIQUES

A. pH and solvent effects

The effect of pH on the ultraviolet absorption spectra of malonaldehyde is shown in Fig. 44 (Ref. 2; see also Ref. 1). The absorption spectra of malonaldehyde and its anion are compared with the spectra of acetaldehyde, acrolein and crotonaldehyde, Fig. 45. The so-called $n \to \pi^*$ bands of malonaldehyde and its anion at 350 nm in this figure are probably mainly due to contamination since this band has an mε of 0·0078, Fig 46[4], and not over 0·1 as shown in Fig. 45. This figure demonstrates the problem in obtaining a correct mε value for an $n \to \pi^*$ band. The complete ultraviolet absorption spectra of carefully purified malonaldehyde at pH 1 (structure **IV**) and pH 7 (structure **V**) are shown in Fig. 46.

In organic solvents somewhat different effects take place. Thus in chloroform the *sym-trans* form, **III**, predominates as shown by nuclear magnetic resonance studies[29] and the presence of a 271 nm band in the ultraviolet

Table 20. Reagents for the analysis of malonaldehyde and its standards

Reagent	λ_{max} (mε) or $F_{exc/em}$	Ref.
Acid	250 (2·1)[a]	1–5
Alkali	267·5 (27·1)[b]	2, 3, 5, 6
4'-Aminoacetophenone	504 (67)[c]	7
	F520/580	7
p-Aminobenzoic acid	F475/520[d]	7
p-Aminobenzoate, ethyl ester	F500/550[e]	7
4-Aminodiphenylamine	427 (29)	7
Aniline	387 (48·6)[f]	7
Anthrone	510 (7·9)	10
	F485/560	11
Azulene	702 (142)	7
Barbituric acid	485[g]	12, 13
Benzenediazonium tetrafluoroborate	369 (~20)	15, 16
10,9-Borazaronaphthalene	514	17
9,10-Diacetoxyanthracene	F495/560	11
N-Ethylcarbazole	590 (34)	7
4-Hexylresorcinol	603 (46)	7
Indole	550 (60)	7
3-Methyl-2-benzothiazolinone hydrazone (MBTH)	670 (17)	18
2-Methylindole	555	19
N-Methylpyrrole	558 (85)	7
p-Nitroaniline	580 (74·6)	7
4-Phenylazoaniline	605 (46)	7
Phloroglucinol	543	20, 21
Sulphanilamide	F475/520	
4,4'-Sulphonyldianiline	F475/545	7
Thiobarbituric acid	530 (15·8)[h]	7

[a] At pH 1.[4] However, at pH 2·2 or in 1 N H_2SO_4 λ_{max} 245 nm, mε 13.[1, 2]
[b] In 3 % aq triethylamine.[6] At pH 12 λ_{max} 267 nm, mε 30[2] and above pH 7 λ_{max} 267, mε 31·8.[3]
[c] The pure neutral chromogen absorbs at λ_{max} 395 nm, mε 63·1 and its cationic salt at 409 nm.[8]
[d] The chromogen cation is said to absorb at 400 nm.[8]
[e] The pure neutral chromogen absorbs at λ_{max} 386 nm, mε 56·2, while its cation absorbs at 403 nm.[8]
[f] The pure chromogen cation absorbs at 388 nm, mε 55·5 in ethanol while the anion absorbs at 437 nm, mε 61·7 in dimethylformamide and the neutral chromogen at λ_{max} 360 nm, mε 42·5 in 96 % ethanol.[9]
[g] Pure chromogen absorbs at 495 nm.[14]
[h] mε values of 153,[13] 154[22] and 156[23] have been reported.

absorption spectrum.[4] This band is also found in solutions of malonaldehyde in dichloromethane and in diethyl ether–cyclohexane mixtures, Fig. 47. In a de-chelating agent such as diethyl ether[30] breakage of the intramolecular hydrogen bond would be expected to give a violet shift of the 245 nm $n \to \pi^*$

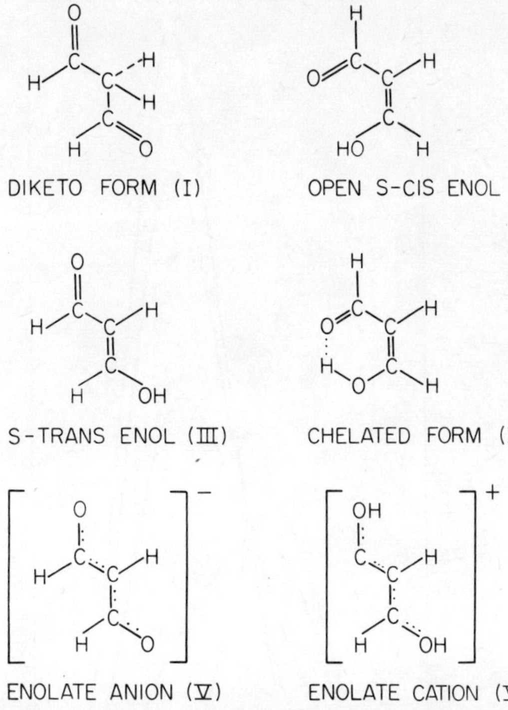

DIKETO FORM (I)

OPEN S-CIS ENOL (II)

S-TRANS ENOL (III)

CHELATED FORM (IV)

ENOLATE ANION (V)

ENOLATE CATION (VI)

FIG. 43. Structures of malonaldehyde in neutral, acid and alkaline solution.

band observed in aqueous solution. Thus, the band at 234 nm in diethyl ether or its cyclohexane mixtures is attributed to the open *sym-cis* form, **II**.[4] However, in cyclohexane the diketo form, **I**, predominates and even in dichloromethane 98% of malonaldehyde is believed to be present in the diketo form.

The spectra of the series $(O=(CH=CH)_n=CH=O)^-$ has been reported, Table 21. Of some interest is the report that the dipotassium salt of muconaldehyde, $(OHC)_2CH-CH(CHO)_2$, absorbs at 270 nm, mε 39·8 in water[31] as compared to the malonaldehyde anion at 267·5 nm, mε 27·1.

B. Iodine

Iodoform can be formed from malonaldehyde by the following reaction[5]

$$OHC-CH_2-CHO + 5 NaOH + 3I_2$$

$$\rightarrow CHI_3 + 3 NaI + 2HCOONa + 3H_2O.$$

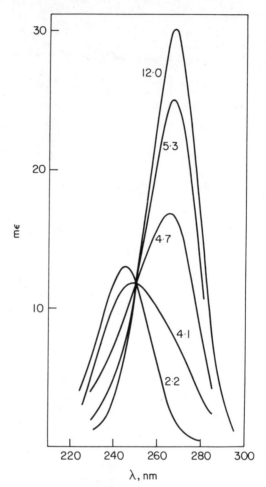

Fig. 44. The effect of pH on the ultraviolet absorption spectrum of malonaldehyde.[2]

The iodoform can then be determined with a quinaldinium salt. An $m\varepsilon$ of about 200 would be possible here.

C. Standards

Stable, readily available standards are necessary in the determination of malonaldehyde and its precursors because of the inconvenience of obtaining and handling pure solutions of malonaldehyde. For example, when 1,3,3-triethoxyprop-1-ene is hydrolysed with 1 N H_2SO_4 for about 3 h at room temp, a malonaldehyde solution can be obtained showing only one peak

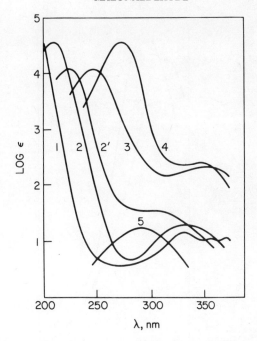

FIG. 45. Ultraviolet absorption spectra. Comparison of malonaldehyde and its anion with acetaldehyde, acrolein and crotonaldehyde.[2] (1) Acrolein in hexane (2) crotonaldehyde in hexane and (2') in water–alcohol (3) malonaldehyde at pH 2·3 and (4) at pH 11·3 (5) acetaldehyde in water.

at λ_{max} 245 nm, mε 13·7 at pH 0·4.[1, 2, 26] This solution is stable for at least one week at room temp. Similarly, 0·1 M aq solutions of malonaldehyde in 1 N H_2SO_4 or HCl are stable for over 15 d at 4°.[21, 32] If the pH of the solution is increased to pH 7 to 8, the solution is still about as stable. The absorption maximum at 350 has an mε of 0·0083, 0·0615 and 0·069 for solutions of pH 0·4, 7·15 and 9·5, respectively.[1] However, most of the standards in Table 22 can be obtained commercially and can be readily purified. The glycine derivative can be obtained in pure crystalline form.[38]

The structures of some of the chromogens and fluorogens obtained in the determination of the malonaldehyde standards are shown in Fig. 48.

D. 4′-Aminoacetophenone

With 4′-aminoacetophenone it is possible to assay for malonaldehyde and its precursors colorimetrically or fluorimetrically.[7] The aldehyde can be determined as its chromogen anion fluorimetrically and as the neutral

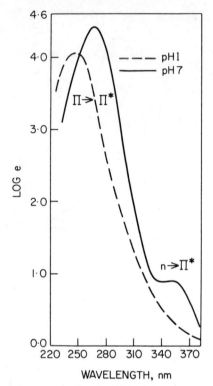

Fɪɢ. 46. Ultraviolet absorption spectra of malonaldehyde in aqueous solution at pH 1 and 7.[4]

Table 21. Absorption spectra[a] of malonaldehyde anion and its homologues[6]

$$[O\dot{=}(CH\dot{=}CH)_n\dot{=}CH\dot{=}O]^-$$

n	λ_{max}	mε
1	267·5	27·1
2	362·5	56
3	455	75·5
4	547·5	63 +
5	644	

[a]All spectra in dimethylformamide containing 3 % triethyl-amine except n = 1 which is in 3 % aq triethylamine.

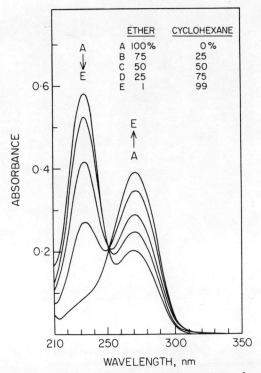

FIG. 47. Ultraviolet absorption spectra of malonaldehyde (4.5×10^{-5} M) in diethyl ether–cyclohexane mixtures.[4]

Table 22. Standards useful in the determination of malonaldehyde and its precursors

Substance	Ref.
β-Ethoxyacrolein diethylacetal or 1,3,3-triethoxyprop-1-ene	1, 24
Malonaldehyde bis sodium bisulphite	33
1,1,3,3-Tetraethoxypropane	3, 23, 34
1,1,3,3-Tetramethoxypropane	7
Sodium malonaldehyde	35–37
N-Prop-2-enal aminoacetic acid	38

chromogen (λ_{max} 390 nm) or its anion (λ_{max} 504 nm) or its cation (λ_{max} 419 nm) colorimetrically. The neutral chromogen does not fluoresce at room temperature but at liquid nitrogen temperatures has a bright green–blue fluorescence while the chromogen anion has a red colour with a brilliant orange fluorescence at room temperature and an orange colour with a

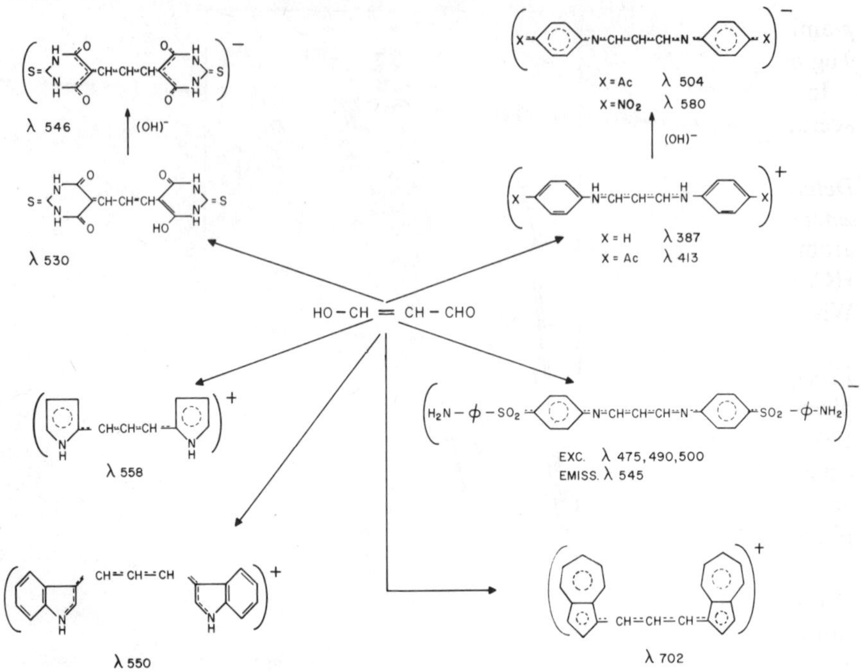

FIG. 48. Structures of some of the chromogens and fluorogens obtained in the determination of malonaldehyde with the appropriate reagents.

brilliant yellow fluorescence at liquid nitrogen temperatures. Procedures for the detection of malonaldehyde with 4'-aminoacetophenone, azulene, 4-hexylresorcinol, indole, N-methylpyrrole, p-nitroaniline, 4,4'-sulphonyldianiline, and thiobarbituric acid have been described.[39]

The pure chromogen obtained from the reaction of p-aminoacetophenone with 1,1,3,3-tetramethoxypropane as the malonaldehyde standard gave the following long wavelength maxima and millimolar absorptivities in the following solvents: dimethylformamide, 308, 20; dimethylformamide–conc HCl (99:1, v/v), 284, 13 and 419, 77; dimethylformamide–10% aq tetraethylammonium hydroxide (98:2, v/v), 527, 89; the spectrophotometric analytical solvent mixture in procedure B, 504, 82; and the spectrophotofluorimetric analytical solvent mixture, 518, 100.[7]

In spectrophotometric procedure B an approx 80% yield of chromogen is obtained from the malonaldehyde standard. With this procedure 1,1,3,3-tetramethoxypropane gave λ_{max} 504 nm, mε 67 while 1,1,3-trimethoxy-1-propene, acrolein and 4-pyridylpyridinium chloride gave long wavelength bands at 504, 482 and 450 nm with mε 45, 7·5 and 60, respectively. In the *p*-aminoacetophenone procedure B, Beer's law was obeyed from 0·44 to 9 μg of the tetramethoxypropane.

In procedure A tetramethoxypropane gave λ_{max} 413, mε 75 with *p*-aminoacetophenone.

Determination of malonaldehyde and some of its precursors with an aromatic amine. Procedure A.[7] Heat 2 ml of the aq test solution with 2 ml of 3% aromatic amine in 2-methoxyethanol containing 5% by volume of conc HCl at 100° for 3 min and then cool under the tap. Read absorbance at 387 nm. With aniline as reagent, the absorbance is stable for at least 8 hours.

Procedure B. Heat 1 ml of aq test solution and 1 ml of 3% *p*-aminoacetophenone in 2-methoxyethanol containing 5% by volume of conc HCl at 100° for 3 min and then cool under the tap. Add 2 ml of 40% methanolic benzyltrimethylammonium methoxide (with *p*-nitroaniline as the reagent use only 1 ml of alkali). Read the absorbance at 504 nm (*p*-aminoacetophenone) or 580 nm (*p*-nitroaniline). The colour is stable for at least 30 min.

Procedure C. To 2 ml of the dimethylformamide test solution add 1 ml of a dimethylformamide solution containing 1% of an aromatic amine and 1% by volume of conc HCl. Heat for 5 min at 100° and then cool to room temp. Add 0·5 ml of 10% aq tetra-*n*-propylammonium hydroxide. Read at $F_{exc/em}$ as shown in Table 23.

Table 23. Aromatic amine determination of malonaldehyde through spectrophotofluorimetry.[7]

Reagent	$F_{exc/em}$	Relative fluor. intensity
Quinine[a]	F350/450	1
4,4'-Sulphonyldianiline	F490/545	8
Ethyl *p*-aminobenzoate	F490/550	5
p-Aminobenzoic acid	F475/520	0·8
p-Aminoacetophenone	F490/580	0·5

[a]Standard

The fluorescence intensity is stable for 30 minutes. A linear relationship is found from 5 to 170 ng of aldehyde. Other aldehydes gave negative results. It is necessary to run this procedure in a highly basic solution so as to obtain maximum ionization of the polymethine dye, as demonstrated by Table 24 for the pure polymethine.[40] When aromatic amines such as 4-aminobenzo-

Table 24. Effect of solvent basicity on ionization and fluorescence intensity

$$Ac-C_6H_4-NH-CH=CH-CH=N-C_6H_4-Ac$$

$+1\%$ BAH[a]	H_	$F_{exc/em}$	Relative fluor. intensity
$CF_3CH_2 . OH$		460/520	0·3
$H . OH$	12·01		0·0
$CH_3 . OH$	12·66	460/525	0·2
$CH_3 . CH_2 . OH$	14·57	485/570	0·3
$(CH_3)_2CH . OH$	16·95	500/575	25·0
$(CH_3)_2C(Et) . OH$	18·09	505/570	40·0
$(CH_3)_3C . OH$	19·14	505/575	100·0

[a] 23% methanolic tetra-n-butylammonium hydroxide.

phenone or 2-aminofluorenone are used in procedure C, an intense visible colour is obtained but no fluorescence.

E. Other aromatic amines

p-Aminobenzoic acid or ethyl p-aminobenzoate can be used in these procedures. Procedure C was standardized with ethyl p-aminobenzoate. Water or alcoholic solvents inhibited the formation of fluorescence. A linear relation was obtained from 5 to 170 ng of aldehyde.

Aniline can be used as the reagent in procedure A: the chromogen, **VII**, results.

$$(C_6H_5-NH\!\!=\!\!=\!\!CH\!\!=\!\!=\!\!CH\!\!=\!\!=\!\!CH\!\!=\!\!=\!\!NH-C_6H_5)^+$$

VII[41]

λ_{max}	mε
242	13·8
384	56·8

Tetramethoxypropane gives λ_{max} 387 nm, mε 48·6 with aniline.[7] Beer's law is obeyed with 0·34 to 5 μg per ml of final solution.

Comparison of **VII** with longer chained N-methyl substituted analogues, **VIII**, clearly shows the importance of the length of the chain of conjugation between resonance terminals on the position of the long wavelength maximum and the intensity of the band.

$$(C_6H_5-\underset{\underset{CH_3}{|}}{N}\!=\!\!=\!(CH\!=\!\!=\!CH)_n\!=\!\!=\!CH\!=\!\!=\!\underset{\underset{CH_3}{|}}{N}-C_6H_5)^+$$

VIII[6]

n	λ_{max}	mε
1[9]	350	45
2	454	111
3	562·5	141
4	671·5	203

However, if N,N'-diphenyl ethylenediamine were used as the reagent for malonaldehyde the shortened straight line distance between resonance terminals in the chromogen, **IX**, decreases mε considerably as compared with **VII**

IX[41]

λ_{max}	m(ε)
230	6·9
380	25·2

The spectra of **VII** and **IX** were obtained in 1% methanol in buffer pH 2·2.

If **VII** and **VIII**, n = 1 are compared to **X**, it can be seen that the extraconjugation of the phenyl group results in absorption at much longer wavelength for **VII** or **VIII**, n = 1.

$$[(CH_3)_2N\!=\!\!=\!CH\!=\!\!=\!CH\!=\!\!=\!CH\!=\!\!=\!N(CH_3)_2]^+$$

X

λ_{max} 311 nm, mε 48·2 in 96% ethanol.

The chromogen obtained from the determination of malonaldehyde and its precursors with aniline is affected by pH, solvent and temperature changes.[9] The effect of pH and solvent is shown in Fig. 49.

Malonaldehyde dianil or 1-phenylamino-3-phenyliminopropene exists in a *cis–trans* equilibrium which is solvent- and temperature-dependent. The position of the equilibrium may be correlated with the tendency of the solvent to form hydrogen bonds. Essentially in some solvents there is competition between the intermolecular hydrogen bonds between solvent and chromogen and the intramolecular hydrogen bond in the chromogen. The effect of

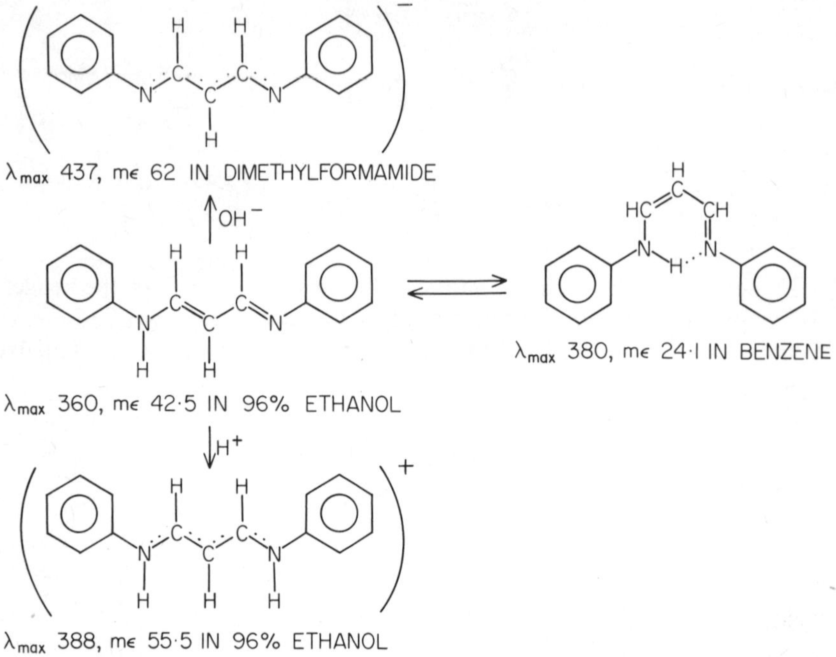

λ_{max} 437, mϵ 62 IN DIMETHYLFORMAMIDE

λ_{max} 380, mϵ 24·1 IN BENZENE

λ_{max} 360, mϵ 42·5 IN 96% ETHANOL

λ_{max} 388, mϵ 55·5 IN 96% ETHANOL

FIG. 49. Effect of pH and solvent on the chromogen obtained in the determination of malonaldehyde with aniline.

various solvents on the long wavelength maximum and the millimolar absorptivity of the pure neutral chromogen is shown in Table 25. In 96% ethanol the chromogen is present as the pure *trans* form; in the non-polar solvents mainly as the *cis–cis* form. With a decrease in temperature from 20° to −180° the wavelength maximum shifts to longer wavelength and greater intensity, e.g. in 96% ethanol λ_{max} 360, mϵ 42·5 at 20° and λ_{max} 373, mϵ 56·5 at −180° and in 2-methyltetrahydrofuran λ_{max} 364, mϵ 25·2 at 20° and λ_{max} 379, mϵ 43 at −180°.[9]

The malonaldehyde dianil cation does not show such striking solvent effects, e.g. in methylene chloride λ_{max} 388 nm, mϵ 48·5 and in ethanol λ_{max} 388 nm, mϵ 55·5.

F. Amino acids

Malonaldehyde–protein/enzyme interactions have been studied.[42–44] It is postulated that malonaldehyde–amino acid interaction is shown by the formation of 1-amino-3-iminopropene derivatives fluorescing at

Table 25. Solvent effect on the long wavelength maximum and millimolar absorptivity of malonaldehyde dianil.[9]

Solvent	λ_{max} (nm)	mε
Benzene	380	24·1
n-Hexane	377	26·0
Methylcyclohexane	379	25·9
Carbon tetrachloride	383	24·7
Chloroform	380	24·4
Triethylamine	375	25·1
1,4-Dioxane	370	24·6
1,2-Dimethoxyethane	364	25·2
2-Methyltetrahydrofuran	364	25·2
Acetonitrile	362	25·6
Acetone	362	26·6
Dimethylformamide	357	36·1
Dimethylsulphoxide	360	38·5
96% Ethanol	360	42·5
Methanol	360	43·2

$F$390/470–480.[42] This phenomenon and its analytical possibilities are worth investigating and will be discussed in the section on malonaldehyde precursors in a subsequent volume of this series.

G. Anthrone

The use of anthrone as a colorimetric[10] and fluorimetric[11] reagent for the determination of malonaldehyde and its standards has been described. It has been shown that α,β-unsaturated aldehydes condense with anthrone in sulphuric acid to give benzanthrone.[10, 11, 45–47] It is postulated that benzanthrone dimerizes to violet–red dibenzanthrone or green iso-dibenzanthrone.[10, 47] Aliphatic aldehydes could interfere in the colorimetric method, Table 26. Benzanthrone in the test solution gives λ_{max} 510 nm and mε 7·8.

Anthrone determination of malonaldehyde.[10] Add 3 ml of 0·2% anthrone in conc H_2SO_4 into the centre of 2 ml of aq test solution while mixing. Allow to stand for 10 min, cool, and read the absorbance at 510 nm.

In the fluorimetric procedure a 61% yield of benzanthrone was obtained in the determination of 1,1,3,3-tetramethoxypropane. The types of compounds reacting, essentially α,β-unsaturated aldehydes, are shown in Fig. 50.[11] The percent standard deviations for 10 determinations were ±4·5 and ±5·9 when determinations were made 5 months apart. The fluorescence intensity

Table 26. Colorimetric determination of malonaldehyde and other α,β-unsaturated aldehydes with anthrone.[10]

Aldehyde	λ_{max} (nm)	mε
Malonaldehyde	510	7·9
Acrolein	510	8·0
Crotonaldehyde	510	8·0
Formaldehyde	488	4·5
Acetaldehyde	476	0·83
Propionaldehyde	455	0·80
Butyraldehyde	476	0·30
Hexaldehyde	476	0·33

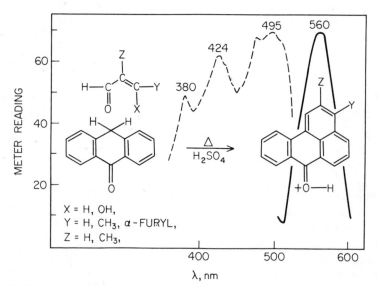

FIG. 50. Reaction of α,β-unsaturated aldehydes with anthrone. Spectra of final fluorogen.[11]

was stable for at least 6 hours. The concentration–intensity relationship was linear through the origin for 3 to 40 μg of the tetramethoxypropane. The data obtained by the following procedure is shown in Table 27.

Anthrone determination of malonaldehyde and other α,β-unsaturated alde-hydes.[11] To 2 ml of aq test solution add 3 ml of fresh 0·1% anthrone in conc H_2SO_4. Allow the mixture to stand for 10 min and then add 3 ml of glacial acetic acid. Cool and read at $F485/560$.

Table 27. Anthrone determination by fluorimetry of malonaldehyde and α,β-unsaturated aldehydes.[11]

Compound	Determination limit (μg)	$F_{exc/em}$
Crotonaldehyde	0·2	472/560
Allylidene diacetate	0·5	485/560
Acrolein	0·25	485/560
3,3-Dimethoxy-1-propene	0·4	485/560
1,1,3,3-Tetramethoxypropane	0·3	485/560
Methacrolein	0·7	485/570
1,3,3-Trimethoxy-1-propene	1	485/560
β-2-Furylacrolein	6	470/560

Pyruvaldehydes and their precursors also react but have to be analysed at $F$460/505.

H. Azulene

Azulene can also be used to determine malonaldehyde colorimetrically. In procedure A the intensity increases from an initial absorbance of 1·84 to 1·87 in 30 minutes. Beer's law is obeyed from 0·20 ($A = 0·1$) to 4 μg of 1,1,3,3-tetramethoxypropane. 1,3,3-Trimethoxypropene gives a band at 702 nm with mε 93. Aliphatic aldehydes give weak bands around wavelength 600 to 625 nm. In procedure B, Beer's law is obeyed from 0·53 ($A = 0·1$) to 11 μg of 1,1,3,3-tetramethoxypropane. The interferences are about the same as in procedure A. However, in procedure A an mε of 135 at 702 nm and a relative standard deviation of 1·7 is obtained as compared to $λ$ 702, mε 142 and relative standard deviation of 5·0 for procedure B. In the latter procedure the colour is stable for about 15 minutes.

Azulene determination of malonaldehyde.[7] *Procedure A*. To 1 ml of aq test solution add 1 ml of 0·5% azulene in glacial acetic acid, followed by 1 ml of 70% aq perchloric acid. Heat for 100° for 5 min, cool to room temp and then dilute to 10 ml with glacial acetic acid. Read absorbance at 702 nm within 5 min after dilution.

Procedure B. To 1 ml of aq test solution add 2 ml of 0·25% azulene in glacial acetic acid, followed by 1 ml of 70% aq perchloric acid. Shake, heat at 100° for 5 min and then cool to room temp. Read absorbance at 702 nm within 15 minutes.

I. Barbituric acid

Barbituric[12–14, 48, 49] and selenobarbituric[50] acids could probably also be used for the analysis of malonaldehyde. Comparison of the chromogens and the wavelength maxima obtained with formaldehyde,[51] malonaldehyde[14] and glutaconaldehyde[52] on reaction with barbituric acid are shown in structure **XI**.

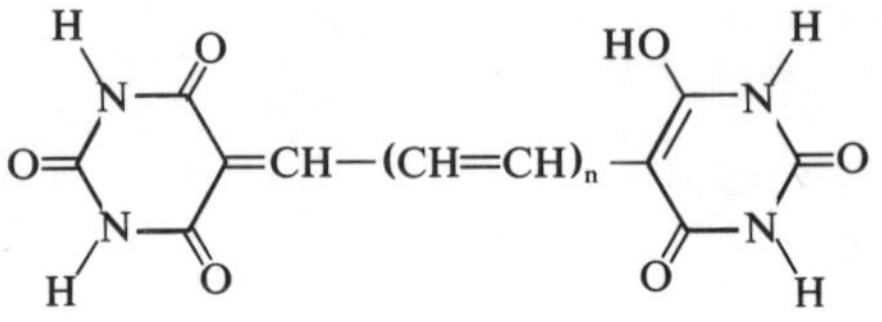
H
O
HO
H
N
N
O
=CH—(CH=CH)n—
O
N
N
H
O
O
H

XI

n	λ_{max}
0	413
1	495
2	570

J. Benzenediazonium salts

Benzenediazonium fluoroborate could also be used to determine malonaldehyde. The consequent chromogen has many tautomeric forms, Fig. 51.[15] In methanol the chromogen absorbs at 369 nm with approximate mε 20.[16]

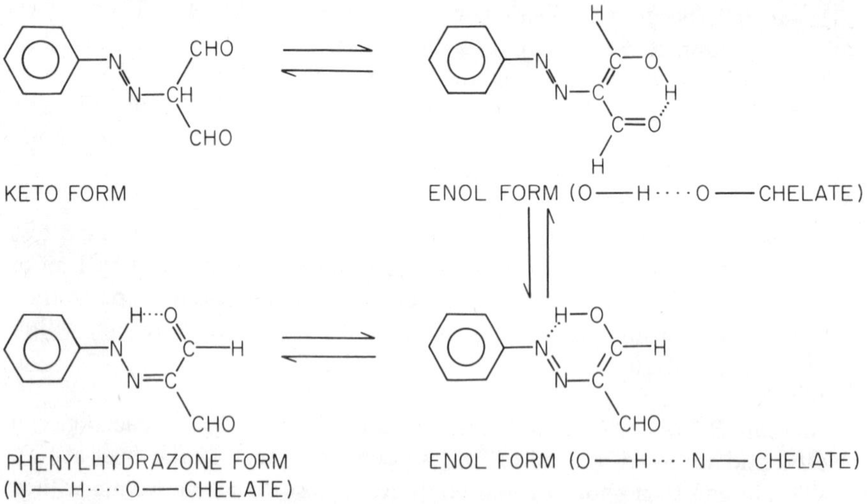
CHO
N
N—CH
CHO
KETO FORM
H
N
C—O
N—C
H
C=O
H
ENOL FORM (O—H····O—CHELATE)
H···O
N
C—H
N=C
CHO
PHENYLHYDRAZONE FORM
(N—H····O—CHELATE)
H—O
N
C—H
N—C
CHO
ENOL FORM (O—H····N—CHELATE)

FIG. 51. Tautomerism of 2-phenylazomalonaldehyde.[15]

K. 10,9-Borazaronaphthalene

Another reagent which could be used to determine malonaldehyde; violet 12,11-borazarophenalenium cation results from the reaction, Fig. 52.[17]

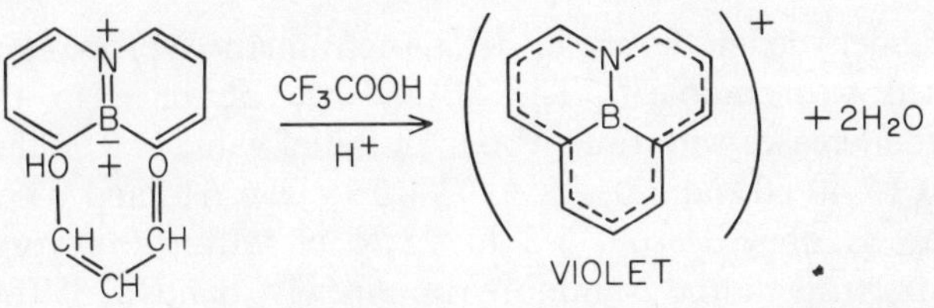

FIG. 52. Reaction of 10,9-borazaronaphthalene with malonaldehyde.[17]

L. 9,10-Diacetoxyanthracene

This can be substituted for anthrone in Procedure I. The same type of fluorescence spectra are obtained as with anthrone.

M. 4-Hexylresorcinol

4-Hexylresorcinol can be used for the determination of malonaldehyde.[7] With 1,1,3,3-tetramethoxypropane an mε of 46 is obtained at 603 nm. The colour is stable for 30 minutes. Acrolein, 2-aminopyrimidine and 1,3,3-trimethoxypropene give a band at 603 nm with mε 0·49, 0·28 and 30, respectively. Negative results are given by aliphatic aldehydes. The trimethine dye, **XII**, is probably the chromogen.

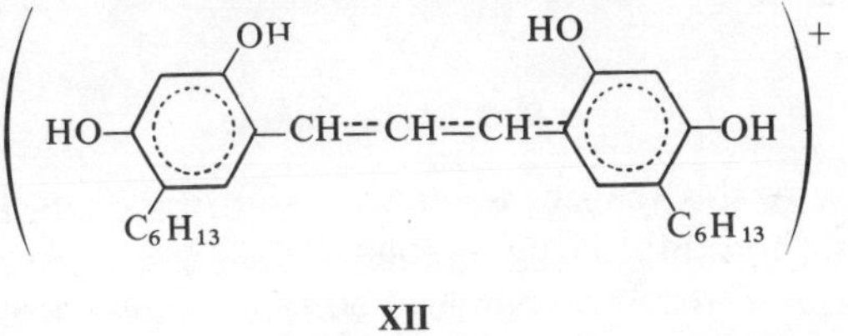

XII

If an aqueous test solution is used in the following procedure a lower millimolar absorptivity is obtained.

4-Hexylresorcinol determination of malonaldehyde.[7] To 2·5 ml of 2-methoxy-ethanol test solution add 0·1 ml of 20% 4-hexylresorcinol in 2-methoxy-ethanol and 2·5 ml of a mixture of trichloroacetic acid (100 g of acid in 10 ml of water)–conc HCl, 9:1, v/v. Heat at 100° for 10 minutes. After 15 min read absorbance at 603 nm. The colour is stable for at least 30 minutes.

N. Indole

Malonaldehyde, in terms of 1,1,3,3-tetramethoxypropane, can also be determined with indole.[7] The absorbance obtained in the analytical procedure increases with time. From an initial value of 0·93 the absorbance rose in 10, 15, 40, 60 and 120 min. to 0·94, 0·95, 0·96, 0·97 and 0·98, respectively. Beer's law is obeyed from 1·2 to 25 μg of tetramethoxypropane. 1,3,3-Trimethoxypropene and 2-aminopyrimidine give bands at 550 nm with mε 41 and 3·3, respectively. Aliphatic aldehydes give bands near 450 to 485 nm with much less intensity.

Substitution of N-ethylcarbazole for indole in the following procedure gave a band at 590 nm with mε 34. This could be improved.

Indole determination of malonaldehyde.[7] To 1 ml of aq test solution add 1 ml of a fresh solution of 2% indole in conc H_2SO_4 (sp. gr. 1·84). Let stand for 7 min and then cool under the tap. Dilute to 10 ml with glacial acetic acid. Read absorbance at 550 nm within 10 minutes.

A relative standard deviation of 2·8 is obtained in this procedure.

O. 3-Methyl-2-benzothiazolinone hydrazone

Malonaldehyde, in the form of 1,1,3,3-tetraethoxypropane, can be determined by the MBTH method for aliphatic aldehydes, wavelength maxima are obtained at 429, 625 and 662 nm with mε 5·4, 17 and 18, respectively.

P. 2-Methylindole

With the use of this reagent for malonaldehyde,[53] Beer's law is obeyed from about 0·2 ($A = 0·1$) to 6 μg malonaldehyde per ml. Glyoxal and pyruvaldehyde also react; they give bands at 505 and 535 nm, respectively. 1,1,3,3-Tetraethoxypropane is used as the standard. It is treated with 3 ml of conc HCl at 45 to 50° for 1 to 3 min and then diluted with water before use in the following procedure.

2-Methylindole determination of malonaldehyde.[53] To 1 ml of aq test solution add 2 ml of reagent (0·1 g 2-methylindole in 100 ml ethanol and just before use add 25 ml conc HCl). After 15 to 20 min read the absorbance at 555 nm.

Q. N-Methylpyrrole

In the N-methylpyrrole procedure Beer's law is obeyed from 1 to 10 μg of the tetramethoxypropane. The colour intensity fades quickly with the absorbance, being approximately halved in 15 minutes. The blank was colourless giving an absorbance of about 0·01 at 558 nm.

N-Methylpyrrole determination of malonaldehyde.[7] Add 1 ml of aqueous test solution followed by 10 ml of 0·5% N-methylpyrrole in methanol. Read absorbance immediately at 558 nm.

R. *p*-Nitroaniline

In the *p*-nitroaniline procedure Beer's law is obeyed from 0·29 to 6 μg of 1,1,3,3-tetramethoxypropane. 1,3,3-Trimethoxypropene gave a band at 580 nm, mε 4·6. Aliphatic aldehydes and ketones gave bands of much weaker intensity at shorter wavelengths.

p-*Nitroaniline determination of malonaldehyde.*[7] Heat 1 ml of aq test solution and 1 ml of 3% *p*-nitroaniline in 2-methoxyethanol containing 5% by volume of conc HCl at 100° for 3 min and then cool under the tap. Add 1 ml of 40% methanolic benzyltrimethylammonium methoxide. Read the absorbance at 580 nm. The absorbance at this wavelength is stable for at least 30 minutes. A relative standard deviation of 2·0 was obtained in this procedure.

S. *p*-Phenylazoaniline

Substitution of *p*-phenylazoaniline (0·5 %) for nitroaniline in the determination of tetramethoxypropane gave a band at 605 nm with mε 46.

T. Quinaldinium salts

If quinaldinium salts such as 1-ethylquinaldinium iodide reacted quantitatively with malonaldehyde to give the pentamethine cation, an mε of about 210 could be obtained at about 710 nm.

U. 4,4′-Sulphonyldianiline

The most sensitive procedures for the determination of malonaldehyde are the fluorimetric ones. Of these the 4,4′-sulphonyldianiline method is probably the most sensitive. A linear relationship between the concentration of the malonaldehyde standard and the fluorescence intensity was obtained from

3 to 150 ng. However, it is possible with a good blank to assay below 0.3 ng of the tetramethoxypropane. The relative standard deviation for 11 runs was 3.24%. The fluorescence intensity in the following procedure is stable for 30 minutes. Negative results were obtained with aliphatic aldehydes. 1,3,3-Trimethoxypropene gave positive results. Previously described Procedure C was used in the determination.

Heating a spot containing malonaldehyde on a paper or thin layer chromatogram with a drop of 1% 4,4'-sulphonyldianiline in dimethylformamide containing 1% conc HCl for 3 min at 100° gives fluorescence at $F450/510$ with a detection limit of 10 ng.[54]

V. 2-Thiobarbituric acid

Thiobarbituric acid can be used to analyse for malonaldehyde and its homologues—formic acid and glutaconaldehyde; the chromogens, **XIII**, n = 0, 1 and 2 are obtained.

XIII

n	λ_{max}
0	452[13, 55, 56]
1	532[13, 57]
2	622[13, 55]

1,3-Diphenyl- and 1,3-diethylthiobarbituric acids can also be used as reagents; wavelength maxima at 537 and 540 nm are obtained.[12] The chromogen, **XIII**, n = 1, absorbs at 532 nm in aq solution, at 538 nm in n-amyl alcohol.[58]

The following procedure can be used with 1,1,3,3-tetraethoxypropane as the standard.

Thiobarbituric acid determination of malonaldehyde.[13, 34] Heat 5 ml of aq test solution containing about 1 to 5 µg of standard with 5 ml of 0.3% 2-thiobarbituric acid in 90% acetic acid at 95° for 35 minutes. Cool and read the absorbance at 532 nm.

The effect of solvents on the reaction of the tetraethoxy standard with thiobarbituric acid is shown by the mε values obtained at 530 nm when 2×10^{-8} mol of the standard and 0.02 M thiobarbituric acid are heated in the solvents shown in Table 28.

Interferences in this procedure have been investigated. Impurities reacting with thiobarbituric acid have been found in various solvents.[22, 59] Pigments with absorption maxima at 450 and 532 nm are formed in solvents such as petroleum ether, diethyl ether, methanol, ethanol, chloroform and hexane.[59]

Table 28. Effect of solvent on thiobarbituric acid determination of malonaldehyde.[22]

Solvent	$m\varepsilon$
Water	154
90% Acetic acid	140
90% Acetic acid[a]	136
12% HCl	126
20% Trichloroacetic acid	115

[a]Prepared two weeks in advance.

Heat and hydrogen peroxide have been shown to aggravate this interference.[22] However, solvents can be readily purified by preliminary treatment with thiobarbituric acid. With a purified reagent, little or no interference from solvent impurities and thiobarbituric acid decomposition products is found after heating with acids, oxidizing agents or hydroperoxides.[60]

Sugars and aldehydes yield yellow interfering pigments with absorption maxima in the range 450 to 490 nm.[60] A large number of aldehydes have been tested in the thiobarbituric acid procedure.[61] Thus, acetaldehyde, acrolein and crotonaldehyde give a weak band at 496 nm while other saturated aliphatic aldehydes give weak bands at 452 nm. Glyoxal and furfural are stated to give weak bands near 550 and 508 nm, respectively.

Many of the TBA procedures would not only determine free malonaldehyde but also some forms of combined malonaldehyde or malonaldehyde precursors. The following procedure is one way of determining free malonaldehyde. The free malonaldehyde content has been reported to indicate the termination of the rancidity–induction period of ground-nut and safflower oils more precisely than do peroxide and TBA values.[62] In the following method the calibration graph is prepared from dilutions of standard solution of 1,1,3,3-tetraethoxypropane, to give 10 to 50 nanomoles of malonaldehyde in 5 ml of solution, which are treated as for the determination.

Determination of free malonaldehyde in vegetable oils with TBA.[62] Dissolve the 2 g test sample in 10 ml of carbonyl-free benzene or cyclohexane. Extract the malonaldehyde into 10 ml of 0.67% aq TBA by shaking for 20 min. Separate the aq layer and heat at 100° for 30 min to develop the colour. Read the absorbance at 530 nm.

REFERENCES

1. P. Szabó and L. Szabó. *Carbohyd. Res.* **4**, 206 (1967).
2. F. Mashio and Y. Kimura. *J. Chem. Soc. Japan* **81**, 434 (1960).
3. T.-W. Kwon and B. M. Watts. *J. Food. Sci.* **28**, 627 (1963).
4. T.-W. Kwon and J. Van der Veen. *J. Agric. Food. Chem.* **16**, 639 (1968).
5. F. Mashio and Y. Kimura. *Yuki Gosei Kagaku Kyokai Shi* **19**, 647 (1961).
6. S. S. Malhotra and M. C. Whiting. *J. Chem. Soc.* 3812 (1960).
7. E. Sawicki, T. W. Stanley and H. Johnson. *Anal. Chem.* **35**, 199 (1963).
8. J. Nys and A. Van Dormael. *Bull. Soc. Chim. Belg.* **65**, 809 (1956).
9. K. Feldmann, E. Daltrozzo and G. Scheibe. *Z. Naturforschg.* **22**, 722 (1967).
10. T.-W. Kwon and B. M. Watts. *Anal. Chem.* **35**, 733 (1963).
11. E. Sawicki, R. A. Carnes and R. Schumacher. *Mikrochim. Acta*, 929 (1967).
12. K. Täufel and R. Zimmerman. *Naturwissenschaften* **47**, 133 (1960).
13. V. S. Waravdekar and L. D. Saslaw. *J. Biol. Chem.* **234**, 1945 (1959).
14. R. C. Shepherd. *J. Chem. Soc.* 4410 (1964).
15. C. Reichardt and W. Grahn. *Chem. Ber.* **103**, 1065 (1970).
16. C. Reichardt and W. Grahn. *Chem. Ber.* **103**, 1072 (1970).
17. M. J. S. Dewar and R. Jones. *Tetrahedron Letters*, 2707 (1968).
18. M. A. Paz, O. O. Blumenfeld, M. Rojkind, E. Henson, C. Furfine and P. M. Gallop. *Arch. Biochem.* **109**, 548 (1965).
19. H. Scherz, G. Stehlik, E. Bancher and K. Kaindl. *Mikrochim. Acta* 915 (1967).
20. S. Patton, M. Keeney and G. W. Kurtz. *J. Am. Oil Chemist's Soc.* **28**, 291 (1951).
21. P. Fleury, J. Courtois, W. Hammam and L. L. Dizet. *Bull. Soc. Chim.* 1290 (1955).
22. B. G. Tarladgis, A. M. Pearson and L. R. Dugan, Jr. *J. Am. Oil Chemist's Soc.* **39**, 34 (1962).
23. R. O. Sinnhuber and T. C. Yu. *Food Technol.* **12**, 9 (1958).
24. R. Huttel. *Ber.* **74**, 1825 (1941).
25. T.-W. Kwon, D. B. Menzel and H. S. Olcott. *J. Food. Sci.* **30**, 808 (1965).
26. J. Saunders and J. R. K. May. *Chem. Ind. (London)* 1355 (1963).
27. T.-W. Kwon and B. M. Watts. *J. Food Sci.* **29**, 294 (1964).
28. T.-W. Kwon. *J. Chromatog.* **24**, 193 (1966).
29. A. A. Bothner-By and R. K. Harris. *J. Org. Chem.* **30**, 254 (1965).
30. B. Eistert, F. Weygand and E. Csendes. *Ber.* **84**, 745 (1951).
31. S. Trofimenko. *J. Am. Chem. Soc.* **85**, 1357 (1963).
32. P. Fleury. *Bull. Soc. Chim. France* 1126 (1955).
33. L. D. Saslaw and V. S. Waravdekar. *J. Org. Chem.* **22**, 843 (1957).
34. D. C. Holland. *J. Am. Oil Chemist's Soc.* **54**, 1024 (1971).
35. D. L. Crawford, T. C. Yu and R. O. Sinnhuber. *J. Food Sci.* **32**, 332 (1967).
36. T. V. Protopopova and A. P. Skoldinov. *J. Gen. Chem. USSR* **28**, 241 (1958).
37. N. Bacon. *Chem. and Ind.* 1377 (1965).
38. D. L. Crawford, T. C. Yu and R. O. Sinnhuber. *J. Agric. Food Chem.* **14**, 182 (1966).
39. E. Sawicki, T. W. Stanley and H. Johnson. *Chemist-Analyst* **52**, 4 (1963).
40. E. Sawicki, T. W. Winfield and C. R. Sawicki. *Microchem. J.* **15**, 294 (1970).
41. B. Eistert and F. Haupter. *Chem. Ber.* **93**, 264 (1960).
42. W. T. Roubal. *Lipids* **6**, 62 (1971).
43. K. S. Chio and A. L. Tappel. *Biochemistry* **8**, 2827 (1969).
44. K. S. Chio and A. L. Tappel. *Biochemistry* **8**, 2821 (1969).

45. O. Bally and R. Scholl. *Ber.* **44**, 1656 (1911).
46. H. Meerwein. *J. Prakt. Chem.* **97**, 235 (1918).
47. E. H. Rodd, Ed., "Chemistry of Carbon Compound IIIb," Elsevier, Amsterdam, 1956.
48. F. Feigl, V. Anger and V. Gentil. *Clin. Chim. Acta* 155 (1960).
49. A. W. Dox and G. P. Plaisance. *J. Am. Chem. Soc.* **38**, 2164 (1916).
50. H. G. Mautner. *J. Am. Chem. Soc.* **81**, 6470 (1959).
51. G. Schwarzenbach and H. Gysling. *Helv. Chim. Acta* **32**, 1314 (1949).
52. E. Asmus and H. Garschagen. *Z. Anal. Chem.* **138**, 404 (1953).
53. H. Scherz, G. Stehlik, E. Bancher and K. Kaindl. *Mikrochim. Acta* 915 (1967).
54. T. W. Stanley and E. Sawicki. *Anal. Chem.* **37**, 938 (1965).
55. H. Schmidt. *Fette Seifen Anstrichmittel* **61**, 883 (1959).
56. H. Schmidt. *Naturwissenschaften* **46**, 379 (1959).
57. R. O. Sinnhuber, T. C. Yu and Te. C. Yu. *Food Research* **23**, 626 (1958).
58. E. W. Turner, W. D. Paynter, E. J. Montie, M. W. Bessert, G. M. Struck and F. C. Olson. *Food Technol.* **8**, 326 (1954).
59. S. Y. Ho and W. D. Brown. *J. Food Sci.* **31**, 386 (1966).
60. T. C. Yu and R. O. Sinnhuber. *J. Am. Oil Chemist's Soc.* **41**, 540 (1964).
61. K. Taufel and R. Zimmermann. *Fette Seifen Anstrichmittel* **63**, 226 (1961).
62. S. S. Arya and N. Nirmala. *J. Food Sci. Technol.* **8**, 177 (1971).

44. 5-METHYLFURFURAL

$$H_3C-\underset{O}{\boxed{}}-CHO$$

I. PHYSICAL AND SPECTRAL PROPERTIES

B.p. 187°, D_4^{25} 1·1219, $n_D{}^{25}$ 1·5147. Soluble in 30 parts water. Volatile with steam.

The aldehyde absorbs at λ 285 nm, mε 15·9[1] and in 0·001 N HCl at λ_{max} 228, 291·5 nm and mε 3·0, 16·2, respectively.[2] Its spectra have been discussed in the furfural section (Chapter 26).

This compound can be determined with azulene.[3] The procedure has been given in the furfural section (Chapter 26): 5-methylfurfural gives λ_{max} 535 nm and mε 64.

Spraying of 5-methylfurfural with 1% hydrazine dihydrochloride in water–conc HCl (4:1) gave a yellow fluorescent spot down to 0·4 μg. At a 10 μg level direct fluorescence examination gave bands at $F405/500$.

The aniline acetate method is useful for determining 5-methylfurfural as well as furfural.[2] Double distillation can be used to separate furfural and 5-methylfurfural with a 98 to 99% recovery from 5-hydroxymethylfurfural which is present in the distillate in less than 1% amounts.

The methylfurfural used in this procedure was prepared from rhamnose by acid decomposition in boiling 50% H_3PO_4 in 20% Na_2SO_4 solution, with overall yield of 11% pure methylfurfural. Rhamnose yields only the single aldehyde.[2, 4, 5]

With the following procedure 5-methylfurfural can be determined in the presence of furfural. It gives a band at 368 nm with mε 10·9, while 5-hydroxy-methylfurfural gives a band at 354 nm with mε 6·9 and furfural gives absorbance (but no band) in this region with mε 2.

A. Aniline determination of 5-methylfurfural[2]

To 1 to 5 ml of test solution or distillate (pH <4) maintained at 25 ± 1° add an equal volume of reagent (to 10 ml pure aniline add 10 ml water and

80 ml of redistilled acetic acid with cooling, and dilute to 100 ml with water).
Incubate at 25° for 5 to 8 min while protecting from light. Read the absorbance
at 368 nm 10 min after adding the reagent.

REFERENCES

1. G. Kallinich. *Arch. Phar.* **295**, 90 (1961).
2. T. E. Friedemann, P. K. Keegan and N. F. Witt. *Anal. Biochem.* **8**, 300 (1964).
3. E. Sawicki and C. R. Engel. *Anal. Chim. Acta* **38**, 315 (1967).
4. W. A. Van Ekenstein and J. J. Blanksma. *Ber.* **43**, 2355 (1910).
5. J. A. Middendorf. *Rec. Trav. Chim.* **38**, 1 (1919).

45. 1-NAPHTHALDEHYDE

I. PHYSICAL AND SPECTRAL PROPERTIES

M.p. 33 to 34°; b.p. 292°, 156° at 19 mm, 150° at 9 mm.

This compound absorbs at λ_{max} 315 nm, $m\varepsilon$ 7·7 and λs 328, $m\varepsilon$ 7·2 in 95 % ethanol and at λ_{max} 425 nm, $m\varepsilon$ 10·3 in conc H_2SO_4–95 % ethanol (19:1, v/v).

One could expect solvent effects to play an important role in the fluorescence and phosphorescence of this aldehyde.

The compound could be determined by the azulene method[1] described in the furfural section (Chapter 26) or by some of the methods described in the aromatic aldehydes section.

1-Naphthaldehyde can be analysed through its nitrophenylhydrazones, Table 29. The 4-nitrophenylhydrazone, **I**, and its anion, **II**, would be especially useful in analysis.

140

Table 29. Absorption spectra of the nitrophenylhydrazones of 1-naphthaldehyde in neutral and alkaline solution

Phenylhydrazone	DMF		Alk. DMF[a]	
	λ_{max}	$m\varepsilon$	λ_{max}	$m\varepsilon$
2-Nitro	450	11·2	600	16·8
4-Nitro	425	35·0	580	52·6
2,4-Dinitro	362[b]	27·4	510[c]	30·0

[a] In dimethylformamide containing 2% of 10% aq tetraethylammonium hydroxide.
[b] In chloroform λ_{max} 391, $m\varepsilon$ 30·2.[2]
[c] Also a band at λ 450 nm, $m\varepsilon$ 30.

One would expect **I** to be non-phosphorescent. It has a green fluorescence in dioxane and is non-fluorescent in alcohol at room temperature.[3]

REFERENCES

1. E. Sawicki and C. R. Engel. *Anal. Chim. Acta* **38**, 315 (1967).
2. E. A. Braude and P. Gore. *J. Chem. Soc.* **41** (1959).
3. E. Sawicki and J. Pfaff. *Microchem. J.* **12**, 7 (1967).

46. 2-NAPHTHALDEHYDE

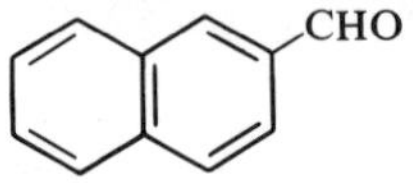

I. PHYSICAL PROPERTIES

M.p. 60°; b.p. 160° at 19 mm. Soluble in alcohol and ether and slightly soluble in hot water. Volatile with steam. Forms addition compound with excess saturated aqueous sodium bisulphite.

II. REAGENTS

A. Acid

A methanolic solution of 2-naphthaldehyde treated with a drop of conc H_2SO_4 showed the expected violet shift in spectra, Fig. 53. Acetal formation

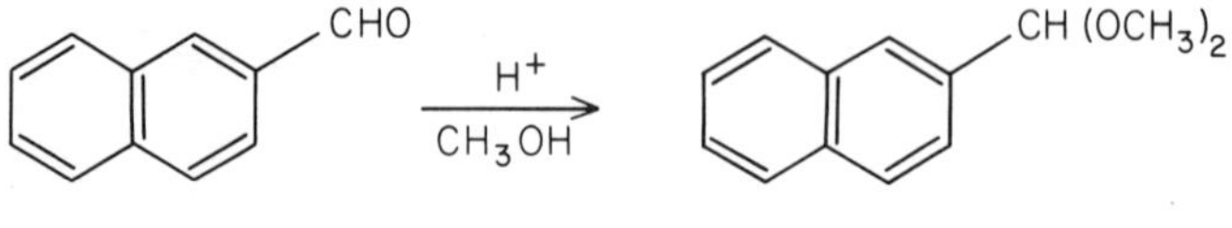

FIG. 53. Effect of acid on a methanolic solution of 2-naphthaldehyde.

is shown but if the hemiacetal were formed in the acidic solution the same spectral changes would be found.[1] The aldehyde in methanol has a strong band at 247 nm and a weaker one at 344 nm; the acetal in acidified methanol has a weak band at 275 nm. In methanol the compound showed a weak fluorescence due to the small amount of hemiacetal present.[2] Relative to quinine, $F350/450$ at $1 \mu g/ml$ of $0.1 N$ H_2SO_4 and $K_Q = 1$ the aldehyde at $F280/322$ had K_Q 0.09 and 0.12 in methanol and acidic methanol, respectively. The aldehyde showed no fluorescence in ether. In water the aldehyde fluoresced at $F$264, 300, 345/445. 2-Naphthaldehyde does not fluoresce in pure hydrocarbon solvents.[3]

B. Azulene

Azulene can be used to determine 2-naphthaldehyde by the procedure for furfurals[4] in that section; at λ_{max} 500 nm an mε of 20 is obtained. The procedure could be further optimized for 2-naphthaldehyde. The chromogen would have the cationic resonance structure **I**.

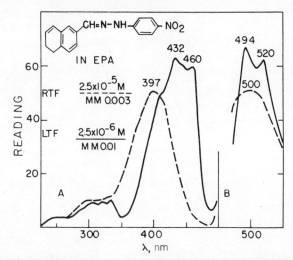

C. Nitrophenylhydrazines

The 2,4-dinitrophenylhydrazone of 2-naphthaldehyde absorbs at λ 384, mε 32·4 in chloroform.[5]

2-Naphthaldehyde 4-nitrophenylhydrazone fluoresces green in dioxane but is non-fluorescent in alcohol at room temperature.[6] It fluoresces at

FIG. 54. Fluorescence excitation (A) and emission (B) spectra of 2-naphthaldehyde 4-nitrophenylhydrazone in EPA at room temperature (-----) and $F$397/500 and at liquid nitrogen temperature and $F$432/520 (———).[6]

much greater intensity and with more fine spectral structure in ethyl ether–isopentane–ethanol (5:5:2) at lower temperatures, Fig. 54. The 2- and 3-nitrophenylhydrazones as well as the 2,4-dinitrophenylhydrazone are non-fluorescent.

REFERENCES

1. E. P. Crowell, W. A. Powell and C. J. Varsel. *Anal. Chem.* **35**, 184 (1963).
2. E. P. Crowell and C. J. Varsel. *Anal. Chem.* **35**, 189 (1963).
3. K. Brederek, T. Forster and H. G. Oesterlin, in H. P. Kallmann and G. M. Spruch, Eds, "Luminescence of Organic and Inorganic Materials", Wiley, New York, 1962, p. 161.
4. E. Sawicki and C. R. Engel. *Anal. Chim. Acta* **38**, 315 (1967).
5. E. A. Braude and P. Gore. *J. Chem. Soc.* 41 (1959).
6. E. Sawicki and J. Pfaff. *Microchem. J.* **12**, 7 (1967).

47. p-NITROBENZALDEHYDE

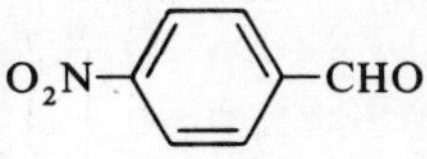

$$O_2N\!\!-\!\!\langle\ \rangle\!\!-\!\!CHO$$

I. PHYSICAL AND SPECTRAL PROPERTIES

M.p. 106°. Sublimes. Soluble in acetic acid, alcohol and benzene. Sparingly soluble in water, ether and petroleum ether. Slightly volatile in steam.

Some of the reported absorption spectra are given in Table 30. The spectra of some nitro- and dinitrophenylhydrazone derivatives are given in Table 31.

Table 30. Absorption spectra of p-nitrobenzaldehyde

Solvent	λ_{max}	mε	Ref.
Ethanol	204, 211s, 265, 306	9.3, 7·1, 11·5, 1·8	1–6
Isopropanol	262	14·1	7
Water	266, 301s, 314s	14·5, 3·0, 1·8	8
Hexane	259, 284s, 295s, 305s	14, 3·4, 2·1, 1·8	8, 9
Gasoline	246	15·1	10
44% H_2SO_4	270	13·5	11
96% H_2SO_4	282	17·8	11

The oxime of p-nitrobenzaldehyde absorbs at λ 368 nm with an mε of about 14.[16] The Schiff base obtained with N,N-dimethyl-p-phenylene-diamine absorbs at λ 445 nm, mε 12.[17]

The 4-nitrophenylhydrazone of p-nitrobenzaldehyde has a moderately green fluorescence in dioxane and is non-fluorescent in alcohol.[18]

p-Nitrobenzaldehyde can also be determined with indole. As low as 0·1 μg of the aldehyde can be estimated with an error of ±0·01 μg. Various aldehydes, ketones, oxidizing agents, HCl and H_3PO_4 interfere.

145

Table 31. Absorption spectra of some nitro- and dinitrophenylhydrazone derivatives of 4-nitrobenzaldehyde

$$4\text{-}O_2N\text{—}C_6H_6\text{—}CH\text{=}N\text{—}NH\text{—}C_6H_3 \text{ or } _4(NO_2)_2 \text{ or } _1$$

Phenylhydrazone	Solvent	λ_{max}	$m\varepsilon$	Ref.
4-Nitro	Ethanol	430	31·6	12
	Alk. DMF[a]	651	60·4	
	Alk. DMF	667	63·1	13
	Alk. DMF-20% H_2O	625	53·7	13
	Alk. DMF-50% H_2O	607	38·0	13
3-Nitro	Ethanol	400	20	12
2-Nitro	Ethanol	365	12·6	
		430	20	12
	Alk. DMF[a]	665	44·8	
2,4-Dinitro	Chloroform	382	37	14, 15
	Basic ethanol	537	45·7	14
	Alk. DMF[a]	575	34	

[a]Dimethylformamide containing 2% of 10% aq tetraethylammonium hydroxide. In this solvent the unsubstituted phenylhydrazone absorbs at λ 689, $m\varepsilon$ 49·2.

A. Indole determination of *p*-nitrobenzaldehyde[19]

To 1 ml of the test solution add 0·1 ml of fresh 0·5% ethanolic indole and 5 to 8 ml of conc H_2SO_4 with mixing. After 20 min read the absorbance at 540 nm.

REFERENCES

1. W. D. Kumler and P. P. T. Sah. *J. Am. Pharm. Ass., Sci. Ed.* **41**, 375 (1952).
2. P. Grammaticakis. *Bull. Soc. Chim. France* **20**, 821 (1953).
3. W. F. Forbes and W. A. Mueller. *J. Am. Chem. Soc.* **79**, 6495 (1957).
4. S. Patai and J. Zabicky. *J. Chem. Soc.* 2030 (1960).
5. S. Patai and Y. Israeli. *J. Chem. Soc.* 2025 (1960).
6. P. Klinke and H. Gibian. *Chem. Ber.* **94**, 26 (1961).
7. V. Petrow, O. Stephenson and B. Sturgeon. *J. Chem. Soc.* 4066 (1953).
8. W. F. Forbes. *Can. J. Chem.* **36**, 1350 (1958).
9. A. Burawoy and J. P. Critchley. *Tetrahedron* **5**, 340 (1959).
10. W. M. Schubert, J. M. Craven, H. Steadly and J. Robins. *J. Org. Chem.* **22**, 1285 (1957).
11. K. Yates and R. Stewart. *Can. J. Chem.* **37**, 664 (1959).
12. P. Grammaticakis. *Bull. Soc. Chim. France* **21**, 1372 (1954).
13. E. Sawicki, T. R. Hauser and T. W. Stanley. *Anal. Chem.* **31**, 2063 (1959).
14. L. A. Jones and C. K. Hancock. *J. Org. Chem.* **25**, 226 (1960).

15. G. D. Johnson. *J. Am. Chem. Soc.* **75**, 2720 (1953).
16. D. P. Johnson. *Anal. Chem.* **40**, 646 (1968).
17. G. Smets and A. Delvaux. *Bull. Soc. Chim., Belges* **56**, 106 (1947).
18. E. Sawicki and J. Pfaff. *Microchem. J.* **12**, 7 (1967).
19. R. Saba, D. Monnier and F. E. Khalil. *Mitt. Geb. Lebensmittelunters Hyg.* **57**, 381 (1966).

48. 5-NITRO-2-FURFURAL

$$O_2N-\underset{}{\overset{O}{\boxed{}}}-CHO$$

I. PHYSICAL AND SPECTRAL PROPERTIES

M.p. 35–36°; b.p. 128–132° at 10 mm. Moderately soluble in water. Unstable in alkali at pH $\geqslant$ 9.[1]

The absorption spectra of this aldehyde and some of its analogs and vinylogs are shown in Table 32. Addition of alkali ($>4 \times 10^{-3}$ M) to a polar solution of the aldehyde shifts the long wavelength maxima about 150 nm.

Table 32. Absorption spectra of 5-nitro-2-furfural and its analogs and vinylogs

$$O_2N-\underset{X}{\overset{}{\boxed{}}}-(CH{=}CH)_n-CHO$$

X	n	Solvent	λ_{max}	mε	Ref.
O	0	Water	225, 310	8·3, 11·6	2–6
		Acetic acid	298	8·3	2
O	1	Water	355	17·0	5
O	1	Ethanol	238, 347	14·8, 23·4	7
O	1	—	237, 347	11·8, 16·2	8
S	0	Ethanol	236, 316·5	7·9, 17·4	9
S	0	Hexane	231, 301	6·2, 11·8	9
S	1	Dioxane	249, 354	8·5, 21·4	10
S	1	Methanol	356	21·4	11
Se	0	Methanol	310	9·3	12
Se	0	Ethanol	212, 315	5·2, 9·8	13
Se	0	Hexane	221, 307	4·0, 12·0	13

3-(5-Nitro-2-furyl)acrolein has been determined at 360 nm in baths for acetylating poly(vinyl alcohol) fibre.[14]

Some of the reactions considered in the furfural(s) section could be used in the analysis of this aldehyde.

The aldehyde could also be determined as the neutral hydrazone or its anion after reaction with *p*-nitrophenylhydrazine. After reaction with MBTH the aldehyde could be determined as the chromogen, **I**.

I

REFERENCES

1. J. P. Stradins, G. O. Reickman and R. A. Gavars. *Elektrokhimiya* **1**, 955 (1965).
2. A. A. Ponomarev and M. D. Lipanova. *Zhur. Obschei Khim.* **32**, 2974 (1962).
3. F. B. Ebitino, J. J. Carroll and G. Gever. *J. Med. Pharm. Chem.* **5**, 513 (1962).
4. R. F. Raffauf. *J. Am. Chem. Soc.* **72**, 753 (1950).
5. H. E. Paul, F. L. Austin, M. F. Paul and V. R. Ells. *J. Biol. Chem.* **180**, 345 (1949).
6. V. Egerts, J. Stradins and M. Shimanska. "Analysis of 5-Nitrofuran Derivatives' Ann Arbor Science Publishers, Ann Arbor, 1970, p. 82.
7. H. Saikachi and H. Ogawa. *J. Am. Chem. Soc.* **80**, 3642 (1958).
8. K. K. Venter and S. A. Giller. *Doklady Akad. Nauk. SSR.* **137**, 83 (1961).
9. G. Pappalardo. *Gazz. Chim. Ital.* **89**, 551 (1959).
10. H. Saikachi *et al.*, *J. Pharm. Soc. Japan* **82**, 1262 (1962).
11. G. Carrara *et al.*, *J. Am. Chem. Soc.* **76**, 4391 (1954).
12. Y. K. Yur'ev and E. L. Zaitseva. *Zhur. Obschei Khim.* **29**, 1057 (1959).
13. A. Belotti and L. Chierici. *Gazz. Chim. Ital.* **90**, 1125 (1960).
14. M. P. Vasil'ev, G. L. Alekseeva, T. P. Makarova, L. A. Vol'f and V. V. Kotetskii. *Zav. Lab.* **35**, 927 (1969).

49. OXYBENZALDEHYDES

I. INTRODUCTION

By this name is meant all mono- and poly-hydroxy and alkoxybenzaldehydes not discussed in a separate section in these volumes. Some of these aldehydes covered in this volume include *p*-hydroxybenzaldehyde, salicylaldehyde and vanillin.

II. TECHNIQUES

A. Spectra

The absorption spectra of a variety of these aldehydes have been reported, Table 33. All of these aldehydes could be analysed in the neutral or cationic

Table 33. Ultraviolet absorption spectra of some oxybenzaldehydes.

X	Solvent	λ_{max}	mε	Ref.
2-CH$_3$O	Hexane	211	20·0	1–3
		246	10·5	
		253s	8·5	
		306	4·6	
		314s	4·2	
2-CH$_3$O	Ethanol	253–255	10–11·8	3–5
		315–321	4·2–5	
3-CH$_3$O	Hexane	216	23·4	1–4
		220	22·4	
		246	9·1	
		251s	8·9	
		304	3·0	
		313s	2·7	

Table 33—*continued*

X	Solvent	λ_{max}	mε	Ref.
3-CH$_3$O	Ethanol	252–255	8·3–10	3–5
		309–314	2·5–3	
4-CH$_3$O	Hexane	215	15·9	2, 3, 6
		220	14·8	
		266	20·0	
		273	16·6	
		280	12·9	
		288	5·9	
		312	0·066	
		323	0·06	
		331s	0·047	
		337s	0·041	
		345	0·033	
		353s	0·017	
		361	0·013	
4-CH$_3$O	95% Ethanol	277	15–20	3–10
		283	15–20	
4-CH$_3$O	95% H$_2$SO$_4$[a]	344	17·0	11
4-CH$_3$O[b]	Benzene	320	28·2	12
4-CH$_3$O	Chloroform	321	30·9	12
4-CH$_3$O	Benzene-acid[c]	345	28·2	12
3,5-DiHO[d]	Ethanol	220	15·1	13
		255	10·0	
		334	3·5	
2,4-DiHO[e]	Ether	232	8·5	14
		280	13·8	
		310	6·6	
2,4-DiHO	Water, pH 6·98	280	12·0	15
		326	17·0	
2,4-DiHO	Water, pH 3	211	15·1	16
		229	10·7	
		278	15·9	
		320s	6·3	
2,4-DiHO	Ethanol	235	9·3	17
		280	15·1	
		318	8·1	
2,4-DiHO	Water, pH 11	230s	12·0	16
		250s	7·9	
		331	20·4	
2,4-DiHO	Ethanol, KOH	255	6·9	17
		334	30·9	
3,4-DiHO[f]	Water	209	13·5	18
		231	12·6	
		279	9·3	
		312	7·6	

Table 33—*continued*

X	Solvent	λ_{max}	$m\varepsilon$	Ref.
3,4-DiHO	Ethanol	233	12·9	19
		279	9·1	
		314	8·5	
3.4-DiHO	Ethanol, NaOEt	252	8·9	19
		295s	—	
		350	22·9	
3,4-DiHO	Ethanol, NaOEt, H_3BO_3	245	14·1	19
		292	6·8	
		338	14·5	
3,4-DiHO	Water, pH 9·7[g]	248	9·8	20
		347	20·0	
3,4-DiHO	Water, pH 9·7[h]	258	17·0	20
		359	15·5	
2-HO–3–CH_3O[i]	Dioxane	265	10·0	21
		340	3·2	
2-HO–4–C_2H_5O	Ethanol	230	14·8	22
		278	20·4	
		319	8·3	
3-HO–4–CH_3O[j]	0·1 N HCl	231	13·8	23
		280	11·2	
		314	8·7	
3-HO–4–CH_3O	0·01 N NaOH	249	21·9	23
		292	8·3	
		360	6·0	
2,3-DiCH_3O	Ethanol	219	20·9	24
		258	9·8	
		318	2·8	
3,4-DiCH_3O	Water	230	15·5	25
		278	11·2	
		308	9·3	
3,4-DiCH_3O	95% Ethanol	230	17·1	
		275	11·4	
		319	9·2	
3,4-DiCH_3O	95% H_2SO_4	239	9·1	25
		341	20·4	
3,4-CH_2O_2[k]	95% Ethanol	231	17·1	26
		273	7·6	
		313	9·4	
3,4-CH_2O_2[k]	95% H_2SO_4[a]	225	9·1	
		247	10·2	
		334	12·0	
		390	15·7	
2,3,5-TriHO	Ethanol	276	10·0	27
		332	2·0	
2,4,6-TriHO	Ethanol	293	25·1	28
		340s	2·5	

Table 33—*continued*

X	Solvent	λ_{max}	mε	Ref.
4-HO–3,5-DiCH$_3$O	Ethanol	215	20·4	29–31
		231	17·8	
		308	14·5	
4-HO–3,5-DiCH$_3$O	Ethanol, KOH	250	10·7	31
		370	27·5	
2-HO-4,6-DiCH$_3$O	Ethanol	215	15·9	32
		294	20·4	
		330s	3·8	
2-HO-4,6-DiCH$_3$O	48% EtOH–0·05 N NaOH	235s	15·9	32
		294	16·2	
		359	6·2	
2,4,6-TriCH$_3$O	Ethanol	288	20·0	28
		322s	4·0	
3-CH$_3$O-4,5-CH$_2$O$_2$	Ethanol	287	3·9	33
3,4,5-TriCH$_3$O	95% Ethanol	219	22·3	
		288	10·0	
3,4,5-TriCH$_3$O	95% H$_2$SO$_4$[a]	385	17·7	

[a] Containing 5% of 95% ethanol.
[b] 4-Methoxycinnamaldehyde.
[c] Benzene containing 1·8 M CCl$_3$COOH.
[d] α-Resorcylaldehyde
[e] β-Resorcylaldehyde
[f] Protocatechualdehyde.
[g] Sodium potassium derivative.
[h] Copper derivative.
[i] o-Vanillin.
[j] Isovanillin.
[k] Piperonal.

forms while those with hydroxy groups could be analysed in the anionic form also. Syringaldehyde has been analysed after paper chromatography and elution with methanol[34] and after silica gel thin layer chromatography, elution with ethanol and treatment with alkali.[35] Ethylvanillin in vanilla extracts has been determined with the help of its absorption spectra in 0·002 N H$_2$SO$_4$ and 0·002 N NaOH.[36] Many of these aldehydes could probably be separated through cation exchange chromatography as described for some of these aldehydes and precursor derivatives, Fig. 55.[37] The eluate from the column is passed through a quartz flow cell (1 cm optical path length, volume 0·1 ml) of a spectrophotometer and the absorbance is measured at 280 nm. The output of the spectrophotometer is recorded on a laboratory potentiometric recorder and fed into a digital integrator which automatically prints out the area under each peak.

B. Acetal formation

Acetal formation in conjunction with UV spectrophotometry can be used in the characterization and analysis of the oxybenzaldehydes.[38] In the

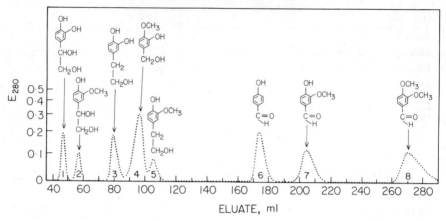

FIG. 55. Separation of 5 phenolic alcohols and 3 phenolic aldehydes by cation exchange chromatography. 1 = 3,4-Dihydroxyphenylglycol (200 μg); 2 = 3-methoxy-4-hydroxyphenylglycol (200 μg); 3 = 3,4-dihydroxyphenylethanol (200 μg); 4 = 3-hydroxy-4-methoxybenzyl alcohol (100 μg); 5 = 3-methoxy-4-hydroxyphenylethanol (200 μg); 6 = 4-hydroxybenzaldehyde (60 μg); 7 = vanillin (100 μg); 8 = veratraldehyde (200 μg). Conditions: column, 0·9 × 60 cm; resin, 16 ± 6 μ PA-28; eluent, 0–15 min sodium citrate buffer, pH 3·28, 15–150 min. sodium citrate–boric acid buffer, pH 4·53; flow rate, 50 ml h⁻¹; pressure, 15–20 atm; column temperature, 55°.[37]

procedure a drop of H_2SO_4 is added to the methanolic solution of the aldehyde. The results are strikingly demonstrated for 2,5-dimethoxy-benzaldehyde, Fig. 56. Hemiacetal formation is shown but acetal formation could also take place. This same spectral change is shown by vanillin, 4-hydroxy-3-ethoxybenzaldehyde, syringaldehyde, *o*-anisaldehyde, *p*-anis-aldehyde, *m*-anisaldehyde, veratraldehyde, 3,5-dimethoxybenzaldehyde, 2,3-dimethoxybenzaldehyde, 4-ethoxy-3-methoxybenzaldehyde, 3,4,5-tri-methoxybenzaldehyde and piperonal. 2,5-Dimethoxybenzaldehyde is one of

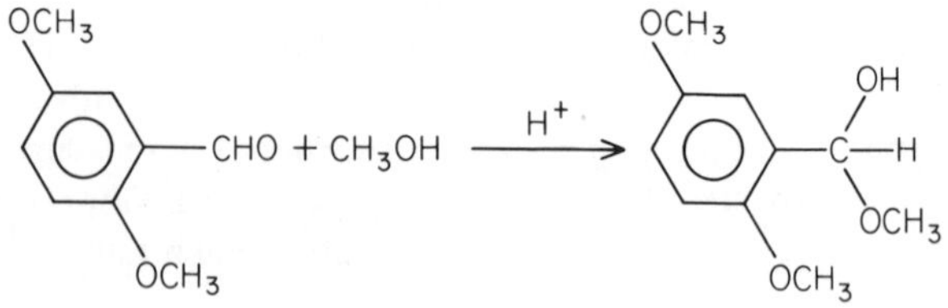

λ_{max} 270, 324   279, 283
REL. INT. 1·0, 0·35   0·42, 0·42
F 263, 358/460   F 298/327
REL. INT. 0·48   0·26

FIG. 56. Reaction of 2,5-dimethoxybenzaldehyde with methanol in the presence of acid.[38]

the few oxybenzaldehydes that has a strong fluorescence in methanol derived from itself and not from hemiacetal formation.[39] But even this aldehyde loses its fluorescence in ether solution. The other oxybenzaldehydes become fairly fluorescent in acidic methanol in the hemiacetal and/or acetal form. No fluorescence was observed with the acetals of the trioxy derivatives of benzaldehyde. This is in agreement with the reported lack of fluorescence of trihydroxybenzenes.

C. o-Aminothiophenol

o-Aminothiophenol can be used to determine the oxybenzaldehydes. It has been used for p-anisaldehyde.[40] The reaction and the chromogens are shown in Fig. 57. The effect of pH on the fluorescence of the fluorogen,

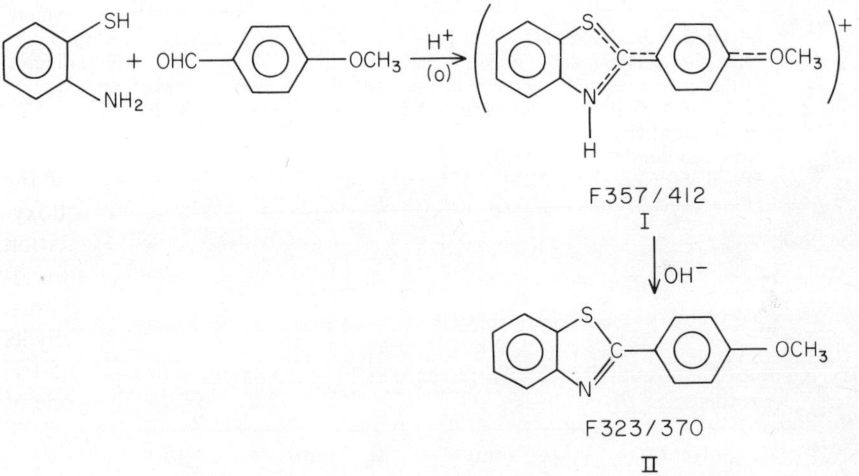

F357/412

I

F323/370

II

FIG. 57. Reaction of o-aminothiophenol with p-anisaldehyde.

2-(4-methoxyphenyl)benzothiazolium cation, **I**, is shown in Table 34. Solvent effects on the fluorescence of **II** are shown in Table 35. By the following method 1·0 to 100 μg of p-anisaldehyde can be determined.

o-*Aminothiophenol determination of* p-*anisaldehyde.*[40] To 10 ml of aq test solution add 1 ml of 0·5% o-aminothiophenol HCl followed by 5 ml of 30% (w/v) H_2SO_4. Heat at 100° for 1 h, cool, and dilute to 20 ml with water. Read the fluorescence intensity at F357/412.

F*

Table 34. pH Effects on fluorescence of 2-(4-methoxyphenyl)-benzothiazole.[40]

pH	λ_{ex}[a] (nm)	λ_{em}[b] (nm)	RFI[c]
0 >[d]	357	412	79
0 >[e]	357	412	79
0·3	357	412	79
0·35	357	412	79
0·45	356	412	71
0·55	355	412	71
0·82	355	412	71
0·98	355	412	62
1·82	352	411	26
2·75	325	390	10
3·7	325	380	10
7	325	380	15·5
12·8	324	380	44
14 <[f]	324	380	1

[a] Excitation maximum.
[b] Emission maximum.
[c] Relative fluorescence intensities, uncorrected; fluorescence readings at same intensity of instrument (excitation slit width: 6·5 nm, emission slit width: 6·5 nm, recorder sensitivity: 3).
[d] Final concentration of H_2SO_4: 30% (w/v).
[e] Final concentration of H_2SO_4: 15% (w/v).
[f] Final concentration of NaOH: 10% (w/v).

Table 35. Solvent effects on fluorescence of 2-(4-methoxyphenyl)-benzothiazole.[40]

Solvent	λ_{ex}[a] (nm)	λ_{em}[b] (nm)	RFI[c]
Ethanol	323	370	10
Methanol	323	370	10
n-Butanol	324	370	8·5
Chloroform	324	368	7·5
Cyclohexane	322	358	4·0
Benzene	325	365	6·5
Toluene	325	365	6·5

[a] Excitation maximum.
[b] Emission maximum.
[c] Relative fluorescence intensities, uncorrected: fluorescence readings at same sensitivity of instrument (excitation slit width: 6·5 nm, emission slit width: 6·5 nm, recorder sensitivity: 3).

D. Anionic, cationic and neutral forms

The low temperature fluorescence and phosphorescence properties of the oxybenzaldehydes in the neutral, anionic and cationic forms need to be investigated.

E. Azulene and Barbituric Acid

Azulene[41] and barbituric acid[42, 43] can be used to locate oxybenzaldehydes on chromatograms and could also be used in their determination. In the case of barbituric acid yellow to green fluorescent chromogens are obtained, e.g. **III** is obtained from *p*-methyoxybenzaldehyde.

III

F. Hydrazines

2,4-Dinitrophenylhydrazine can also be used in the assay of these compounds. The dinitrophenylhydrazones can be separated on silica gel TLC by employing a combination of chlorobenzene (first direction) and isopropyl ether–chlorobenzene (1:2, v/v) (second direction)[44] or ethyl acetate–ligroine (1:2, v/v) in the second direction.[45] The ultraviolet absorption spectra of these compounds have been reported. Table 36.[44] See also Ref. 46 for a separation and spectra of these derivatives.

One per cent hydrazine sulphate in 1 N HCl can be used as a spray for oxybenzaldehyde spots on chromatograms. The fluorescences of the spots are observed under ultraviolet light before and after heating at 100°[47, 48] or treatment with ammonia.[49] An example of the type of fluorescence spectra obtained is shown in Fig. 58.[41] The paper and thin-layer chromatographic properties, the neutral absorption spectra and the fluorescence properties of many of the oxybenzaldehyde azines have been reported.[50] Results are shown for the azine of 3,4,5-trimethoxybenzaldehyde, Fig. 59. Another possible variable that can be used is the oxidation by hypochlorite of azines of the *p*-hydroxybenzaldehydes, as shown for syringaldazine by the intense colour of the chromogen, **IV**.[51]

IV

λ_{max} 530 nm, mε 65

Table 36. Ultraviolet absorption spectra of the 2,4-dinitrophenylhydrazones of oxybenzaldehydes in methanol.[44]

Benzaldehyde	λ_{max}	mε
—[a]	376	30·9
3-HO	221, 291, 381	31·6, 10·7, 36·3
4-HO	300, 392	12·0, 36·3
2-HO	387	30·2
4-CH$_3$O[b]	387	33·1
3,4-DiHO[c]	310, 399	11·8, 31·6
3-HO–4-CH$_3$O[d]	305, 393	8·9, 29·5
2-HO–3-CH$_3$O[e]	260, 295, 389	10·5, 7·6, 29·5
3,4-CH$_2$O$_2$[f]	225, 391	8·5, 12·3
3,5-DiCH$_3$O–4-HO[g]	310, 397	12·9, 35·5
3,4,5-TriCH$_3$O[h]	225, 300, 388	19·1, 7·8, 24·0

[a] Benzaldehyde 2,4-dinitrophenylhydrazone.
[b] p-Anisaldehyde.
[c] Protocatechualdehyde.
[d] Isovanillin.
[e] o-Vanillin.
[f] Piperonal or heliotropin.
[g] Syringaldehyde.
[h] Gallaldehyde trimethyl ether.

G. Thioglycolic acid

p-Anisaldehyde can be determined with thioglycolic acid in H$_2$SO$_4$.[52] With 0·05 μmole of the aldehyde, an absorbance of 0·252 was obtained at 550 nm. Other oxybenzaldehydes can also be determined.

H. Vinylogs

Vinylogs of the oxybenzaldehydes have been found in the smoke of Chinese incense, anti-mosquito coils and heated hard-wood dust, e.g. sinapyl aldehyde, Va, coniferyl aldehyde, Vb, as well as syringaldehyde and vanillin.[53]

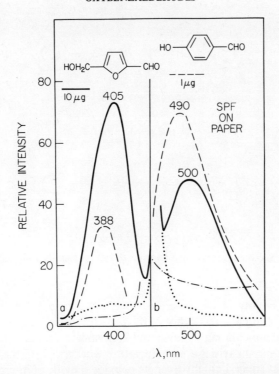

FIG. 58. Fluorescence excitation (a) and emission (b) spectra of the azine salts formed on paper after spraying with hydrazine dihydrochloride reagent. 5-Hydroxymethylfurfural (10 μg): (———) excitation spectrum at emiss. $\lambda 550$ nm and $MM = 0.003$; (———) emission spectrum at exc. 405 nm and $MM = 0.01$; (·········) blank for above; $F = 405/500$ for 5-hydroxymethylfurfural azine salt. 4-Hydroxybenzaldehyde (1 μg): (– – – –) excitation spectrum at emiss. $\lambda 525$ nm and $MM = 0.01$; (– – – – –) emission spectrum at exc. $\lambda 350$ nm and $MM = 0.01$; (–·–·–·) blank for above; $F = 388/490$ for 4-hydroxybenzaldehyde azine salt.[41]

These aldehydes are readily separated by silica gel TLC with *n*-hexane–diethyl ether–dichloromethane–glacial acetic acid (4:3:2:1) as developer.

$$HO-\underset{H_3CO}{\overset{X}{\bigcirc}}-CH{=}CH{-}CHO$$

V

	X	Aldehyde
(a)	CH_3O	Sinapyl
(b)	H	Coniferyl

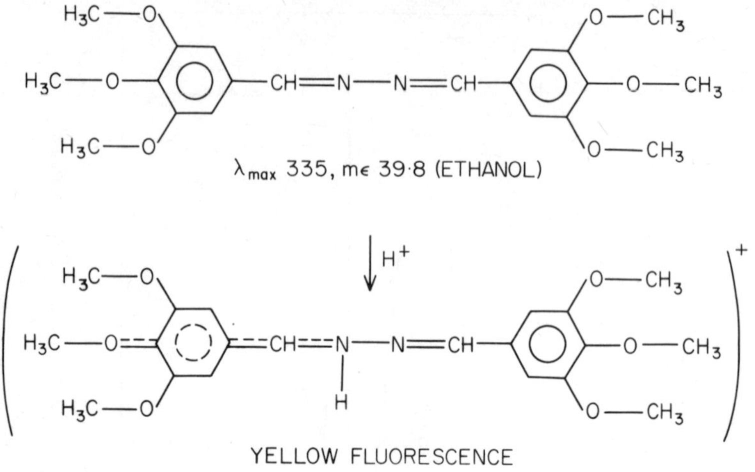

λ_{max} 335, mϵ 39·8 (ETHANOL)

YELLOW FLUORESCENCE

FIG. 59. Spectral properties of 3,4,5-trimethoxybenzaldehyde azine and its salt.

Assay could be any of the described methods. These aldehydes and their epoxides are of interest in studies of the possible etiological factors of naso-pharyngeal tumors among Chinese and Kenyans[54] and in connection with tumors of the nasal cavities among furniture workers.[55] In the latter case it is believed that sinapyl aldehyde or its epoxide may be of interest.[53]

REFERENCES

1. J. C. Dearden and W. F. Forbes. *Can. J. Chem.* **37**, 1305 (1959).
2. J. C. Dearden and W. F. Forbes. *Can. J. Chem.* **36**, 1362 (1958).
3. P. Grammaticakis. *Bull. Soc. Chim. France* **20**, 821 (1953).
4. A. Burawoy and J. T. Chamberlain. *J. Chem. Soc.* 2310 (1952).
5. N. J. Leonard, R. T. Rapala, H. L. Herzog and E. R. Blout. *J. Am. Chem. Soc.* **49**, 2997 (1949).
6. E. Spinner. *Spectrochim. Acta* **17**, 545 (1961).
7. S. Patai and Y. Israeli. *J. Chem. Soc.* 2025 (1960).
8. S. Patai and J. Zabicky. *J. Chem. Soc.* 2030 (1960).
9. L. Skulski and T. Urbanski. *Roczniki Chem.* **34**, 443 (1960).
10. L. A. Cohen. *J. Org. Chem.* **22**, 1333 (1957).
11. K. Yates and R. Stewart. *Can. J. Chem.* **37**, 664 (1959).
12. A. Wasserman. *J. Chem. Soc.* 1014 (1958).
13. N. A. Valyashko and N. N. Valyashko. *Zhur. Obshchei Khim.* **26**, 146 (1956).
14. E. A. Braude, A. A. Webb and M. V. S. Sultanbawa. *J. Chem. Soc.* 3328 (1958).
15. S. Dagley and M. D. Patel. *Biochem. J.* **66**, 227 (1957).
16. L. Doub and J. M. Vandenbelt. *J. Am. Chem. Soc.* **77**, 4535 (1955).
17. H. W. Lemon. *J. Am. Chem. Soc.* **69**, 2998 (1947).

18. P. Klinke and H. Gibian. *Chem. Ber.* **94**, 26 (1961).
19. W. J. Horton and M. G. Stout. *J. Org. Chem.* **26**, 1221 (1961).
20. S. Senoh, Y. Tokuyama and B. Witkop. *J. Am. Chem. Soc.* **84**, 1719 (1962).
21. A. N. Wilson and S. A. Harris. *J. Am. Chem. Soc.* **70**, 2331 (1949).
22. E. Wenkert, L. H. Liu and W. D. Fellows. *J. Org. Chem.* **27**, 2278 (1962).
23. R. A. Robinson and A. K. Kiang. *Trans. Faraday Soc.* **51**, 1398 (1955).
24. B. Weinstein and T. A. Hylton. *Tetrahedron* **20**, 1725 (1964).
25. O. Goldschmid. *J. Am. Chem. Soc.* **75**, 3780 (1953).
26. W. D. Kumler and P. P. T. Sah. *J. Am. Pharm. Ass., Sci. Ed.* **41**, 375 (1952).
27. R. E. Corbett, C. H. Hassall, A. W. Johnson and A. R. Todd. *J. Chem. Soc.* 1 (1950).
28. P. Grammaticakis. *Compt. Rend.* **231**, 278 (1950).
29. R. A. McIvor and J. M. Pepper. *Can. J. Chem.* **31**, 298 (1953).
30. I. A. Pearl and D. L. Beyer. *J. Am. Chem. Soc.* **72**, 1743 (1950).
31. H. W. Lemon. *J. Am. Chem. Soc.* **69**, 2998 (1947).
32. C. Eneback. *Acta Chem. Scand.* **11**, 895 (1957).
33. P. Crabbe, P. R. Leeming and C. Djerassi. *J. Am. Chem. Soc.* **80**, 5258 (1958).
34. D. E. Bland and C. Stamp. *Aust. J. Appl. Sci.* **6**, 353 (1955).
35. M. J. Reale. *Anal. Biochem.* **13**, 162 (1965).
36. L. G. Ensminger. *J. Ass. Offic. Agr. Chemists* **36**, 679 (1953).
37. H. W. Lange and K. Hempel. *J. Chromatog.* **59**, 53 (1971).
38. E. P. Crowell, W. A. Powell and C. J. Varsel. *Anal. Chem.* **35**, 184 (1963).
39. E. P. Crowell and C. J. Varsel. *Anal. Chem.* **35**, 189 (1963).
40. S. Nakano, H. Taniguchi and T. Furuhashi. *Yakugaku Zasshi* **92**, 411 (1972).
41. C. R. Engel and E. Sawicki. *Microchem. J.* **13**, 202 (1968).
42. V. Anger and S. Ofri. *Z. Anal. Chem.* **203**, 422 (1964).
43. V. Anger, in P. W. West, A. M. G. MacDonald and T. S. West, Eds. *Anal. Chem. 1962*, Elsevier, New York, London, 1963, p. 58.
44. C.-H. Yang and J. Chow. *J. Chinese Chem. Soc.* **15**, 97 (1968).
45. G. Ruffini. *J. Chromatog.* **17**, 483 (1965).
46. Y.-Y. Chin, H. Liu and C. Yang. *Chemistry, Taipei*, 2 (1972).
47. E. Sundt and A. Saccardi. *Food Tech.* **16**, 89 (1962).
48. M. H. Klouwen, R. ter Heide and J. G. J. Kok. *Fette, Seifen, Anstrichmittel* **65**, 414 (1963).
49. K. G. Bergner and H. Sperlich. *Dtsch. Lebensm.-Rundschau* **47**, 134 (1951).
50. E. D. Barber. *J. Chromatog.* **27**, 398 (1967).
51. R. Bauer and C. O. Rupe. *Anal. Chem.* **43**, 421 (1971).
52. G. Kunovits. *Anal. Chim. Acta* **55**, 221 (1971).
53. S. Gibbard and R. Schoental. *J. Chromatog.* **44**, 396 (1969).
54. C. S. Muir and K. Shanmugaratnam, Eds., *Cancer of the Nasopharynx*, UICC Monograph Series I, Munksgaard, Copenhagen, 1967.
55. E. D. Acheson, R. H. Cowdell, E. Hadfield and R. G. Macbeth. *Brit. Med. J.* **2**, 587 (1968).

50. PALMITALDEHYDE

$$CH_3—(CH_2)_{14}CHO$$

I. PHYSICAL PROPERTIES

M.p. 34°. Insol. in water; soluble in organic solvents. On standing, it polymerizes incompletely to a trimer, m.p. 73°.

Palmitaldehyde, stearaldehyde and other pure fatty aldehydes can be prepared through conversion of the alcohol tosylate with dimethyl sulphoxide to the corresponding aldehyde.[1, 2] GLC can then be used to demonstrate purity. The p-nitrophenylhydrazone of palmitaldehyde can be prepared from the bisulphite addition product and crystallized from ethanol to a constant melting point of 96·5.[3]

Free fatty aldehydes have been reported as naturally occurring components of lipid extracts.[4—6] Methods have been devised for the measurement of these aldehydes in the presence of plasmalogens.[7, 8]

To measure the free aldehydes in the presence of plasmalogen without hydrolysing the plasmalogen, it is necessary to use sulphuric acid at a concentration of 0·001 N.[8] The success of this selective assay was proven with radio-labelled plasmalogens. The recoveries of p-nitrophenylhydrazones of stearaldehyde and palmitaldehyde down to acetaldehyde obtained with the following procedure and other methods are compared in Table 37.

A. Determination of free aldehydes in tissue lipids[8]

Evaporate the lipid sample in a 40 ml conical centrifuge tube to dryness. Redissolve in 0·2 ml of chloroform. To each sample add 8 ml of 90% aq methanol (v/v), 1 ml of 0·01 N H_2SO_4 and 1 ml of 0·02 M p-nitrophenyl-hydrazine in 80% aq methanol (v/v). Mix the samples, heat for 25 min at 60°, and then cool in an ice bath. To each sample add 10 ml hexane and 5 ml water. Shake the tubes for 30 sec and separate the phases by centrifugation. Discard the lower phase. Wash the hexane phase at least twice with 10 ml of 35% aq ethanol (v/v) by shaking, centrifuging and discarding the lower phase. Evaporate an 8 ml aliquot of the hexane phase under nitrogen almost

Table 37. Recoveries of p-nitrophenylhydrazones of various chain lengths.[8]

Hydrazone shorthand designation	Per cent recovery by method[a]			
	A	B	C (7)	D (9)
2:0	0	0	0	0
4:0	0	0	0	0
8:0	56	53	39	47
10:0	74	72	57	65
12:0	88	88	73	80
14:0	92	91	80	87
16:0	100	99	83	95
18:0	101	100	87	99

[a] A, Present work, 0·008 N acid medium. B, Present work 0·001 N or 0·06 N acid medium.[8] C, Pries and Böttcher,[7] total medium. D, Wittenberg, et al.[9]

to dryness. Dissolve the residue in 3 ml of 95% aq ethanol and read the absorbance at 395 nm against a reagent blank.

The free aldehyde content of mouse tissue, such as heart, liver, kidney, brain and skeletal muscle, can be determined by this method.

REFERENCES

1. V. Mahadevan. *J. Am. Oil Chemist's Soc.* **41**, 520 (1964).
2. C. S. Marvel and V. C. Sekara. Organic Syntheses, Coll. Vol. 3, 366 (1955).
3. M. A. Wells and J. C. Dittmer. *Biochemistry* **5**, 3405 (1966).
4. R. A. Gelman and J. R. Gilbertson. *Biochem. Biophys. Res. Commun.* **20**, 427 (1965).
5. J. R. Gilbertson, W. J. Ferrell and R. A. Gelman. *J. Lipid Res.* **8**, 38 (1967).
6. W. J. Ferrell and J. R. Gilbertson. *Proc. W. Va. Acad. Sci.* **39**, 263 (1967).
7. C. Pries and J. F. Böttcher. *Biochem. Biophys. Acta* **98**, 329 (1965).
8. W. J. Ferrell, J. R. Radloff and A. B. Jackiw. *Lipids* **4**, 278 (1969).
9. J. B. Wittenberg, S. R. Korey and F. H. Swenson. *J. Biol. Chem.* **219**, 39 (1956).

51. PROPIONALDEHYDE

$$CH_3—CH_2—CHO$$

I. PHYSICAL PROPERTIES

M.p. $-81°$; b.p. $48\cdot8°$; D_4^{20} $0\cdot8066$; $n_D{}^{19}$ $1\cdot36460$. Soluble in 5 parts water at $20°$. Volatile with steam.

II. SPECTRA

This aldehyde in water has 2 bands in the ultraviolet at 210 nm, mε $0\cdot032$ and 275 nm, mε $0\cdot013$, the latter being a weak band derived from an $n \rightarrow \pi^*$ transition.[1] In isooctane the latter band had much fine structure, e.g. λ_{max} 280s, 285, 292·5, 302·5 and 310s with mε $0\cdot019$, $0\cdot020$, $0\cdot021$, $0\cdot019$, and $0\cdot014$, respectively.[2] These bands are too weak to use in analysis, except when the aldehyde is present almost exclusively and in high concentration.

III. REAGENTS

A. 1,3-Diketones

1,3-Cyclohexanedione, dimedone and 2,4-pentanedione can also be used to determine propionaldehyde colorimetrically or fluorimetrically. The procedures have been given in the aliphatic aldehydes section. As little as $0\cdot2$ μg of propionaldehyde can be estimated.[3]

B. 2,4-Dinitrophenylhydrazine

2,4-Dinitrophenylhydrazine could be used in the assay of this aldehyde in appropriate mixtures or after chromatography. Spectral data for the dinitrophenylhydrazone are given in Table 38. Mixed saturated carbonyl compounds can be converted to their dinitrophenylhydrazones and separated by partition between petroleum ether and nitromethane on a silica gel[11] or a diatomaceous[12] column. Fractions are read at λ 425 nm and λ 530 nm.

Table 38. Absorption spectra of propionaldehyde 2,4-dinitrophenylhydrazone in various solvents

Solvent	λ_{max} (nm)	mε	Ref.
Hexane	340	22·4	4
Chloroform	357	22·4	5–8
Ethanol	359	22	9, 10
Ethanol–NaOEt	431	22·4	7
Ethanol–chloroform–NaOEt	438	22·4	8

C. 3-Methyl-2-benzothiazolinone hydrazone

MBTH can be used to estimate propionaldehyde in the absence of other aliphatic aldehydes. In the following procedure 2 bands are obtained at λ_{max} 604, mε 38 and λ_{max} 660 nm, mε 35. The sensitivity of the procedure is capable of further improvement.

MBTH determination of propionaldehyde. To 2 ml of aq test solution add 1 ml of 0·5% aq MBTH . HCl. Heat at 100° for 3 min and cool. Add 0·5 ml of 2% aq ferric chloride. Read the absorbance at 604 or 660 nm in 15 minutes.

D. Ninhydrin

Propionaldehyde is stated to react specifically with ninhydrin in H_2SO_4 to give a deep red–blue colour which can be read at 595 nm and mε 29.[13] Other aliphatic aldehydes (such as formaldehyde, acetaldehyde, acrolein, crotonaldehyde and isobutyraldehyde), aromatic aldehydes (such as benzaldehyde, salicylaldehyde and vanillin) and heterocyclic aldehydes (such as furfural) produce no colour with ninhydrin. *n*-Butryaldehyde gives a red colour, λ_{max} 470 nm. Formaldehyde inhibits the reaction so it must be removed. Ketones and amino acids do not react with the reagent under the conditions of the test. In the analysis of atmospheric propionaldehyde air is first passed through 20 ml of 2% glycine solution in saturated sodium carbonate so as to remove the formaldehyde. The propionaldehyde is then collected in 20 ml of 5% sodium bisulphite solution contained in the next 2 tubes, and the following procedure is used for the analysis.

Ninhydrin determination of propionaldehyde.[13] To 0·5 ml of the 5% aq sodium bisulphite test solution add cautiously 4 ml of conc H_2SO_4. Mix and cool to 25°. Add 0·2 ml of 3% ninhydrin in 5% sodium bisulphite solution and mix. Stopper and let stand for 1 h at 25°. Dilute to 12·5 ml with conc H_2SO_4, mix and read the absorbance at 595 nm.

Because of its remarkable specificity and lack of independent confirmation, this method should be investigated thoroughly.

E. Nitrophenylhydrazines

The 2-nitrophenylhydrazone of propionaldehyde absorbs at about λ 438 nm, mε 6·3 in ethanol,[14] while the 4-isomer[15] absorbs at λ_{max} 274, 341 and mε 12, 6·8, respectively, in hexane and λ_{max} 250, 393 and mε 8·9, 22·4, respectively, in 80% methanol in acetic acid.[15]

Propionaldehyde 4-nitrophenylhydrazone can be determined phosphorimetrically with a determination limit of 6 ng/0·1 ml solution. In EPA its spectral bands are at P255, 395, 408i/525, 550s, Fig. 60.[16]

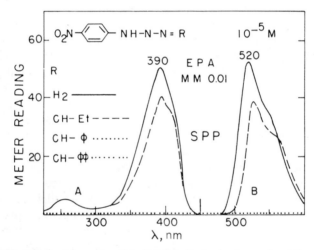

FIG. 60. Phosphorimetric spectra of 4-nitrophenylhydrazine (———) and the 4-nitrophenylhydrazone of propionaldehyde (– – – –) in EPA at a concentration of 10^{-5} M. The 4-nitrophenylhydrazones of benzaldehyde and 2-naphthaldehyde are non-phosphorescent.[16]

F. *m*-Dinitrobenzene

Propionaldehyde has been shown to react with *m*-dinitrobenzene in the presence of alkali to form a highly coloured anionic resonance structure.[17] This aldehyde reacts with *s*-trinitrobenzene in the presence of triethylamine to form the anion, I, λ_{max} 470, 566 nm.[18]

I

Other aldehydes and ketones containing the α-C hydrogen would be expected to react. The reaction has not been applied to the analysis of propionaldehyde.

REFERENCES

1. G. Mackinney and O. Temmer. *J. Am. Chem. Soc.* **70**, 3586 (1948).
2. A. P. I. Research Project No. 44, I, 0329 (1949).
3. E. Sawicki and R. A. Carnes. *Mikrochim. Acta* 148 (1968).
4. F. H. Lohman. *Anal. Chem.* **30**, 972 (1958).
5. G. D. Johnson. *J. Am. Chem. Soc.* **75**, 2720 (1953).
6. G. W. H. Cheeseman *et al. J. Chem. Soc.* 1516 (1949).
7. L. A. Jones and C. K. Hancock. *J. Org. Chem.* **25**, 226 (1960).
8. L. A. Jones, J. C. Holmes and R. B. Seligman. *Anal. Chem.* **28**, 191 (1956).
9. A. Takamizawa, S. Hayashi and H. Sato. *J. Pharm. Soc. Japan* **85**, 158 (1965).
10. J. D. Roberts and C. Green. *J. Am. Chem. Soc.* **68**, 214 (1946).
11. P. J. G. Kramer and H. Duin. *Rec. Trav. Chim.* **73**, 63 (1954).
12. K. J. Monty. *Anal. Chem.* **30**, 1350 (1958).
13. L. R. Jones and J. A. Riddick. *Anal. Chem.* **26**, 1035 (1954).
14. P. Grammaticakis. *Bull. Soc. Chim. France* **21**, 1372 (1954).
15. Y. Yagi. *Bull. Chem. Soc. Japan* **36**, 487 (1963).
16. E. Sawicki and J. Pfaff. *Microchem. J.* **12**, 7 (1967).
17. S. Gitis, A. Kaminskii and A. Varlanova. *J. Org. Chem. (USSR)*, **4**, 472 (1968).
18. M. J. Strauss. *Tetrahedron Letters*, 2021 (1969).

52. PEPTIDE AND PROTEIN ALDEHYDES

I. PHYSICAL PROPERTIES

The presence of trace quantities of aldehydic components in commercial gelatins and collagen has been reported.[1–5] Ichthyocol and other tropocollagens contain 1 to 2 equivalents (per tropocollagen of mol. wt. 300,000) of a component which reacts as an aldehyde or from which an aldehyde is easily derived.[1] The chemical reactivities and the ultraviolet absorption spectra of derivatives made with MBTH or 2,4-dinitrophenylhydrazine suggest that the aldehyde-containing component has aldol-like properties in the manner of β-hydroxyaldehydes.[6]

In the study of the reaction of thiosemicarbazide with collagen spectral evidence has been obtained for the presence of aldehyde groups on α chains and β components.[7]

Aldehydes may be intermediates in the formation of the desmosins, **I**,[8] which are the cross-links in elastin and are polyfunctional amino acids believed to be derived from four lysyl residues in peptide linkage.[8–13] Since lathyrogens inhibit cross-linking in elastin,[13–15] and elastin from the aortas of lathyritic chicks are deficient in aldehyde groups when compared to normal elastin,[16] it would appear that lathyrogenic agents block the conversion of lysine to an aldehyde intermediate and, thus, inhibit cross-linking in elastin.[3]

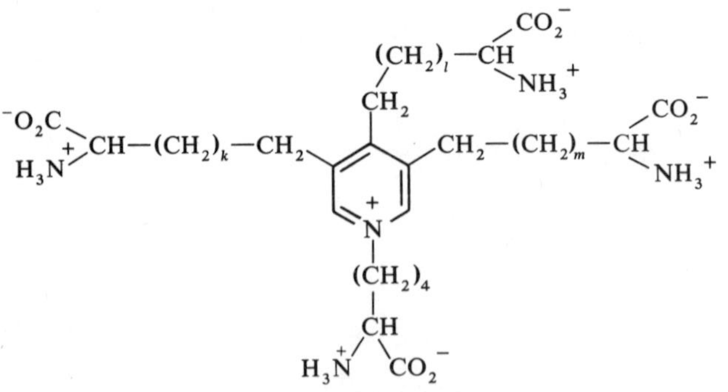

$$\mathbf{I}\ (k + l + m = 4)$$

See the 2-aminoadipaldehydic acid precursors and peptide aldehyde precursors sections for more details.

REFERENCES

1. M. Rojkind, O. O. Blumenfeld and P. M. Gallop. *Biochem. Biophys. Res. Commun.* **17**, 320 (1964).
2. O. O. Blumenfeld, M. A. Paz and P. M. Gallop. *Fed. Proc.* **22**, 648 (1963).
3. P. M. Gallop. *Biophys. J.* **4**, 79 (1964).
4. J. M. Landucci. *Bull. Soc. Chem.* **21**, 191 (1956).
5. C. I. Levine. *J. Exp. Med.* **116**, 119 (1962).
6. M. Rojkind, O. O. Blumenfeld and P. M. Gallop. *J. Biol. Chem.* **241**, 1530 (1966).
7. M. L. Tanzer, D. Monroe and J. Gross. *Biochemistry* **5**, 1919 (1966).
8. S. M. Partridge, D. F. Elsden, J. Thomas, A. Dorfman, A. Telser and P. Ho. *Biochem. J.* **93**, 30C (1964).
9. J. Thomas, D. F. Elsden and S. M. Partridge. *Nature,* **200**, 651 (1963).
10. S. M. Partridge, D. F. Elsden and J. Thomas. *Nature,* **197**, 1297 (1963).
11. S. M. Partridge, D. F. Elsden, J. Thomas, A. Dorfman, A. Telser and P. Ho, *Nature* **209**, 399 (1966).
12. E. J. Miller, G. R. Martin and K. A. Piez. *Biochem. Biophys. Res. Commun.* **17**, 248 (1964).
13. E. J. Miller, G. R. Martin, C. E. Mecca and K. A. Piez. *J. Biol. Chem.* **240**, 3623 (1965).
14. B. L. O'Dell, D. F. Elsden, J. Thomas, S. M. Partridge, R. H. Smith and R. Palmer. *Biochem. J.* **96**, 35P (1965).
15. B. L. O'Dell, D. F. Elsden, J. Thomas, S. M. Partridge, R. H. Smith and R. Palmer. *Nature* **209**, 401 (1966).
16. E. J. Miller and H. M. Fullmer. *J. Exptl. Med.* **123**, 1097 (1966).

53. 1-PYRENEALDEHYDE

I. SPECTRAL PROPERTIES

The absorption spectra of the compound in methanol and in conc H_2SO_4 are shown in Fig. 61.

The compound is not fluorescent in non-polar solvents but is fluorescent in polar solvents while its 4-isomer fluoresces in polar and non-polar

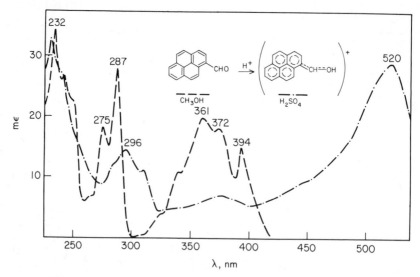

FIG. 61. The ultraviolet-visible absorption spectra of 1-pyrenecarboxaldehyde in methanol (–––––) and in sulphuric acid (–·–·–·).

solvents.[1] However, on the addition of trichloroacetic acid to a heptane solution of 1-pyrenealdehyde the compound becomes fluorescent.

The fluorescence excitation and emission spectra in ethanolic solution on glass fibre paper and in a cell are shown in Fig. 62.[2] Dioxane quenches the fluorescence. The effect of solvent on the fluorescence intensity of the aldehyde is shown in Table 39.[2]

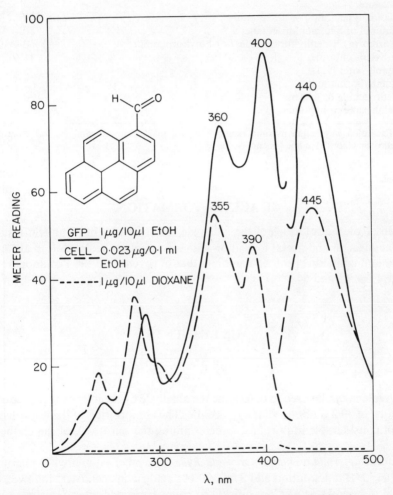

FIG. 62. Fluorescence excitation and emission spectra of 1-pyrenecarboxaldehyde on glass-fibre paper: spot wet with ethanol (———); spot wet with dioxane (·········); and in a cell in ethanol solution (– – – –).[2]

Table 39. Effect of the intermolecular hydrogen bond on the fluorescence intensity of 1-pyrenealdehyde[a].[2]

Solvent	Relative fluorescence intensity
2,2,2-Trifluoroethanol	1000
Ethanol–water (1:1)	600
Formamide	600
Methanol	200
Ethanol, n-pentanol, or n-heptanol	100
t-Butanol or s-tetrachloroethane	80
Chloroform, N-methylformamide, or t-butylformamide	60
Methylene chloride	15
Phenol–water (9:1)	5
Dimethylformamide	2
Triethylamine or toluene	0
Cyclohexane or heptane	0

[a]Excitation wavelength maxima ranges from 390 to 395 nm; emission maxima from 415 (methylene chloride) to 460 [phenol–water (9:1)].

II. ACETAL FORMATION

In alcoholic solutions of the aldehyde, addition of a mineral acid results in hemiacetal and acetal formation with a consequent violet shift to absorption and emission spectra resembling that of pyrene and the 1-aminopyrene salt, Figs. 63 and 64.[3]

III. REAGENTS

A. Azulene

Azulene can be used to determine the aldehyde by the following procedure. An mε of 39·2 is obtained at λ_{max} 606 nm. The composition of the test solvent is of considerable importance in determining the sensitivity of the method.

Azulene determination of 1-pyrenealdehyde. To 2 ml of a dimethylformamide–water (3:1) test solution add 3 ml of 0·1 % azulene in acetic acid followed by 3 ml of conc H_2SO_4. Cool quickly to room temp and after 5 min read the absorbance at λ 606 nm.

The method needs further study for optimization.

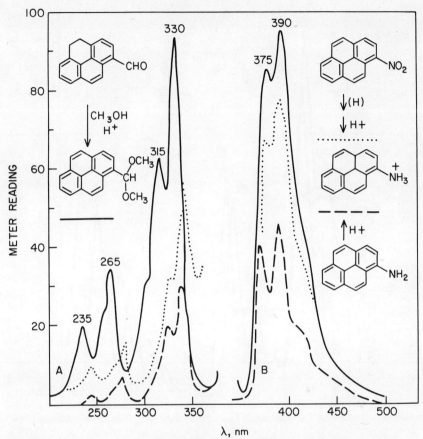

FIG. 63. Comparison of the fluorescence excitation and emission spectra of
1-pyrenecarboxaldehyde in acidifed methanol (———) with reduced 1-nitropyrene (········)
and 1-aminopyrene (– – – –) both in acid solution.[3]

B. Borohydride

Reduction with borohydride can also be used in the characterization
and assay of polynuclear aldehydes.[3] Striking changes are shown in the
absorption spectra, Fig. 65 and in the fluorescence spectra, Fig. 66. The
similarity of the spectra of pyrene, reduced 1-pyrenealdehyde and reduced
1-acetylpyrene are depicted in Fig. 67. The broad long wavelength band
near 470 nm is derived from the excimer. The reduced pyrenealdehyde can be
dissolved in conc sulphuric acid to give the entirely different spectrum of the
cation. Fig. 65.

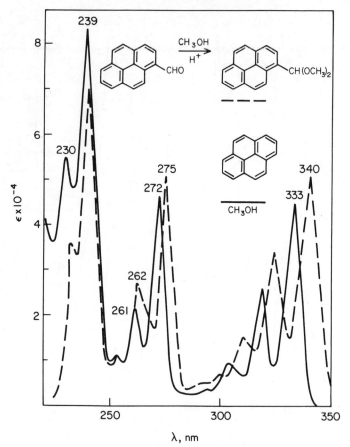

FIG. 64. Comparison of the ultraviolet absorption spectra of 1-pyrenecarboxaldehyde in acid methanol (-----) with pyrene in methanol (———).[3]

The following procedure can be used in this type of characterization or assay.

Analysis of 1-pyrenealdehyde with borohydride followed by sulphuric acid.[3] *Reagent.* Dissolve 0·5 g of potassium borohydride in a mixture of 20 ml of water and 50 ml of methanol. Add 1 ml of 0·05 % cupric chloride and dilute to 100 ml with methanol.

Procedure. Dilute 1 ml of test solution in a 10 ml volumetric flask to the mark with the reagent. Run the absorption and fluorescence excitation and emission spectra from 200 to 500 nm.

Dilute 1 ml of this solution to 10 ml with conc H_2SO_4 acid and assay through the reduced form spectrally.

Obtain fluorescence spectra by adding one drop of reagent to a spot of the compound on glass fibre paper. Add a drop of conc HCl and obtain the fluorescence excitation and emission spectra of the reduced form.

C. Phenylhydrazines

4-Nitrophenylhydrazine can also be used to determine 1-pyrenealdehyde. The p-nitrophenylhydrazone dissolved in dimethylformamide containing a small amount of tetraethylammonium hydroxide forms the blue anion absorbing near 610 nm.

Phenylhydrazine shows a somewhat different phenomenon. 1-Pyrenealdehyde phenylhydrazone absorbs at λ 408 nm with $m\varepsilon$ 36 in dimethyl-

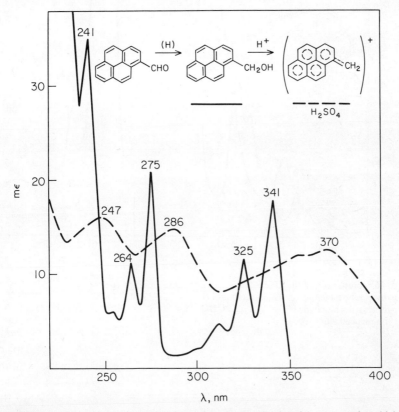

FIG. 65. Comparison of the ultraviolet absorption spectra of reduced 1-pyrenecarboxaldehyde in methanol (———) and in conc H_2SO_4 (-----).

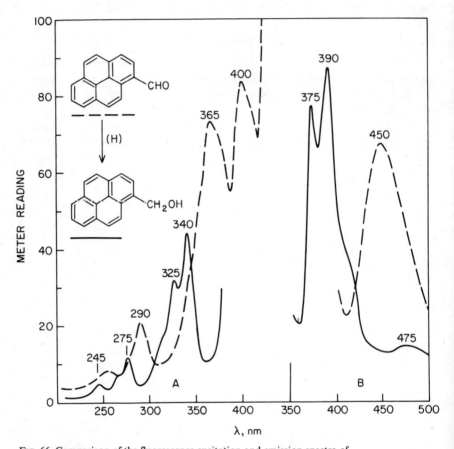

FIG. 66. Comparison of the fluorescence excitation and emission spectra of
1-pyrenecarboxaldehyde in water–methanol (1:4) (−−−−−) and reduced
1-pyrenecarboxaldehyde (————). 1 μg PCHO. MM = 0·01 for the aldehyde and MM = 0·03
for the reduced aldehyde.

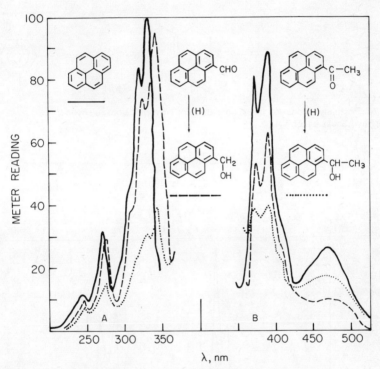

FIG. 67. Comparison of fluorescence excitation and emission spectra of pyrene (————),
reduced 1-pyrenecarboxaldehyde (————), and reduced 1-acetylpyrene (·········).

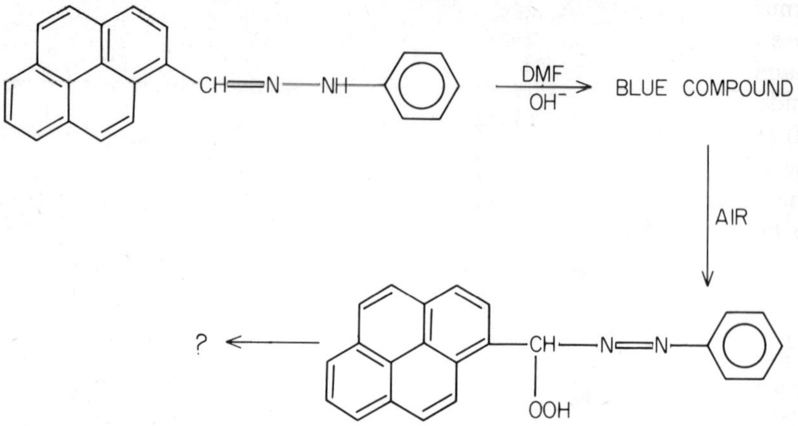

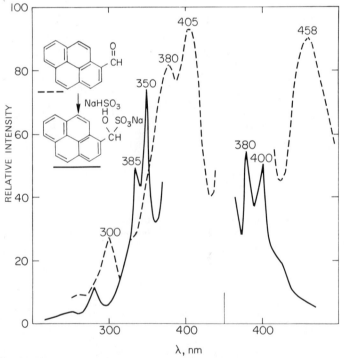

FIG. 68. Postulated oxidation of the blue anion of 1-pyrenecarboxaldehyde phenylhydrazone by air.

FIG. 69. Comparison of the fluorescence excitation and emission spectra of 1-pyrenecarboxaldehyde (10 ng) (-----) and its sodium bisulphite addition product on paper.

formamide. The addition of 2% of 10% aq tetraethylammonium hydroxide gives an unstable blue colour which in 3 h fades to a light yellow colour. Examination of the absorption spectrum shows the presence of the following bands (relative intensities)—λ 278 (1·85), 305s (0·75), 319 (0·97), 333 (1·5) and 350 (1·8). The postulated equation for this reaction is shown in Fig. 68. The short wavelength band is derived from the phenylazo group while the other bands are derived from the insulated pyrene group. A similar reaction has been postulated for benzaldehyde phenylhydrazone.[4]

D. Bisulphite

Sodium bisulphite can also be used in the analysis of the aldehyde as shown in the drastic change in fluorescence spectra of 10 ng of 1-pyrene-aldehyde on paper treated with 1 μl of 10% aq sodium bisulphite, Fig. 69.

REFERENCES

1. K. Bredereck, T. Foster and H. G. Oesterlin, in H. P. Kallmann and G. M. Spruch, Eds., "Luminescence of Organic and Inorganic Materials," Wiley, New York, 1962, p. 161.
2. E. Sawicki, T. W. Winfield and C. R. Sawicki. *Microchem. J.* **15**, 294 (1970).
3. H. Johnson and E. Sawicki. *Talanta* **13**, 1361 (1966).
4. H. C. Yao and P. Resnick. *J. Org. Chem.* **30**, 2832 (1965).

54. PYRIDOXAL

I. INTRODUCTION

Vitamin B_6 activity resides in the 3 compounds, pyridoxine, pyridoxamine and pyridoxal. All three are found in natural sources of vitamin B_6. Probably the most important forms of vitamins B_6 are pyridoxal and its 5'-phosphate.

II. STRUCTURES

The various possible structures postulated to be in equilibrium are shown in Fig. 70.[1] The equilibrium involves lactam ⇌ lactim and ring ⇌ chain tautomerisms. Hydration forms are also possible in water. The zwitterion

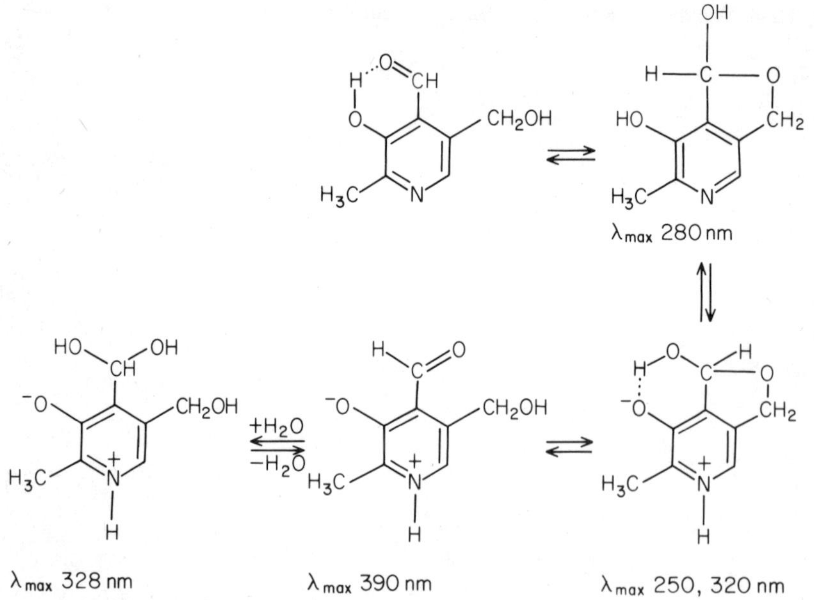

FIG. 70. Equilibrium between the various pyridoxal structures.[1]

180

predominates in aqueous solution, while the non-zwitterion is present to about 8%. Somewhat similar structures have been postulated for the 5-desoxy derivative of pyridoxal, Fig. 71; in addition, structures for the

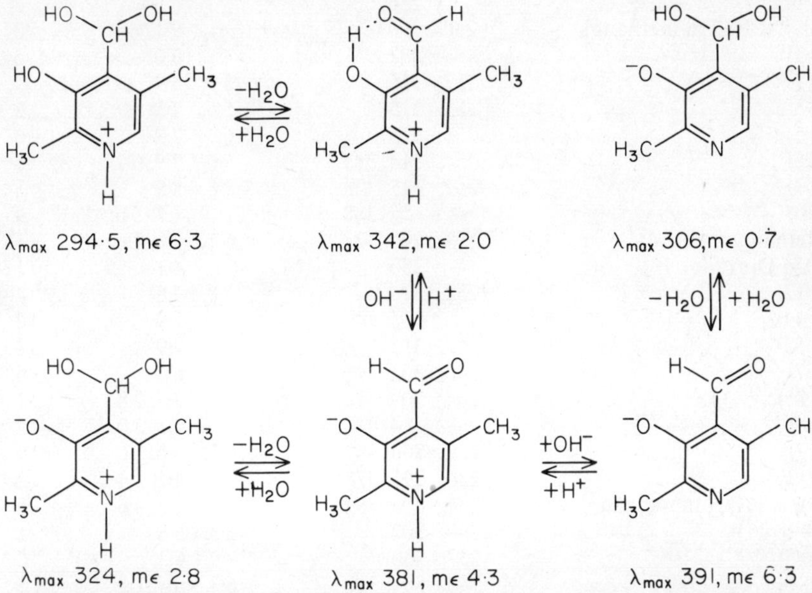
$-H_2O$
$+H_2O$
λ_{max} 294·5, mε 6·3
λ_{max} 342, mε 2·0
λ_{max} 306, mε 0·7
OH^-
H^+
$-H_2O$
$+H_2O$
λ_{max} 324, mε 2·8
λ_{max} 381, mε 4·3
λ_{max} 391, mε 6·3
$+OH^-$
$+H^+$

FIG. 71. Equilibrium between the various desoxypyridoxal structures in neutral, acid and alkaline solution.

cationic and anionic derivatives have been postulated. Varying ultraviolet absorption spectra have been reported for pyridoxal, Table 40. The drastic effect of a change in solvent is shown for aqueous methanol solutions in Table 41.

The hemiacetal structures exist in aqueous solutions.[5] In acidic solution the hemiacetal structure, **I**, predominates. In alkaline solution structures **II** and **III** predominate.

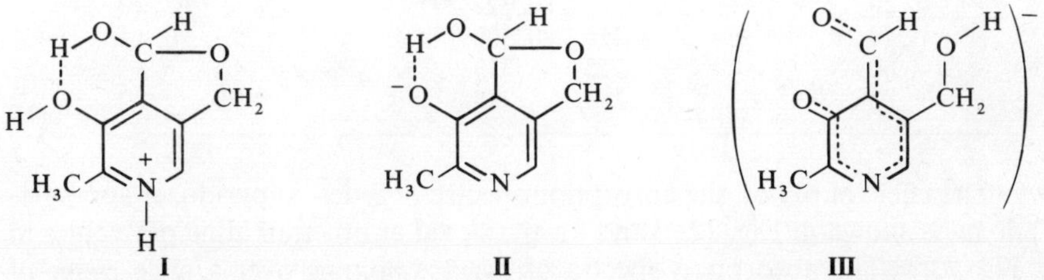

I λ_{max} 285 nm

II λ_{max} 303 nm

III λ_{max} 240, 390 nm

Table 40. Absorption spectra of pyridoxal

Solvent or (pH)	λ_{max} (nm)	mε	Ref.
0·1 N HCl	288	8·9	1
(1·0)	286	8·5	2
10^{-2} M HCl in methanol	230s, 290	9·1	3
(1·9)[a]	283	10·0	5
(4·97)	253, 315	5·0, 5·9	2
(5·50)	253, 315	5·5, 7·5	2
(6·5)	251, 315	6·3, 7·9	6
(6·8)[b]	254, 314, 383	5·0, 7·9, 0·1	8
(6·9)	252, 317	5·8, 8·9	1
(7·0)	388	5·0	9
Methanol (neutral)	220s, 280, 328	6·7, 4·6, 1·0	3
60% Dioxane	280	4·1	1
(7·13)	252, 315	5·8, 7·8	2
(7·44)	315	7·9	10
(7·55)	250, 315	6·3, 7·9	11
(8·7)	240, 303	6·3, 6·3	6
(8·85)	284, 309, 412	4·1, 3·7, 2·8	2
(9·4)	284, 411	4·3, 3·0	2
(9·7)[c]	239, 300, 389	6·3, 5·0, 1·6	8
(10·13)	230, 295, 378	9·4, 4·2, 2·4	2
0·02 M KOH in methanol	234, 303, 389	11·2, 3·5, 4·6	3
(10 to 11)	240, 302	8·3, 5·8	1
(10·7)	237, 300	7·9, 6·3	6
(11·0)	240, 304, 391	6·3, 6·3, 1·3	5
(13·0)	241, 300, 377	8·2, 5·8, 1·3	2

[a] At pH 2 λ_{max} 286·5 and $E_{1\,cm}^{1\%}$ = 440 reported.[4]
[b] λ_{max} 330 nm at pH 6·75 reported.[7]
[c] From pH 8 to 13 λ_{max} is 385 nm; from pH 10 to 13, mε is 1·3.[12]

Table 41. Ultraviolet absorption spectra of pyridoxal in neutral aqueous methanol mixtures.[3]

H_2O, %	λ_{max}	mε
0	280, 328	4·6, 1·0
20	280, 322	3·7, 2·3
40	256, 280, 320	3·7, 3·0, 4·1
60	255, 319	4·5, 5·9
80	254, 318	5·0, 7·2

The effect of pH on the absorption spectra of 5-desoxypyridoxal and pyridoxal is shown in Fig. 72.[1] and for pyridoxal at other alkaline pH values in Fig. 73.[2] The absorption spectra of pyridoxaloxime over a wide range of pH has also been reported.[2]

The equilibrium constants and spectra of pyridoxal, 5-desoxypyridoxal and various pyridine derivatives have been compared for purposes of assigning the structures[1, 13] previously discussed. Comparison of the spectra of 3-hydroxypyridine-4-aldehyde, desoxypyridoxal and pyridoxal has shown

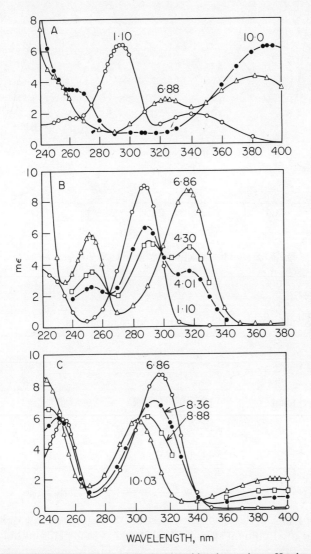

FIG. 72. The spectra of 5-desoxypyridoxal and pyridoxal at various pH values: A. 5-desoxypyridoxal; B, pyridoxal in acid solutions; C, pyridoxal in basic solutions. The figures beside the curves denote the pH of the solutions.[1]

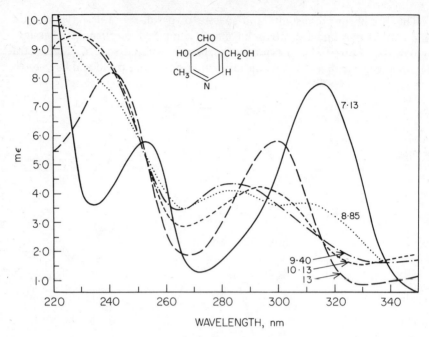

FIG. 73. Absorption spectra of pyridoxal (pH 7·13 or greater).[2]

Table 42. Calculated values of pK_a with standard deviations

	pK_a		
	(14)	(1)	(6)
5-Desoxypyridoxal	4·16 ± 0·003 (25°)	4·17 (25°)	
	8·02 ± 0·004	8·14	
Pyridoxal	4·13 ± 0·008 (50°)	4·20 (25°)	4·23
	8·37 ± 0·008	8·66	8·70
	13·04 ± 0·023	13·0	

that the locations of the absorption maxima of each species are quite similar, whereas the predominant species of pyridoxal at each pH is entirely different from those of the other two compounds.[13] Equilibrium constants are given for pyridoxal and 5-desoxypyridoxal in Table 42.[14]

Some of the methods for analysis of pyridoxal are given in Table 43.

Table 43. Reagents in the determination of pyridoxal

Reagent	Chromogen λ_{max} or fluorogen $F_{exc/em}$	Ref.
—[a] at pH 7	315	15
—[a] at pH 13	389	15
—[a] at pH 6·75	325	16
—[a] at pH 6·75	F330/385	17, 18
Acetone	420	15, 19
Amino acid	365[b]	20–22
Cyanide	F360/430	11, 23–33
Diazotized aromatic amines		34–37
2,6-Dichloroquinone-4-chloroimide	650	37–42
N,N-Diethyl-p-phenylenediamine[c]	605	43
Dithionate		44
Hydrazine[d]	Y fluor.	45
MBTH	380[e]	46
Oxidizing agent	F350/450	47–49
Phenylhydrazine	410	37, 50
Pyridoxal kinase[f]	—	51
Semicarbazide	G. fluor.	52
Thiophene		15

[a] Unchanged compound analysed.
[b] With ethanolamine.[20]
[c] Developed for pyridoxine.
[d] Used only as a spot test.
[e] mε 22·4.
[f] Reaction not yet used in analysis.

III. SPECTRAL PROPERTIES

The free aldehyde is analysed best at λ 315 nm at pH 7 or at 389 nm at pH 13.[15] The total concentration of vitamin B_6 (pyridoxal, pyridoxamine and pyridoxine) can be determined at λ 325 nm in an aq solution of pH 6·75, under which conditions all 3 compounds have an $E_{1\,cm}^{1\%}$ of 440.[16]

The fluorescence properties of the vitamin B_6 family have been reported. Their fluorescence quantum yields vary with temperature.[53] The quantum yield of pyridoxal changes gradually from about 0·03 at 40° to 0·08 at 5° while pyridoxamine changes from about 0·08 at 40° to 0·21 at 5° and pyridoxamine phosphate from about 0·095 at 40° to 0·26 at 5°. Some of the fluorescence properties of the hemiacetal of pyridoxal are shown in Table 44. The quantum yield of fluorescence of pyridoxal at 25° in 0·05 M potassium phosphate buffer of pH 7·0 has been reported to be 0·048 ± 0·003 at the excitation wavelength of 315 nm.[53]

Since the acidity or basicity of a compound can be entirely different in the excited state than in the ground state, sometimes at a particular pH value the

Table 44. Fluorescence characteristics of pyridoxal hemiacetal at various pH values.[54]

Compound	Molecular species	λ_{max}	$F_{exc/em}$	Intensity of maximum fluorescence[a]	pH range of maximum fluorescence[b]
Pyridoxal hemiacetal	Neutral form[c]	280	291/330	—	in Ethanol
	Dipolar ion	317	330/382	210	pH 6
	Cation	288	300/350	11	Ho −3·7 to −3·4
	Cation (excited)	—	300/382	125	pH 0
	Anion	302	310/365	280	pH 12
3-Hydroxypyridine	Neutral form	278	None	0	
	Dipolar ion	315	325/392	6	pH 1-2
	Cation	283	298/340	2	~Ho −4
	Cation (excited)	—	298/398	7	pH 1-2
	Anion	298	309/365	100	pH 10-14

[a] Fluorescence intensity of the 3-hydroxypyridine anion at pH 11 taken as 100.
[b] Ho is the acidity function of Hammett.[54]
[c] In dioxane.

molecule may absorb in the neutral form (or as a salt) in the ground state and fluoresce as a salt (or a neutral compound) in its excited state. This is called excited state ionization and has been reviewed.[54, 55] Thus, in the excited state the pK_a^* of 3-hydroxypyridine and pyridoxal are -3.0 and -3.3, respectively.[54, 56] This phenomenon is useful in analysis.

IV. DIRECT PHOTOMETRIC ANALYSIS

The native fluorescence of pyridoxal can also be used for its assay.[17, 18] Since pyridoxamine is believed to be the only interference of the vitamin B_6 group in whole blood, 2 blanks are run in the following procedure. In one blank pyridoxal is destroyed with hydrogen peroxide, in the other all the vitamin B_6 congeners are destroyed by exposure of samples to the ultraviolet light of a quartz mercury vapour lamp. Quantitative recoveries of pyridoxal are obtained. Ultraviolet determination can also be accomplished by the variable reference technique.[57]

Determination of pyridoxal in whole blood.[17] Extract 1 ml of fresh whole blood with 25 ml of acetone in an amber glass container. Shake for 30 min, centrifuge, and evaporate the supernatant acetone layer to dryness. Take up the residue in 5 ml of $0.1 M$ phosphate buffer of pH 6·75. Either centrifuge at 20,000 rev min^{-1} for 30 min or filter through a sintered glass filter. Read the fluorescence intensity (of pyridoxal and pyridoxamine) at $F335/385$. To the 1 ml of sample in the cuvette add 0·01 ml of 30% H_2O_2 and read the intensity (pyridoxamine) at $F335/385$.

Neither pyridoxic acid nor pyridoxine interfere since they could not be detected in blood.

Pyridoxal can be reduced; this can be useful in analysis. For example, when the background materials can seriously interfere in the determination, an appropriate blank can be formed by reducing the pyridoxal in the mixture before the reagent is added. Thus, pyridoxal can be reduced by 2,6-dimethyl-3,5-dicarboethoxy-1,4-dihydropyridine in boiling methanol or by this same pyridine derivative and N'-(n-propyl)-1,4-dihydronicotinamide in about 50% aq methanol at 30°.[58] The apparent second-order rate constants for the reaction of 2,6-dimethyl-3,5-dicarboethoxy-1,4-dihydropyridine with pyridoxal are comparable at 30° in aq methanol and in boiling neat methanol. The reduction is a non-free-radical mediated direct hydrogen transfer from dihydropyridine to aldehyde which does not require trace metals as catalysts.

Pyridoxal can be separated from the other forms of vitamin B_6.[59] The method separates pyridoxine, pyridoxal and pyridoxamine and their 5'-phosphates, and 4-pyridoxic acid, from each other.

Determination of pyridoxal in the presence of the various forms of vitamin B_6.[59]
Apply the test solution to a column of Dowex AG 50W-X8 (200 to 400 mesh)
in 0·01 M ammonium formate (pH 3·2). Elution at 0·5 ml per min is started
with 200 ml 0·1 M ammonium formate and continued with 100 ml of 0·05 M
ammonium formate (pH 4·25) to which 0·5 M ammonium formate (pH 7·5)
is added at 0·5 ml per minute. Measure the absorbance of the eluate fractions
at 295 nm.

A modified procedure has been used for the determination of pyridoxal
in brain tissue.[18] The tissue is homogenized and centrifuged. The vitamin
B_6 analogues are separated on a column of Amberlite CG120. The column is
percolated with water followed by buffers. The pyridoxal is separated at
pH 6 and determined fluorimetrically at $F330/385$.

V. REACTIONS

A. Acetone

An acetone condensation procedure has been described for pyridoxal
in the presence of pyridoxine and pyridoxamine.[15, 19] Beer's law is obeyed
from 10 to 400 µg. The procedure has proved useful in studying nonenzymatic
transamination with vitamin B_6 of some amino and keto acids. Alanine,
glutamic acid, pyruvic, α-ketoglutaric acid, other similar amino and keto
acids, pyridoxine, and pyridoxamine do not produce colour in the procedure.
The optimum colour intensity develops rapidly in the first 12 min, and then
gradually increases from 30 min (e.g. $A = 0·64$) to 180 min ($A = 0·76$). The
equation for the reaction is shown in Fig. 74.

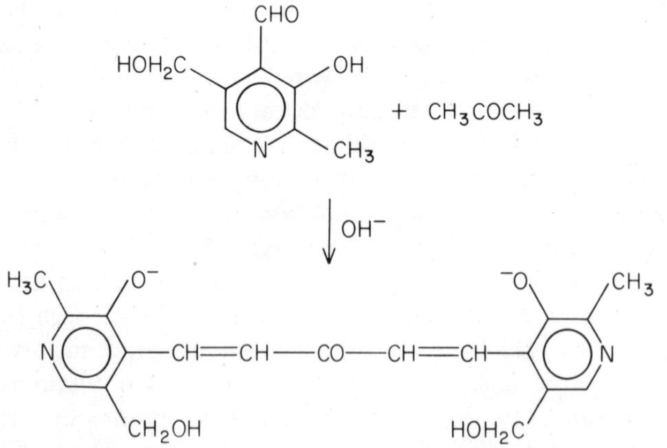

FIG. 74. Reaction of pyridoxal with acetone in alkaline solution.

Acetone determination of pyridoxal.[19] To 1 ml of aq test solution containing 20 to 400 µg of pyridoxal in a cuvette add 0·6 ml of acetone and 0·4 ml of 10% NaOH. Shake, and after 15 min standing read the absorbance at λ 420 nm.

The procedure could probably be improved through optimization.

B. Ammoniacal silver nitrate

Pyridoxal can be oxidized with ammoniacal silver nitrate to pyridoxic acid.[48, 60, 61] Pyridoxic acid can be dehydrated in acidic medium to give a strongly fluorescent pyridoxic lactone, Fig. 75.[62] The lactone fluoresces 25 times as intensely as the acid.

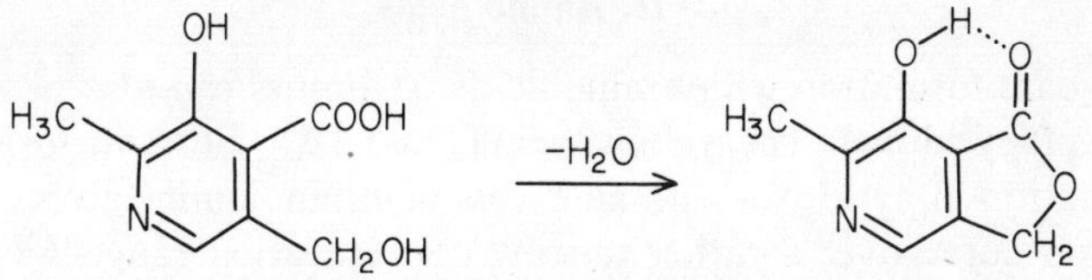

FIG. 75. The dehydration of pyridoxic acid to its lactone.

Table 45. Reaction of pyridoxal (P) and its 5'-phosphate (P·PO$_4$) with acid hydrazides.[63]

Acid hydrazide	Relative fluorescence intensity	
	P	P·PO$_4$
Benzoic	1·2	2·0
Picolinic	1·0	0·5
Isonicotinic	1·0	9·6
Acetic	56·0	29·5
Propionic	44·0	27·5
Butyric	82·0	26·8
Isobutyric	97·0	30·9

C. Acid hydrazides

The fluorescence reaction of pyridoxal and pyridoxal-5'-phosphate with hydrazides has been examined, Table 45.[63] Pyridoxal and its phosphate react with isobutyric acid hydrazide to form hydrazones in an acetate buffer solution which fluoresce green in an alkaline medium. Isobutyric acid hydrazide gives best results. Analysis is at $F$380/495. About 0·01 to 1 µg of pyridoxal or 0·1 to 1 µg of its phosphate can be determined. Ten-fold amounts of pyridoxine and equal amounts of pyridoxamine do not interfere.

Solvents affect the fluorescence intensity. Highest intensities are obtained for both aldehydes in dimethylformamide, with gradually decreasing intensities in ethanol, methanol and water. The fluorescence intensity was about 1.5% of that obtained in dimethylformamide.

Mixtures of pyridoxal and its phosphate can be analysed with a combination of the isobutyric acid hydrazide method and an enzymatic method using acid phosphate. Since pyridoxal reacts much better than its phosphate, the hydrolysis of the phosphate to pyridoxal makes the method for the phosphate more sensitive. Utilizing these 2 methods, recoveries of the 2 aldehydes in mixtures containing them gives 97.4% to 100% recoveries of pyridoxal and 97.5 to 102% recoveries of the phosphate.

D. Amino acids

Schiff-base formation with amino acids or amines can also be used in the analysis of pyridoxal. The yellow Schiff base $(\lambda_{max}$ 365 nm) formed in the determination of pyridoxal with an excess of ethanolamine gives a nonlinear calibration curve over a rather narrow concentration range.[20] The metal complexes of the Schiff base formed between pyridoxal and alanine fluoresce in the visible region.[21] The fluorescence can be seen on paper chromatograms and can be measured in solution. Pyridoxal can be combined with an amino acid and the Schiff base reduced with sodium borohydride to a fluorescent pyridoxyl derivative which could be separated chromatographically.[22] The fluorescent spots on paper could be chromatographed.

In attempting to understand the absorption spectra of the Schiff bases of pyridoxal, the electronic absorption spectra of N-salicylidene valine and N-(3-hydroxy-4-pyridylmethylene)-valine have been studied in acidic and basic[64] and neutral[65] methanol and dioxane solutions. In attempts to assign structures to bands the absorption spectra of pyridoxal amino acids in aqueous solution,[10] in neutral and alkaline methanol solution,[3, 66] and in aq solutions at various pH values[14] have been reported. On the basis of these studies the structures of pyridoxalvaline[3] and pyridoxalalanine[14] in neutral, acidic and alkaline solution have been assigned, Fig. 76. The pyridoxylidene-DL-alanine salt in strong acid solution exists in very small amounts[14] and is rapidly decomposed to pyridoxal and the amino acid.[3]

In the reaction of pyridoxal and an amino acid, Schiff base formation is incomplete even when the concentration of amino acid is as much as 100 times the concentration of pyridoxal, while in methanol solution Schiff base formation is complete in relatively dilute solution in the presence of two- or threefold concentration of amino acid.[3] Pyridoxylidenevaline absorbs in methanol at λ 255s, 337 and 418 with mε 8.0, 3.5 and 2.8, respectively, and in methanolic 2×10^{-2} M KOH at λ 373 and mε 5.3.

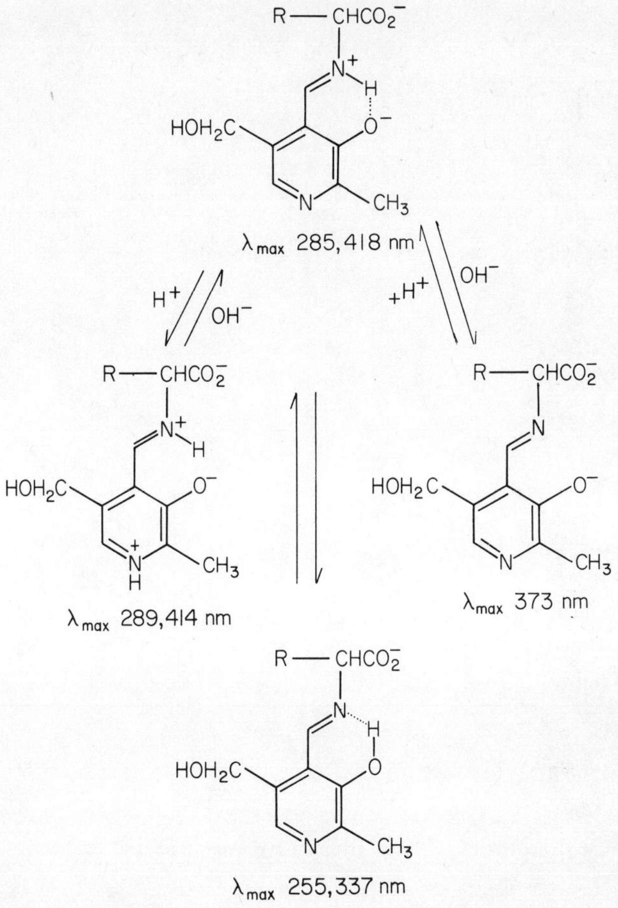

FIG. 76. The structure of pyridoxal amino acids in neutral, acid and alkaline solutions.

The spectra of solutions of glycine butyl ester with pyridoxal[67] are similar to those reported for methanolic solutions of N-(3-hydroxy-4-pyridyl-methylene)valine.[68] The reaction scheme in Fig. 77 is closely similar to that given in the previous Figure 76. The reaction scheme is somewhat similar for solutions of glycine butyl ester and pyridoxal-N-methochloride, Fig. 78. These spectra are similar to those described for aqueous solutions of pyridoxal N-methochloride and valine.[69]

The spectrum of solutions of 10^{-2} M diethyl aminomalonate and 7×10^{-5} M pyridoxal HCl in ethanol are similar to those of glycine butyl ester and pyridoxal in alcohol. However, when sodium methoxide is added to yield a

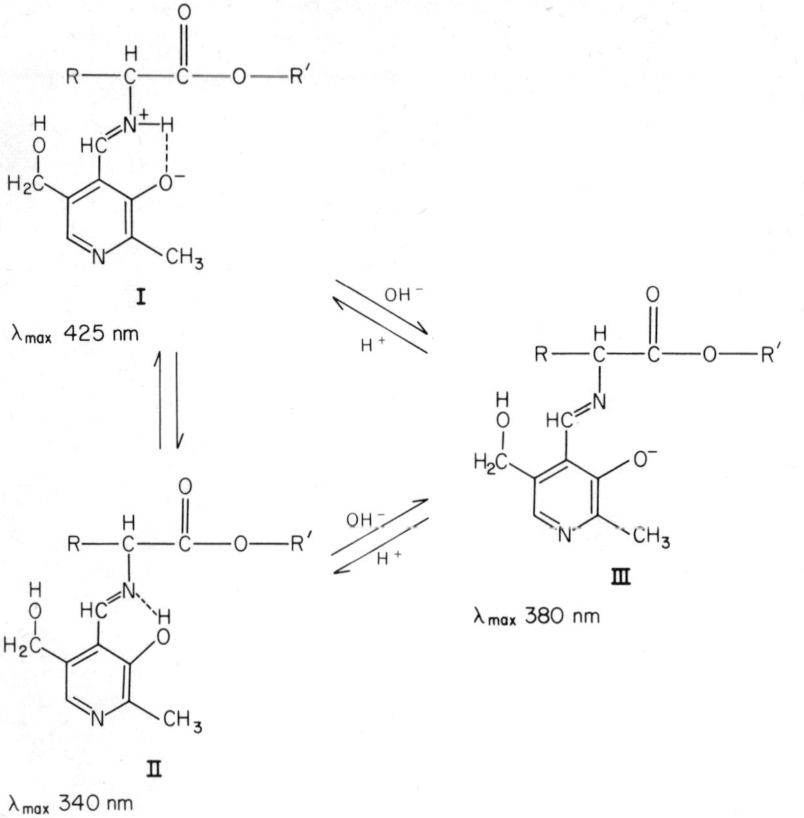
I
λmax 425 nm
OH⁻
H⁺
III
λmax 380 nm
OH⁻
H⁺
II
λmax 340 nm

FIG. 77. The structures of pyridoxal glycine butyl ester in neutral, acid and alkaline solutions.(67)

concentration of 10^{-2} M, the long wavelength band shifts to 470 nm. This band is probably derived from **IV**, a structure with a long chain of conjugation.

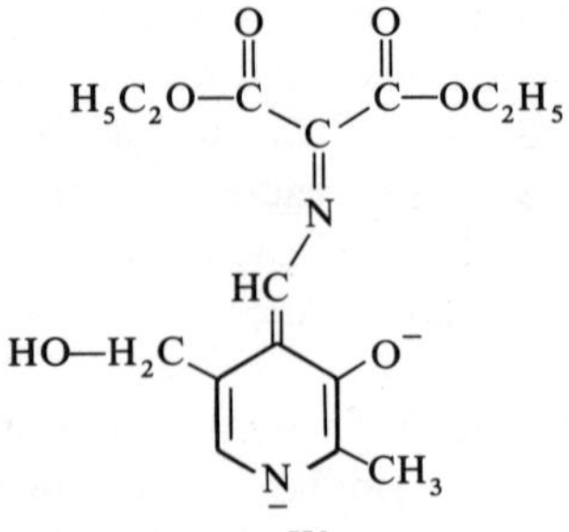

IV

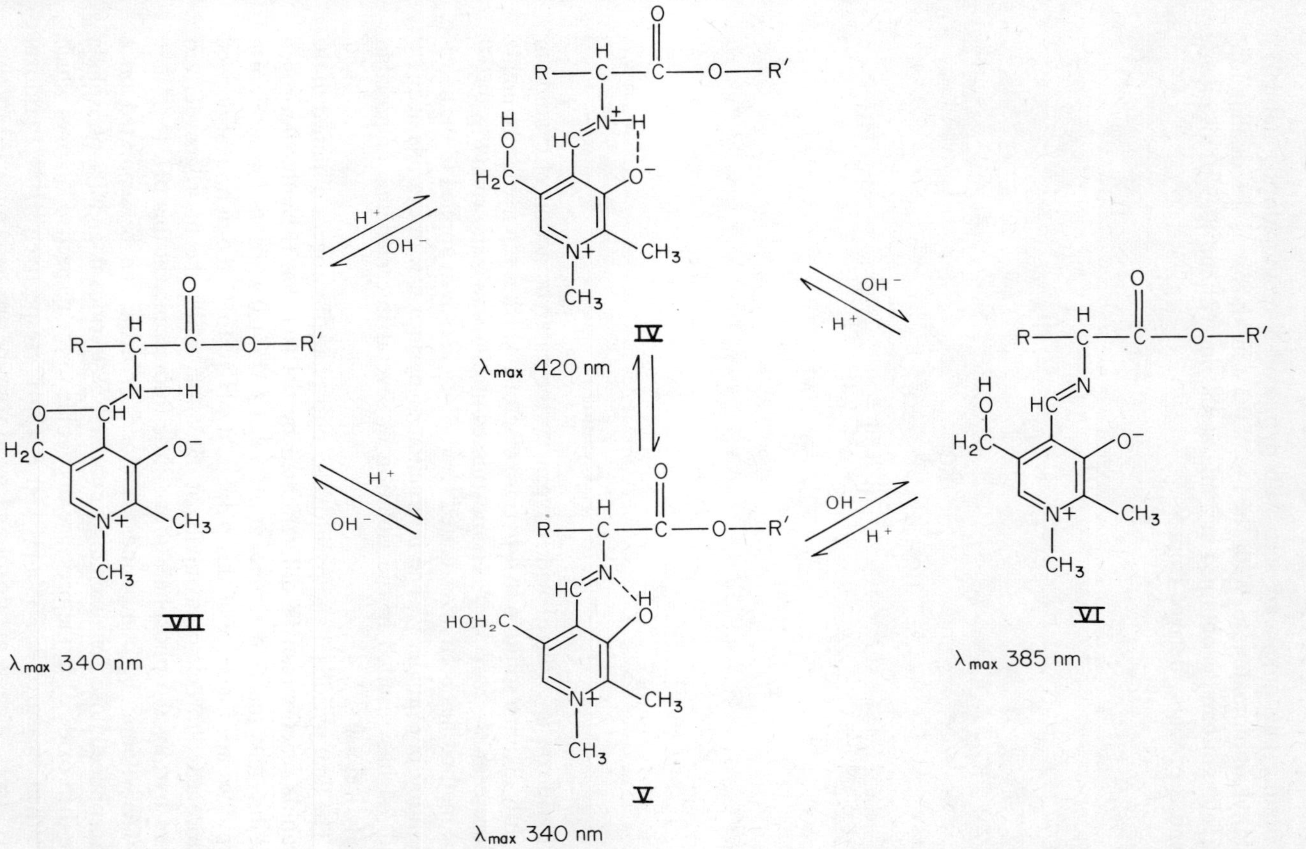

FIG. 78. The structures of pyridoxal-N-methochloride glycine butyl ester in neutral, acid and alkaline solutions.[67]

Similar phenomena are seen with pyridoxal N-methochloride and 0·05 M diethyl aminomalonate. With the use of 0·2 M imidazole as the alkali, a long wavelength band is obtained in 2 min at 480 nm with mε 40.[67] This intense band is probably derived from **V**.

V

E. Cyanide

Pyridoxal is oxidized with oxygen by the catalytic action of cyanide in slightly alkaline solution to 4-pyridoxolactone which is reported to be highly fluorescent.[25, 27–30, 32, 33] The postulated mechanism is shown in Fig. 79.[25] The method has been investigated[11, 23–33, 70] and even applied to the determination of cyanide.[71] The interaction of pyridoxal with cyanide at pH 6 and 7·4 has resulted in the isolation of several intermediates of possible analytical use.[72]

The final pyridoxal and pyridoxal-5-phosphate fluorogens obtained in the cyanide reaction can be differentiated by the fact that the latter fluorogen exhibits maximal fluorescence at pH 3·8 at $F315/420$ while the former fluorogen does not fluoresce at this pH.[11] At pH 10 to 11 the pyridoxal-derived fluorogen fluoresces maximally at $F358/438$ while the fluorogen derived from pyridoxal-5-phosphate shows little fluorescence at this pH.[24, 70]

The vitamin B_6 compounds in blood or urine can be separated on a phosphocellulose ion exchange column.[31] Pyridoxal and its phosphate are then oxidized in the presence of cyanide to the respective lactones which are then measured at $F350/434$ and $F318/417$, respectively.[11, 24] Pyridoxal precursors, such as pyridoxol and pyridoxamine are also converted to pyridoxolactone and measured. Similarly, the pyridoxal phosphate precursor,

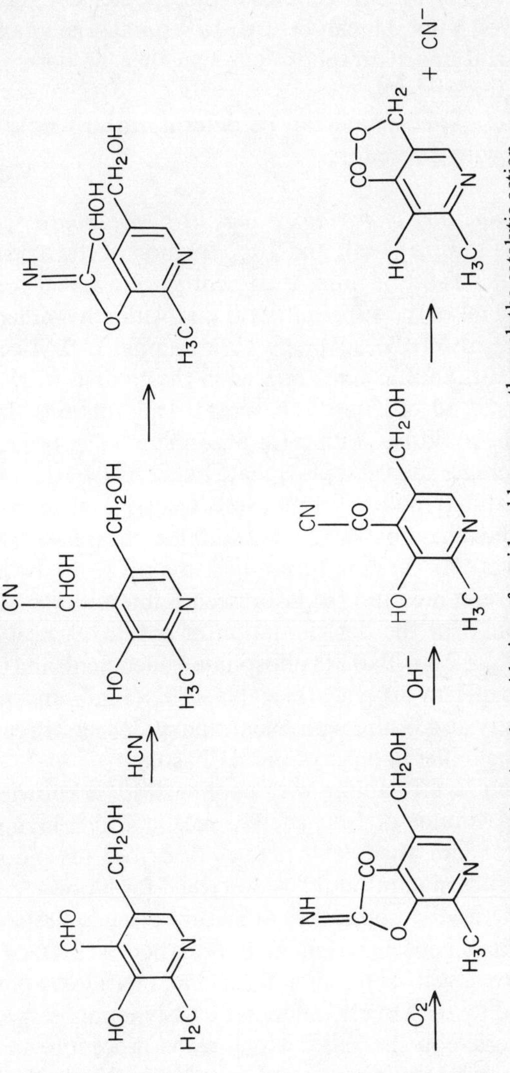

FIG. 79. Reactions showing the oxidation of pyridoxal by oxygen through the catalytic action of cyanide in alkaline solution to 4-pyridoxolactone.[25]

pyridoxamine phosphate, is converted to pyridolactone phosphate and measured.

Thin layer electrophoresis on cellulose with the help of sodium acetate buffer (pH 5·1) at 750 V for 3 h can be used to separate the vitamin B_6 compounds.[23] Pyridoxal and its 5′-phosphate can then be determined fluorimetrically with cyanide.[11, 24]

Pyridoxal and its 5′-phosphate can be determined in whole blood or in organs by the following procedure.

Fluorimetric determination of pyridoxal and its 5′-phosphate.[24] *Blood:* To H_2O (2 ml) add the sample (1 ml) and 10% trichloroacetic acid soln. (3 ml), heat the mixture at 50° for 15 min, then centrifuge at 4000 rev min^{-1} for 10 min, and wash 4 ml of the supernatant liquid with ethyl ether (2 × 4 ml). Apply a portion (2 ml) of the aq phase to a column of SM-cellulose (1 g, equilibrated with 0·01 N acetic acid), and wash the column with 0·01 N acetic acid; reject the first 1 ml of eluate. The next 10 ml contains the pyridoxal phosphate. Elute the pyridoxal with 0·1 M phosphate buffer of pH 7·4 (10 ml). To 2 ml of the first eluate add 0·2 M phosphate buffer (pH 7·4) (2 ml) and 0·05 M KCN in 0·1 M phosphate buffer (0·1 ml); to a second 2 ml of the eluate (the blank) add 0·2 M phosphate buffer (2 ml) and 0·1 M phosphate buffer (0·1 ml) Heat both solns at 50° for 30 min, then adjust the pH to 3·8 by adding 0·5 N tartaric acid (1 ml), and measure the fluorescence intensities at 420 nm, with excitation at 325 nm. For the determination of pyridoxal, heat 2 ml of the second eluate at 50° for 2 h with 0·2 M phosphate buffer (5 ml) and 0·05 M KCN (0·1 ml); adjust the pH to 10 with 0·6 M Na_2CO_3 (1 ml), and measure the fluorescence intensity at 438 nm, with excitation at 358 nm. Prepare a blank with 0·1 M phosphate buffer in place of the KCN soln.

Organs: Homogenize the sample with cooling, with a known volume of H_2O; add an equal volume of 10% trichloroacetic acid soln, and heat the mixture at 50° for 15 min, then centrifuge as described for blood samples. Treat the resulting supernatant liquid as described for blood.

The following method is applicable to serum, plasma, tissues and foodstuffs.[32] The limiting concentration in the method is 2–10 ng pyridoxal. Interfering substances, such as pyridoxylic acid and pyridoxal phosphate are completely removed by the Dowex column. Large amounts of NAD, vitamin B_1 or B_2 could interfere in the assay. Note in the procedure shown in Fig. 80 that pyridoxal phosphate is converted to pyridoxal by acid phosphatase and the total pyridoxal is then determined.

F. Diazotized amines

Diazotized amines, such as sulphanilic acid,[36] *p*-aminoacetophenone,[34, 35] and o-dianisidine[37] can be used in analysing pyridoxal. With the use of p-aminoacetophenone a dye such as **VI** is formed. The neutral hemiacetal is shown but the chromogen could also be determined as the anion, mono-cation and di-cation.

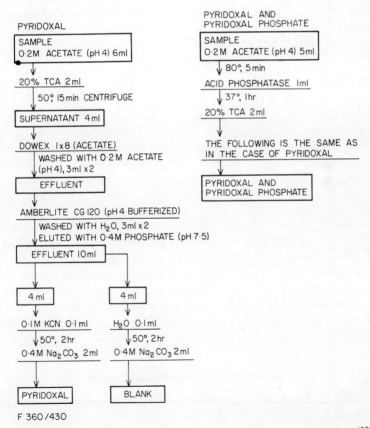

VI

F 360/430

FIG. 80. Schematic for the microdetermination of pyridoxal and its 5'-phosphate.[32]

G. Oxidation

Pyridoxal can also be oxidized by permanganate[47–49] or silver oxide[48, 73] to pyridoxic acid and then in the presence of hot acid converted to the fluorescent lactone. Preliminary separations of the vitamin B_6 components are necessary. Separations involved column chromatography through Amberlite IRA-410 and then Amberlite IR-112[48] or Dowex AG 50-WX 8 (100–200 mesh), Fig. 81[73] and two-dimensional paper chromatography, first with isopropyl alcohol–water (4:1) adjusted to pH 3·5 with acetic acid, then with the upper phase of amyl alcohol–acetone–water (2:1:2).[47]

H. 2,6-Dichloroquinone chloroimide

Since pyridoxal and other members of the vitamin B_6 complex are phenols, they can be determined by the indophenol test for phenols unsubstituted in the para position.[73] Thus, coupling of pyridoxal with 2,6-dichloroquinone chloroimide in a veronal buffer produces a blue chromogen, **VII**, which can be extracted into an organic solvent.[39, 42]

VII

This anion, λ_{max} 620 nm, fades in the alkaline solution. The indophenol would absorb at widely differing wavelengths in the neutral, monocationic and polycationic forms. Use of ammonia–ammonium chloride buffer with sodium acetate gives a 50% increase in sensitivity and shifts the wavelength maximum from 620 to 650 nm.[41] Pyridoxal can be readily differentiated from pyridoxine since the latter forms with boric acid a chelate which no longer reacts with the chloroimide while pyridoxal does not form the chelate and so reacts.[40]

I. N,N-Diethyl-p-phenylenediamine

This reagent can also be used to determine pyridoxal and the other members of the vitamin B_6 complex.[43, 74–76] Essentially the procedure consists of the following steps.

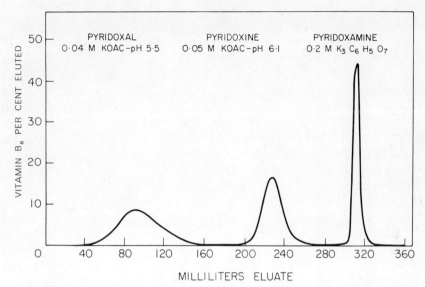

FIG. 81. Chromatographic fractionation of vitamin B_6 components with Dowex Ag 50-WX 8 (100–200 mesh) resin.[73]

Determination of pyridoxal.[43] To 10 ml of neutral test solution in a small separatory funnel add 3 ml of pH 7 phosphate buffer, 1 ml of fresh 0·1% diethylaminoaniline sulphate and exactly 10 ml of benzene. Add fresh 1% aq potassium ferricyanide down the side of the funnel and shake immediately for about 30 seconds. Discard the aq phase. Dry the benzene layer over a little anhydrous sodium sulphate, filter, and read the absorbance at 605 nm.

Other phenols also react. With pyridoxal the chromogen, **VIII**, is formed.

VIII

The method has been automated.[75, 76] The relative responses of the members of the vitamin B_6 family are shown in Fig. 82.[76] The colour obtained in the procedure for pyridoxine is stable over 4 hours.[75]

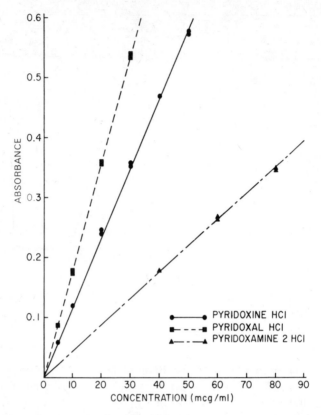

FIG. 82. Relative responses of pyridoxine . HCl, pyridoxal . HCl and pyridoxamine . 2HCl with the automated assay for pyridoxine without the addition of boric acid.[76]

J. Miscellaneous reactions

Dithionate and bisulphite produced marked changes in the spectrum of pyridoxal.[44] Pyridoxal reacts with hydrazine on paper to give a yellow fluorescent spot.[45, 77] Pyridoxal condenses with MBTH at pH 3·4 to give the azine, **IX**, absorbing at λ_{max} 430 nm with mε 27·4.[12] This azine is only slightly soluble in neutral and alkaline aqueous solutions. 2-Oxoglutarate and pyruvate do not interfere in the determination of pyridoxal. The precision is about ±3%. These various reactions could prove analytically useful in the study of biological materials.

IX

Pyridoxal can also be condensed with phenylhydrazine at 60° and determined at 410 nm.[37, 50] 2-Hydrazinobenzoic acid has also been used.[37]

REFERENCES

1. D. E. Metzler and E. E. Snell. *J. Am. Chem. Soc.* **77**, 2431 (1955).
2. A. K. Lunn and R. A. Morton. *Analyst* **77**, 718 (1952).
3. Y. Matsushima and A. E. Martell. *J. Am. Chem. Soc.* **89**, 1322 (1967).
4. M. Hochberg, D. Melnick and B. L. Oser. *J. Biol. Chem.* **155**, 109, 119 (1944).
5. D. Heyl, E. Luz, S. A. Harris and K. Folkers. *J. Am. Chem. Soc.* **73**, 3430 (1951).
6. V. R. Williams and J. B. Neilands. *Arch. Biochem.* **53**, 56 (1954).
7. D. Melnick, M. Hochberg, H. W. Himes and B. L. Oser. *J. Biol. Chem.* **160**, 1 (1945).
8. H. F. Schott and W. G. Clark. *J. Biol. Chem.* **196**, 449 (1952).
9. N. Lucas, H. K. King and S. J. Brown. *Biochem. J.* **84**, 118 (1962).
10. D. E. Metzler. *J. Am. Chem. Soc.* **79**, 485 (1957).
11. V. Bonavita. *Arch. Biochem.* **88**, 366 (1960).
12. W. W. Umbreit, D. J. O'Kane and I. C. Gunsalus. *J. Biol. Chem.* **176**, 629 (1949).
13. K. Nakamoto and A. E. Martell. *J. Am. Chem. Soc.* **81**, 5863 (1959).
14. K. Nagano and D. E. Metzler. *J. Am. Chem. Soc.* **89**, 2891 (1967).
15. A. Gaudiano and M. Polizzi-Sciarrone. *Annali Ist. Sup. Sanitá* **1**, 588 (1965).
16. M. Hochberg, D. Melnick and B. L. Oser. *J. Biol. Chem.* **154**, 313 (1944).
17. D. B. Coursin and V. C. Brown. *Proc. Soc. Exptl. Biol. Med.* **98**, 315 (1958).
18. Y. H. Loo and L. Badger. *J. Neurochem.* **16**, 801 (1969).
19. F. P. Siegel and M. I. Blake. *Anal. Chem.* **34**, 397 (1962).
20. D. E. Metzler and E. E. Snell. *J. Am. Chem. Soc.* **74**, 979 (1952).
21. P. Fasella, H. Lis, N. Siliprandi and C. Baglioni. *Biochim. Biophys. Acta* **23**, 417 (1957).
22. C. Turano, P. Fasella, P. Vecchini and A. Giartosio. *J. Chromatog.* **14**, 201 (1964).
23. C. E. Colombini and E. E. McCoy. *Anal. Biochem.* **34**, 451 (1970).
24. M. Yamada, A. Saito and Z. Tamura. *Chem. Pharm. Bull. Tokyo* **14**, 482 (1966).
25. S. Takanashi, Z. Tamura, A. Yoshino and Y. Iidaka. *Chem. Pharm. Bull.* **16**, 758 (1968).
26. V. Bonavita and V. Scardi. *Anal. Chim. Acta* **29**, 47 (1959).
27. S. Oishi and S. Fukui. *Vitamins* **33**, 457 (1966).
28. S. Oishi and S. Fukui. *Vitamins* **34**, 238 (1966).
29. S. Oishi and S. Fukui, The 20th Annual Meeting of the Chemical Society of Japan, Abstracts of Papers, III, p. 704 (Tokyo 1967).

30. S. Takanashi and Z. Tamura. *J. Vitaminol.* **16**, 129 (1970).
31. S. F. Contractor and B. Shane. *Clin. Chim. Acta* **21**, 71 (1968).
32. S. Takanashi, I. Matsunaga and Z. Tamura. *J. Vitaminol.* **16**, 132 (1970).
33. N. Oishi and S. Fukui. *Arch. Biochem. Biophys.* **128**, 606 (1968).
34. E. B. Brown, A. F. Bina and J. M. Thomas. *J. Biol. Chem.* **158**, 455 (1945).
35. A. F. Bina, J. M. Thomas and E. B. Brown. *J. Biol. Chem.* **148**, 111 (1943).
36. M. Swaminathan. *Nature* **145**, 780 (1940).
37. H. E. Richter. *Z. Anal. Chem.* **254**, 359 (1971).
38. H. D. Gibbs. *J. Biol. Chem.* **72**, 649 (1927).
39. J. V. Scudi. *J. Biol. Chem.* **139**, 707 (1941).
40. J. V. Scudi, W. A. Bastedo and T. J. Webb. *J. Biol. Chem.* **136**, 399 (1940).
41. J. P. Sweeney and W. L. Hall. *J. Ass. Offic. Agric. Chem.* **38**, 697 (1955).
42. J. V. Scudi, H. F. Konnes and J. C. Keresztesy. *Am. J. Physiol.* **129**, 459 (1940).
43. O. Hrdy and L. Urbanova. *Ceskoslov. Farm.* **6**, 510 (1957); through *Z. Anal. Chem.* **163**, 234 (1958).
44. E. Adams. *Anal. Biochem.* **31**, 484 (1969).
45. L. Ben-Dor. *Chemist-Analyst* **53**, 8 (1964).
46. K. Soda, T. Yorifuji, H. Misono and M. Moriguchi. *Biochem. J.* **114**, 629 (1969).
47. H. Kraut and U. Imhoff. *Nahrung* **12**, 29 (1968).
48. A. Fujita, D. Fujita and K. Fujino. *J. Vitaminol. (Osaka)* **1**, 279 (1955).
49. A. Fujita and K. Fujino. *J. Vitaminol. (Osaka)* **1**, 290 (1955).
50. H. Wada and E. E. Snell. *J. Biol. Chem.* **236**, 2089 (1961).
51. D. B. McCormick and E. E. Snell. *J. Biol. Chem.* **236**, 2076 (1961).
52. R. Håkanson. *J. Chromatog.* **13**, 263 (1964).
53. R. F. Chen. *Science* **150**, 1593 (1965).
54. J. W. Bridges, D. S. Davies and R. T. Williams. *Biochem. J.* **98**, 451 (1966).
55. E. L. Wehry and L. B. Rogers, in D. M. Hercules, Ed., "Fluorescence and Phosphorescence Analysis," Wiley, New York, 1966, p. 81.
56. R. T. Williams and J. W. Bridges. *J. Clin. Pathol.* **17**, 371 (1964).
57. S. S. Schiaffino, H. W. Loy, Jr., O. L. Kline and L. S. Harrow, *J. Ass. Offic. Agric. Chem.* **39**, 180 (1956).
58. S. Shinkai and T. C. Bruice. *Biochemistry* **12**, 1750 (1973).
59. H. Tiselius. *Clin. Chim. Acta* **40**, 319 (1972).
60. A. Fujita, K. Matsuura and K. Fujino. *J. Vitaminol. (Osaka)* **1**, 267 (1955).
61. A. Fujita, D. Fujita and K. Fujino. *J. Vitaminol. (Osaka)* **1**, 275 (1955).
62. J. W. Huff and W. A. Perlzweig. *J. Biol. Chem.* **155**, 345 (1944).
63. T. Uno, S. Nakano and H. Taniguchi. *Japan Analyst* **20**, 1117 (1971).
64. D. Heinert and A. E. Martell. *J. Am. Chem. Soc.* **85**, 188 (1963).
65. D. Heinert and A. E. Martell. *J. Am. Chem. Soc.* **85**, 183 (1963).
66. Y. Matsuo. *J. Am. Chem. Soc.* **79**, 2016 (1957).
67. L. Schirch and R. A. Slotter. *Biochemistry* **5**, 3175 (1966).
68. A. E. Martell, in E. E. Snell, P. Fasella, A. E. Braunstein and A. Rossi-Fanelli, Eds. "Chemical and Biological Aspects of Pyridoxal Catalysis", Macmillan, New York, 1963, p. 13.
69. C. C. Johnston, H. G. Brooks, J. D. Albert and D. E. Metzler in E. E. Snell, P. M. Fasella, A. E. Braunstein and A. Rossi-Fanelli, Eds., "Biological Aspects of Pyridoxal Catalysis", New York, N.Y., Macmillan, 1963, p. 69.
70. M. Yamada, A. Saito and Z. Tamura. *Chem. Pharm. Bull.* **14**, 488 (1966).
71. S. Takanashi and Z. Tamura. *Chem. Pharm. Bull. Japan* **18**, 1633 (1970).
72. W. Korytnyk, H. Ahrens, N. Angelino and G. Kartha. *J. Org. Chem.* **38**, 3793 (1973).

73. M. J. MacArthur and J. Lehmann. *J. Ass. Off. Agric. Chem.* **42**, 619 (1959).
74. K. Sato. *Vitamins* **16**, 561 (1959).
75. T. Tsuda, H. Mizukami and S. Yarimizu. *Ann. Sankyo Res. Lab.* **16**, 114 (1964).
76. K. Tsuji. *Annals N.Y. Acad. Sci.* **153**, 446 (1968).
77. F. Feigl. "Spot Tests in Organic Analysis", Elsevier Amsterdam, 6th ed., 1960, pp. 202, 234.

55. PYRIDOXAL PHOSPHATE (CODECARBOXYLASE)

I. INTRODUCTION

Stable in the solid state but decomposes in solution at a rate of 2 to 4% per month at 0° and 5 to 7% at room temperature. It is hydrolysed in acid solution in a few hours at 100°.

Many enzymes involved in transamination or amino acid metabolism require pyridoxal 5'-phosphate as a coenzyme. The aldehyde group plays an essential part in pyridoxal catalysis probably through the mechanism of reaction with an amino acid substrate to form a Schiff base which then undergoes enzymatic reaction. The phosphate serves as a cofactor for transaminases, decarboxylases and racemases.

II. SPECTRAL PROPERTIES

Ultraviolet absorption spectral data are given for the compound and some of its derivatives and analogues, Table 46. Closely similar spectra are obtained for the iso-pi-electronic molecules: pyridoxal-5'-phosphate, pyridoxal-5'-methylenephosphonate, **I**, pyridoxal-2-nor-5'-phosphate, **II**, pyridoxal-5'-sulphate, **III**, and pyridoxil-diphosphate, **IV** in 0·1 N HCl, pH 7·0 and 0·1 N NaOH.

	X	Y	Z	W
I	CH_2	PO_3H_2	CH_3	H
II	O	PO_3H_2	H	H
III	O	SO_3H	CH_3	H
IV	O	PO_3H_2	CH_3	a

[a] Where W stands for doubling of molecule to a glyoxal derivative.

Table 46. Effect of pH on the ultraviolet absorption spectrum of pyridoxal-5′-phosphate and its derivatives

pH (or solvent)	λ_{max}				mε	Ref.
		Pyridoxal 5′-Phosphate				
0·1 N HCl		295			6·8	1
0·1 N HCl[a]		295,	335		6·3, 2·0	2
1·0		300,	335		6·3, 1·6	3
1·0		278,	324		7·9, 6·3	4
1·0		295,	335		6·7, 1·8	5
1·9		292			5·0	6
2·0		292,	331s		6·3, 1·6	7
4·0		293			5·0	7
6·0		250,	330,	390	4·0, 2·5, 4·0	5
6·0[a]			325,	390	3·2, 4·0	2
6·1	219,	292			10, 3·2	7
7·0			330,	388	2·5, 4·9	1
7·0			330,	388	2·0, 5·0	3
7·0			358		5·0	4
7·38			325,	388	2·9, 5·1	8
7·4			325,	385	2·6, 5·0	9
7·4			320,	385	2·5, 5·0	10
7·4				388	5·0	11
0·01 M NaHCO₃ buffer				388	5·8	12
8·7			289,	390	3·2, 4·0	7
10·5[b]	230,	267s,	310s,	390	8·5, 2·5, 1·1, 5·5	13
11·0[a]	228,	270s,	308,	390	10·7, 2·1, 1·0, 4·7	13
11·0		265s,	305,	384	2·0, 1·3, 4·0	6
11·0		270,	314,	390	2·0, 1·3, 3·8	5
13·0	232,	270,	295,	390	13, 3·0, 20, 4·0	5
0·1 N NaOH[a]	230,		295,	390	12·6, 2·0, 5·0	2
0·1 N NaOH			305,	388	1·1, 6·6	1
0·1 N NaOH	225,		306,	393	15·9, 3·2, 5·0	7
		Pyridoxal-5′-phosphate oxime				
2·0		275,	320		8·6, 7·5	14
11·0		285,	370		8·8, 4·8	14
		Pyridoxal-5′-phosphate-4′-hydrazone				
0·1 N HCl		314,	337		11·9, 14·2	3
7·0		284,	320		10·8, 8·6	3

Table 46—*continued*

pH (or solvent)	λ_{max}	$m\varepsilon$	Ref.
	Pyridoxal-5'-methylenephosphonate		
0·1 N HCl	258, 295, 340	1·8, 6·1, 2·0	15
7·0	327, 380	2·4, 3·4	15
0·1 N NaOH	232, 268, 301, 391	11·8, 2·8, 1·7, 5·3	15
	Pyridoxal-2-nor-5'-phosphate		
0·1 N HCl	290, 328	4·7, 0·9	16
7·0	381	2·9	16
0·1 N NaOH	382	4·3	16
	Pyridoxal-5'-sulphate[c]		
0·1 N HCl	293	5·2	17
7·0	330, 388	1·7, 3·8	17
0·1 N NaOH	315, 388	0·7, 4·4	17
	Pyridoxil diphosphate		
0·1 N HCl	295	8·0	18
7·0	289, 336, 391	5·3, 0·6, 0·7	18
0·1 N NaOH	392	5·3	18
	Pyridoxildiphosphate dioxime		
7·0	330	4·6	18

[a] Calcium salt.　[b] Ammonium salt.　[c] Barium salt.

The absorption spectrum of pyridoxal phosphate characterizes and differentiates this compound from other phosphorylated and free forms of Vitamin B_6, including pyridoxal, and makes it possible to estimate the compound in pure form and in mixtures.[1, 6, 19] Its spectra are almost identical to the spectra of 5-desoxypyridoxal in solutions of similar pH.[2, 20] Common to all members of the Vitamin B_6 group and to their phosphates is a band with a maximum near 285 nm in acid solution (pH 1 to 3), which is common to all beta pyridones. If the beta phenolic group is unsubstituted, neutralization is accompanied by the disappearance of the 285 absorption maximum and to the appearance at alkaline reaction (pH 11 to 13) of maxima near 240 and 305 nm. In alkaline solution, pyridoxal and its 5-phosphate possess an additional yellow colour, associated with the 4-aldehyde, with a maximum at 385 to 390 nm. This band, however, can be used to differentiate the two because of its greater intensity for pyridoxal phosphate at neutral reaction. Pyridoxal phosphate differs from all members of the Vitamin B_6 group in the intensity of its absorption maxima at 305 nm in alkaline reaction (N/10 NaOH); $m\varepsilon = 1·1$; for pyridoxal $m\varepsilon = 5·8$; for pyridoxamine, pyridoxine, and their 5 phosphates $m\varepsilon = 7·0$ to 8·0.

Pyridoxal phosphate can thus be estimated spectrophotometrically by the increase in absorption at 388 nm on neutralization from pH 1 to 7. Free pyridoxal interferes but slightly (mε 0·2 as compared to mε 4·9 for the phosphate) especially when present as a minor impurity.

The fluorescence and phosphorescence of pyridoxal-5'-phosphate in ethanol–water, 96:4, v/v, and in propylene glycol–water, 50:50, v/v, have been reported.[21] In either solvent fluorescence took place at $F290/375$ and phosphorescence at $P290/430$ at 77°K. The phosphorescence lifetime, T_P, was 1·42 in aq ethanol and 1·48 in aq propylene glycol. The quantum yield of fluorescence was 0·12 in aq ethanol as compared to standard benzophenone set at 0·85.

III. REAGENTS

Pyridoxal phosphate is readily reducible by 2,6-dimethyl-3,5-dicarbo-ethoxy-1,4-dihydropyridine and N'-(n-propyl)-1,4-dihydronicotinamide in 50% aq methanol at 30°.[22]

In Table 47 are given some of the reagents which have been used in the determination of pyridoxal-5'-phosphate.

Table 47. Reagents useful in the determination of pyridoxal-5'-phosphate

Reagents	λ_{max} of $F_{exc/em}$	Ref.
Acetone		23
Alkali and cyanide	$F318/417$	10, 11, 24–32
Amines	a	12, 33–35
Bisulphite	330	12, 36–38
Dithionite	360	36
Enzymatic		39–52
MBTH		53
Phenylhydrazine	410	54–57
Semicarbazide	G fl.	58

ᵃWith glycine, λ_{max} at 395 nm;[12, 33] with diethyl aminomalonate λ_{max} at 420 and 440 nm in neutral solution and 460 nm in alkaline solution;[34] and with m-hydroxypropadrine measurement at λ 327 nm.[35]

Unlike pyridoxal the phosphate is mainly present in solution as the aldehyde and thus it can react usually under milder conditions than can pyridoxal.

Ultraviolet absorption spectral methods can be used to determine the phosphate.[59, 60] In a dilute solution buffered with phosphate it can be determined at λ 388 nm.[1]

The analysis of pyridoxal phosphate by microbiological assay and by the various photometric methods has been reviewed in the 1960's.[40]

Treatment of pyridoxal-5'-phosphate with liver homogenates is stated to result in the formation of pyridoxic acid lactone.[61, 62] The lactone fluoresces 25 times as much as the parent acid, probably due to an increase in the quantum efficiency of fluorescence.[63]

A. Alkaline cyanide

The most studied method for pyridoxal phosphate has been the alkaline cyanide procedure. The fluorogen from pyridoxal phosphate exhibits maximal fluorescence at pH 3·8 at $F314/420$ while the one from pyridoxal exhibits maximal fluorescence at pH 9 to 10 at $F358/430$.[10, 11] The enzyme, phosphorylase, treated with cyanide in the presence of 8 M urea exhibits the characteristic fluorescence spectrum of the pyridoxal phosphate-derived fluorogen. The fluorogen has been identified as 4-pyridoxic acid-5'-phosphate, **V**.[31]

V

Pyridoxal phosphate (and other members of the Vitamin B_6 family) can be extracted from rat brain tissue by homogenization with chloroform–methanol, extraction into aq phosphoric acid and separation on a column of Amberlite CG 120 (200 to 400 mesh, Na^+ form) with the help of water and acetate and phosphate buffers.[27] The first 20 ml of the percolate contained the pyridoxal phosphate which was determined fluorimetrically after reaction with cyanide and further fractionation on a column of Dowex 1-Xl (acetate form).

The pyridoxal phosphate contents of alanine racemase (EC 5.1.1.1), phosphorylase a (EC 2.4.1.1), glutamic–aspartic transaminase (2.6.1.1) and glutamic–alanine transaminase (2.6.1.2) can be determined by fluorimetry of the cyanide-formed fluorogen or by spectrophotometry of the pyridoxal phosphate phenylhydrazone.[29] The results by both methods are in good

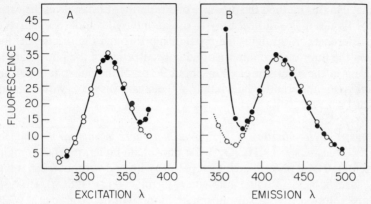

FIG. 83. Excitation spectrum (A) and emission spectrum (B) for pyridoxal phosphate
(0·23 nanomole) (OOOO) and alanine racemase (18 μg) (●●●●) at $F325/420$.[29]

agreement. The coenzyme is readily identified by its characteristic excitation
and emission spectra, Fig. 83.

Determination of pyridoxal phosphate in purified enzymes.[29] Dilute the test
sample of enzyme to 0·2 ml with potassium phosphate (0·005 M, pH 7·4),
add 0·2 ml 11% trichloroacetic acid, and heat at 50° for 15 min. Without
cooling, add 0·14 ml of 3·3 M K_2HPO_4 and 0·05 ml of 0·02 M KCN. Heat again
at 50° for 25 minutes. At this point solutions can stand at room temp for
several hours. Add 0·07 ml of 28% H_3PO_4 (dilute 85% H_3PO_4 1 to 3 with
water) and 1 ml of 2 M potassium acetate (adjust 2 M acetic acid with KOH
to give pH 3·8) so as to achieve a final pH of 3·8. If necessary, centrifuge. Read
fluorescence intensity at $F325/420$.

The fluorescence intensity is stable at 4° for at least 48 hours. A linear
relationship through the origin is obtained for 0·05 to 0·9 nanomoles of
pyridoxal phosphate.

Pyridoxal phosphate has been determined by a procedure[28] shown in the
pyridoxal section. Essentially the phosphate is hydrolysed by acid phosphatase
to pyridoxal which is then oxidized by the catalytic action of cyanide to the
highly fluorescent 4-pyridoxolactone.

The absorption and fluorescence spectra of the reaction product from the
determination of the phosphate with cyanide has been described.[64] The
method has been modified and applied to the analysis of nanogram amounts
of pyridoxal phosphate in microgram samples of microtome sections of fresh
rat liver.[65] Other tissues analysed for the phosphate include cow and rat
adrenal cortex, human adrenals, rat and human liver, human liver carcinoid
tumour (secondary), human jejunal mucosa and human carcinoid tumour

(primary). In this method the presence of interfering substances in the extracts of some tissues makes it necessary to use an internal standard to correct for the interferences. A straight-line relationship through the origin was found between the fluorescence intensity and concentration of the phosphate from 1 to 20 ng in the 45 μl sample. For about 9·3 ng of the phosphate per mg of rat liver tissue the standard deviation of the mean was 4·3 % with a standard error of 1·4 %.

Fluorimetric determination of pyridoxal phosphate in microgram samples of tissue.[65] *Reagents.* 0·8 N $HClO_4$, 0·5 M phosphate buffer, pH 7·0, containing 1·2 N KOH; 0·04 M phosphate buffer, pH 7·0, with and without 0·006 M KCN; 0·91 N tartaric acid; quinine sulphate (1 μg ml^{-1} 0·1 N H_2SO_4). PLP stock standard solution (pyridoxal phosphate monohydrate, A grade, MW 265·2 (Calbiochem), 5 mg ml^{-1} 0·1 N HCl, stored up to three months in the frozen state ($-15°C$). Working standard solutions, stock standard diluted with 0·4 N $HClO_4$ to give 22–444 ng PLP/ml (1–20 ng/45 μl used in the assay), stored up to one week at 2°C.

Procedure. Homogenize fresh tissue in glass-redistilled water in a glass tube immersed in an ice–salt bath (100 mg ml^{-1} homogenate) and add an equal volume of cold 0·8 N $HClO_4$. Mix well and, after 15 min at 0°C, centrifuge at 4° for 5 min at about 1600 g. To each 45 μl aliquot of the supernate add 15 μl of the phosphate–KOH solution, mix, and add 10 μl of the buffer–KCN solution for each analysis and 10 μl of this buffer without KCN for each control (reaction mixture pH 7·0). Stopper the tubes and heat at 50° for 25 minutes. Bring the pH to 3·8 by adding 10 μl of the tartaric acid. Centrifuge for 5 min at 1200 g. Set fluorimeter to read 50 with quinine sulphate solution (F350/460). Read the fluorescence intensity at F325/425 of unknown and blank and subtract blank reading.

The cyanide[9] and glycine[23] methods have been compared; pyridoxal did not interfere in either method.[66]

B. Amines

Amines can also be used to determine pyridoxal phosphate. Glycine has been used.[12, 23, 33, 67] Thus, the phosphate in 0·1 M glycine at pH 7·2 gave bands at 279 and 413 nm with mε 5·8 and 6·6, respectively.[12]

In the following procedure heavy metals have a hypsochromic effect on the Schiff base by chelate formation, so they must be masked with EDTA.[33] Pyridoxal does not interfere. Essentially the test solution containing 10 to 20 μg of phosphate per ml is mixed with 0·1 M glycine and the absorbance is read at 395 nm. To get a blank reading, a few milligrams of $Na_2S_2O_5$ are added and another reading is made at 395 nm.

C. Bisulphite and dithionate

Marked changes in the spectra of pyridoxal phosphate and of pyridoxal phosphate enzymes, e.g. alanine racemase (EC 5.1.1.1), are produced by $S_2O_5{}^{2-}$ and $S_2O_4{}^{2-}$.[36] The spectrum of the phosphate in $S_2O_5{}^{2-}$ solution resembles that of its addition product with cysteine.[36, 38] The spectral changes caused by dithionite and bisulphite are shown in Figs. 84 and 85.[36] Bisulphite addition to pyridoxal phosphate produces a spectrum different from

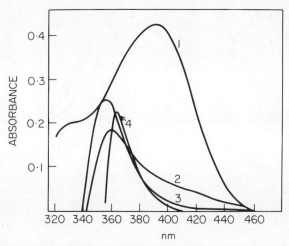

FIG. 84. Effect of sodium dithionite on spectrum of pyridoxal phosphate: (1) 0·1 mM pyridoxal phosphate in 0·05 M potassium phosphate, pH 7·4; (2) immediately after addition of 0·7 mM sodium dithionite; (3) 15 min after 2; (4) immediately after addition of a large excess of 5·8 mM dithionite to 1.[36]

that with dithionite. Both reagents abolish the 390 nm peak of pyridoxal phosphate with the new peak obtained with dithionate at about 360 nm while that with bisulphite is at 330 nm. The changes with bisulphite can be prevented by acetone while those with dithionite cannot. As judged by spectral change pyridoxal phosphate enzymes appear less reactive with bisulphite than with dithionite, relative to the reactivity of the free coenzyme. Dithionite may prove useful in identifying, by difference spectra, the characteristic low 400 nm peak of pyridoxal phosphate enzymes.

Pyridoxal phosphate in a sodium bicarbonate buffered solution (pH 7·2) containing 0·0067 M sodium bisulphite absorbs at λ 330 nm, mε 7·4.[12]

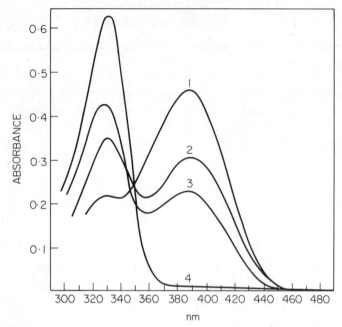

FIG. 85. Effect of increasing concentration of sodium bisulphite on spectrum of pyridoxal phosphate: (1) 0·09 mM pyridoxal phosphate in 0·05 M potassium phosphate buffer, pH 7·4; (2) immediately after adding 0·2 mM bisulphite; (3) immediately after adding further 0·2 mM bisulphite; (4) immediately after adding further 8·8 mM bisulphite.[36]

D. Enzymatic methods

Many enzymatic methods have been developed for the determination of pyridoxal phosphate. In most cases determination depends on restoring activity to apoenzymes.[39, 40] Many enzymes consist of a protein part called the apoenzyme and a removable prosthetic group or coenzyme. The coenzyme is essentially involved in the enzymatic activity. Pyridoxal phosphate is involved as a cofactor in the metabolism of amino acids. It plays a role in the alteration of the side chains while maintaining the α-amino-carboxylic acid grouping, in decarboxylation, and in the transamination to α-keto acids. Several dozen pyridoxal phosphate proteins are known. All these reactions may be derived from one common intermediate, a Schiff's base.

Some of the apoenzymes which have been used include apotrypto-phanase,[43, 47, 49, 51, 52] aspartate apoaminotransferase,[41, 42, 46, 50] and tyrosine apodecarboxylase.[39, 44, 45]

E. Apotryptophanase

Tryptophanase catalyses the essentially irreversible reaction

$$\text{L-Tryptophan} + H_2O \rightarrow \text{pyruvate} + NH_3 + \text{indole.}$$

In the presence of excess apotryptophanase and tryptophan, pyridoxal phosphate can be measured indirectly through the derived indole. The indole could be determined with MBTH,[68, 69] p-dimethylaminocinnamaldehyde[70–72] or p-dimethylaminobenzaldehyde[43, 51, 52, 72–75] colorimetrically or could be determined directly by fluorescence in ethanol at $F285/330$[76] or by phosphorescence at $P285/430fs$.[77, 78]

A large variety of procedures have been used for the determination of indole with p-dimethylaminobenzaldehyde. In one method the chromogen, VI, λ_{max} 570 nm, mε 57·7, was similar spectrally to the chromogen obtained from 3-methylindole and dissimilar spectrally from the chromogen obtained from 2-methylindole.[73]

VI

In another method the chromogen obtained from indole absorbed at 565 nm, mε 77·3 while the chromogens from 2-methyl- and 3-methylindole absorbed at 540 and 580 nm, respectively.[75]

The following p-dimethylaminobenzaldehyde procedure has a sensitivity approaching that of methods using radioactive substrates. It depends upon the ability of pyridoxal phosphate to restore activity to a highly purified apotryptophanase preparation (specific activity 0·75 to 12 units mg protein) from *Escherichia coli* B/It7A.[43, 48, 49] This assay for pyridoxal phosphate depends upon the following sequence of reactions:

$$\text{Apotryptophanase} + \text{pyridoxal phosphate} \rightarrow \text{tryptophanase}$$

$$\text{L-Tryptophan} + \text{water} \xrightarrow{\text{tryptophanase}} \text{pyruvic acid} + \text{indole} + \text{ammonia}$$

$$\text{Indole} + (CH_3)_2N{-}C_6H_4CHO \rightarrow \text{Chromogen, } \lambda_{max} \text{ 575 nm}$$

Since dilute solutions of pyridoxal phosphate are rapidly destroyed by exposure to light, standards should be prepared fresh and assays should be carried out in dim or red light; e.g. 10 ng of pyridoxal phosphate is decomposed by 50% on exposure to ordinary laboratory light for 30 minutes.[43]

The method can be used in assays for enzymes whose product is pyridoxal phosphate, e.g. pyridoxal phosphokinase (ATP:pyridoxal 5-phosphotransferase, EC 2.7.1.35) and pyridoxamine phosphate oxidase (pyridoxamine phosphate:oxygen oxidoreductase (deaminating), EC 1.4.3.5).

Apotryptophanase determination of pyridoxal phosphate.[43] Pyridoxal phosphate standard: 3 to 15 or from 60 to 240 ng per flask, Fig. 86. Buffer: $0.12\,\text{M KH}_2\text{PO}_4$, pH 7·8, containing 0·25 mg bovine serum albumin/ml and 0·2 mM reduced glutathione,[49] prepared fresh daily. Enzyme: 10 units enzyme/ml (1 unit being defined as the amount of enzyme that catalyses the formation of 1 micromole of indole per minute at 37° in the presence of saturating amounts of pyridoxal phosphate and tryptophan). Retains 85% activity after storage at 4° for one week. Colour reagent: prepare fresh daily by mixing 5 vol of 5% p-dimethylaminobenzaldehyde in 95% ethanol with 12 vol of 5 ml conc H_2SO_4 diluted to 100 ml with *n*-butanol. Stable at room temp.

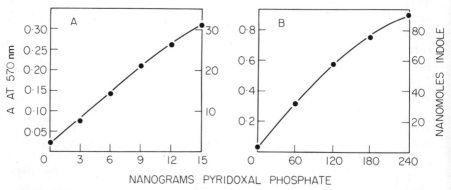

FIG. 86. Standard curves for assay of pyridoxal phosphate with apotryptophanase. By varying reaction conditions, pyridoxal phosphate can be estimated satisfactorily by the apotryptophanase method at concentrations varying from 3 to 15 ng or 60 to 240 ng. The curve in A was prepared by preincubating 3 to 15 ng pyridoxal phosphate with 0·02 unit apotryptophanase for 20 minutes. L-Tryptophan was added and the mixture was incubated 20 min before stopping the reaction with the p-dimethylaminobenzaldehyde reagent. The curve in B was prepared by preincubating 60 to 240 ng pyridoxal phosphate with 0·04 unit apotryptophanase. After adding substrate, the reaction mixture was incubated for 3 min prior to colour development with p-dimethylaminobenzaldehyde. The same colour reagents were used to prepare both curves; in both cases the final volume was 4·9 ml.[43]

Procedure. To a 10 ml Erlenmeyer flask, add 0·3 ml buffer, 1 to 5 μl enzyme, 0 to 0·1 ml pyridoxal phosphate standard or sample, and water to make a final concentration of 0·4 ml. Layer 1 ml toluene over the surface of the reaction mixture. Cover the flask with Parafilm and incubate for 20 min at

37° with gentle shaking to allow reassociation of pyridoxal phosphate with apoenzyme. Start the reaction by adding 0·1 ml 0·02 M L-tryptophan. Tip the flask so that the substrate solution goes under the toluene layer. Swirl and return the flask to shaker. Incubation time depends on the desired sensitivity of the assay. For a satisfactory standard curve in the range of 3 to 15 ng pyridoxal phosphate, incubate for 20 min (see Fig. 86(A)). If a less sensitive assay is acceptable, incubation for 3 min after addition of substrate gives a smooth standard curve for pyridoxal phosphate concentrations of 0 to 240 ng (see Fig. 86(B)).

Stop the reaction by adding 3·5 ml Ehrlich reagent. A clear single phase usually forms. In some biological samples, turbidity may develop. In this case, centrifuge the samples for 15 min at low speed in a clinical centrifuge and decant the clear upper phase from a few drops of aqueous phase into a colorimeter tube.

Allow samples to stand for 20 min after addition of colour reagent to permit full colour development. The colour is stable for 24 h. Read absorbance at 570 nm. For pyridoxal phosphate assays in the 60–240 ng range, the error for duplicate determinations of standard or sample is less than 3%. In the 3–15 ng range, the error is about 7%.

It has been stated that under the authors' experimental conditions indole is attacked in the 2-position by p-dimethylaminobenzaldehyde and in the 3-position by p-dimethylaminocinnamaldehyde.[70] It was shown that in the analysis with the latter aldehyde all methyl indoles except one reacted with the reagent while 3-methylindole and tryptophan and its derivatives did not react. However, under other experimental conditions 3-substituted indoles do react with p-dimethylaminocinnamaldehyde.[79, 80] One of the main chromogens formed in the procedure using excess p-dimethylaminocinnamaldehyde to determine pyridoxal phosphate is **VII**. p-Dimethylaminocinnamaldehyde has been used as a reagent to determine indole in the tryptophanase

VII

reaction.[81] Ninety-nine per cent of the indole that dissolves in 5% trichloroacetic acid can be extracted by toluene.[70] The indole can then be reacted with a solution of p-dimethylaminocinnamaldehyde in propanol to give the chromogen, λ_{max} 625 nm, mε 67·2; another band is present at wavelengths greater than 730 nm (as indicated by a spectral curve). Since the chromogen is

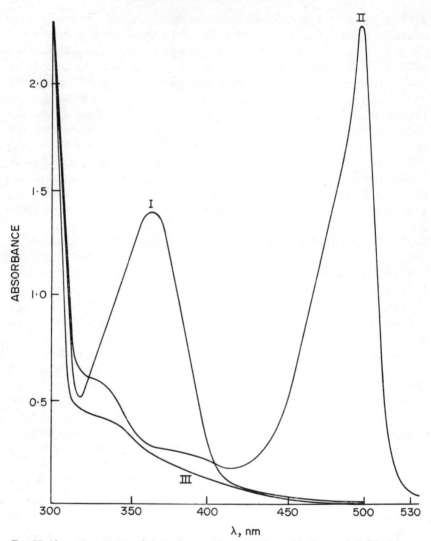

FIG. 87. Absorption spectra of glutamic–aspartic transaminase (15 mg protein/ml) in 0·1 M carbonate buffer of pH 8·5 alone (I) or with 2×10^{-2} M erythro-DL-β-hydroxyaspartate (II) and of apotransaminase (15 mg protein/ml in the same buffer) alone (III) or with 2×10^{-2} M erythro-DL-β-hydroxyaspartate (III).[41]

stable in aq acetic acid, this solvent is used to extract the chromogen from the toluene mixture.[70, 71] An mε of 82 at 625 nm has also been reported.[71]

In the following procedure tryptophan and other 3-substituted indoles do not react and neither is the tryptophan extracted into toluene from aq solution.[70] Beer's law is obeyed from 0·05 to 0·5 µg of indole/ml of 5% tri-chloroacetic acid. Dimedone is used because it combines with the pyridoxal phosphate and renders it unavailable to the reaction with the remaining indole in acidic conditions.[70, 72]

p-*Dimethylaminocinnamaldehyde determination of indole*.[70] Add 0·2 ml of 1% ethanolic solution of 5,5-dimethyl-1,3-cyclohexanedione to 1·8 ml of the test mixture (as obtained from an enzymic reaction). Add 8 ml of 6·25% trichloroacetic acid and centrifuge at 1000 g for 15 min. Remove an aliquot of the supernatant and dilute to 10 ml with 5% trichloroacetic acid and add 5 ml of toluene. Cover the test tube with a Saran Wrap-protected rubber stopper and shake on the Vortex for 30 seconds. Centrifuge at 200 g for 15 minutes. To 4 ml of the toluene extract in a graduated, glass-stoppered centrifuge tube add 1 ml of 0·5% 4-dimethylaminocinnamaldehyde. Stopper the tube, mix and heat at 37° for 10 minutes. Add 0·5 ml of 8% (v/v) H_2SO_4 (sp. gr. 1·84) in 95% ethanol, mix and heat at 37° for 10 minutes. Remove the tube from the water bath, add 4 ml of 50% (v/v) glacial acetic acid in water, and place the tube on ice for 10 minutes. Mix on Vortex for 30 sec and centrifuge at 160 g for 15 minutes. Withdraw the lower green-coloured acetic acid layer into a test tube placed on ice. Read absorbance at 625 nm. Carry out all steps after addition of trichloroacetic acid at 0°.

MBTH could be used directly for the determination of pyridoxal phosphate or indirectly through the determination of the derived indole. In the latter case the chromogen would probably have the structure **VIII**.[69] However

VIII

λ_{max} 508 nm, mɛ 32

this procedure has not been optimized for indole; with such optimization the mɛ value would be higher and the sensitivity would be considerably improved.

F. Apoaminotransferase

Spectrophotometric and colorimetric methods are available for estimating pyridoxal phosphate (and pyridoxamine phosphate) which depend upon the restoration of activity to the apoenzyme of aspartate aminotransferase (L-aspartate: 2-oxoglutarate aminotransferase, EC 2.6.1.1), sometimes called glutamic-oxaloacetic transaminase or glutamic-aspartic trans-aminase.[41, 42, 46, 50] Transaminase activity can be coupled to malate dehydrogenase (L-malate: NAD oxidoreductase (decarboxylating) EC 1.1.1.39) so that the reaction can be followed by disappearance of NADH absorbance at 340 nm, of NADH fluorescence at $F340/457$ or by alkaline treatment of NAD^+ to give fluorescence at $F360/460$.

In the spectrophotometric method dependent on the measurement of decreasing NADH the following reactions take place:[46, 50, 82, 83]

1. Pyridoxal phosphate + aspartate apoaminotransferase → aspartate
aminotransferase (AAT)

2. α-Oxoglutarate + aspartate $\xrightarrow{\text{AAT}}$ glutamate + oxaloacetate

3. Oxaloacetate + NADH + H^+ $\underset{\text{malate dehydrogenase}}{\rightleftharpoons}$ malate + NAD^+

Since the transamination can be followed spectrally when coupled with the malic dehydrogenase reaction, it is possible to determine pyridoxal phosphate by measuring the rate of the disappearance of NADH or the appearance of NAD^+. In the spectrophotometric method, measurement is made at 366 nm[46, 50] so as to increase the selectivity of the procedure.

A few other methods are available for the determination of pyridoxal phosphate through the formation of aspartate aminotransferase. This enzyme forms complexes with both keto substrates and dicarboxylic acid inhibitors; these complexes are noteworthy for their wavelength maximum at 430 nm.[84] The enzyme also undergoes a series of reactions with amino substrates and dicarboxylic amino acid inhibitors.[85] Three typical changes can take place. First, a sharp maximum at 492 nm characterizes the enzyme spectrum after the addition of erythro-DL-β-hydroxyaspartate.[86] Second, a maximum at 430 nm results from the reaction of the enzyme with α-methyl-aspartate.[84, 87] Third, a spectral maximum at 333 nm characterizes the reaction products of the enzyme with aspartate, glutamate and other amino compounds which act as substrates or inhibitors of transaminase.[85–88]

Pyridoxal phosphate and its precursors can be determined by means of the absorption due to the formation of the complex between reconstituted transaminase and the erythro isomer of hydroxyaspartate.[41] Essentially the reaction of the apotransaminase with erythro-DL-β-hydroxyaspartate and increasing quantities of pyridoxal phosphate gives rise to a gradual increase in the absorption of the complex at 492 nm. This reaction can take place at either pH 5·5 or 8·5. If α-ketoglutarate is included in the system, pyridoxamine phosphate can also be determined in a similar fashion. Thus, both pyridoxal phosphate and pyridoxamine phosphate can be determined in a mixture by measuring the absorbance of the apotransaminase system at 492 nm before and after the addition of α-ketoglutarate. Although the method is not essentially a catalytic method, it does have the specificity of an enzymatic reaction. Not only that but 25 ng of pyridoxal phosphate are detectable.

For the following procedure aspartate transaminase was prepared from pig hearts[84] using succinate buffer[89] with additional purification achieved by fractionation on a DEAE-Sephadex A-50 column equilibrated and eluted with 0·02 M phosphate buffer pH 7·2.[41] The enzyme preparations had an absorption ratio (280 nm: 360 nm) of 9·5 to 10·5 at pH 9·0. Apotransaminase was prepared from transaminase with the coenzyme in the pyridoxal phosphate form[90] and from transaminase after extensive dialysis against glutamate at low pH.[91] Purification was achieved by dialysis through a Sephadex G-200 column. The absorption spectra of the transaminase and its complex with hydroxyaspartate are shown in Fig. 87.[41] The apotransaminase by itself or after treatment with hydroxyaspartate shows no spectral bands in the 300 to 530 nm region. The spectral effect of increasing amounts of pyridoxal phosphate on solutions of the apotransaminase and hydroxyaspartate is shown in Fig. 88.[41] Ten times higher quantities of pyridoxal, pyridoxamine, pyridoxine, pyridoxine phosphate and pyridoxamine phosphate did not interfere. A standard curve can be obtained in the procedure with 0·0001 to 0·01 μmol of pyridoxal phosphate. The pyridoxal phosphate content of aspartate transaminase can be determined by the procedure.

Apotransaminase determination of pyridoxal phosphate.[41] The approximate directions are as follows: Add 0·15 ml of 0·2 M erythro-DL-β-hydroxyaspartate in 0·1 M carbonate buffer (pH 8·5) to each of two small tubes each containing 0·45 mg of apotransaminase in 0·3 ml of 0·1 M carbonate buffer. To the first tube add 1 ml of 0·01 μmol ml^{-1} of freshly prepared pyridoxal phosphate in 0·1 M carbonate buffer while 1 ml of the test solution is placed in the second tube. After 15 min at 25°, read the absorbance at 492 nm. Calculate the pyridoxal phosphate content of the unknown sample by comparison as follows:

$$\text{Pyridoxal phosphate (μmol)} = 0\cdot01 \ \text{μmol} \ \frac{A_{unknown}}{A_{0\cdot01 \ \text{μmol standard}}}$$

G. 3-Methyl-2-benzothiazolinone hydrazone

Pyridoxal phosphate condenses with MBTH at pH 8·0 to give the azine, **IX**, λ_{max} 380 nm, mε 22·4.[53] This azine is substantially insoluble under acidic conditions. When 2-oxoglutarate and pyruvate are present measurements must be made at 390 nm. Precision of the method is about ±3%.

H*

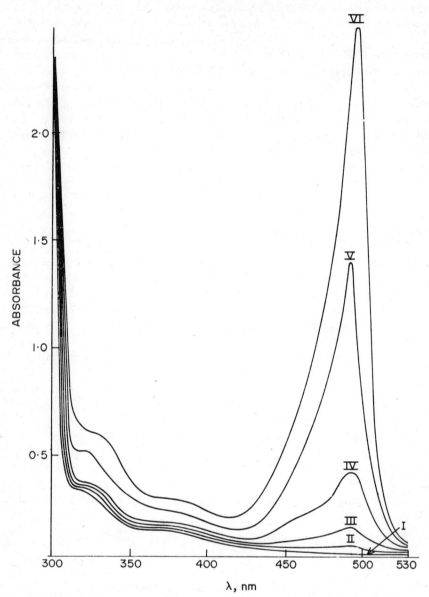

Fɪɢ. 88. Absorption spectra of apotransaminase (4·5 mg protein/0·3 ml) in 0·1 ᴍ carbonate buffer of pH 8·5 and 2 × 10⁻² ᴍ erythro-ᴅʟ-β-hydroxyaspartate alone (I) or with 0·0001 μmole (II) or with 0·0005 μmol (III) or 0·005 μmol (IV) or 0·05 μmol (V) or 0·1 μmol (VI) pyridoxal phosphate.[41]

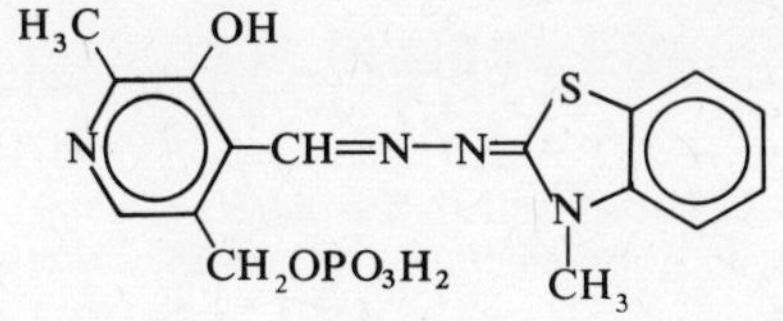

$$H_3C \quad OH$$

$$N \quad -CH=N-N \quad \begin{array}{c} S \\ N \\ CH_3 \end{array}$$

$$CH_2OPO_3H_2$$

IX

IX should absorb at longer wavelengths as a cationic resonance structure in acidic solution.

H. Hydrazines

Pyridoxal phosphate can also be condensed with phenylhydrazine to give the hydrazone, **X**, which can then be determined.[54–57] With microcuvettes

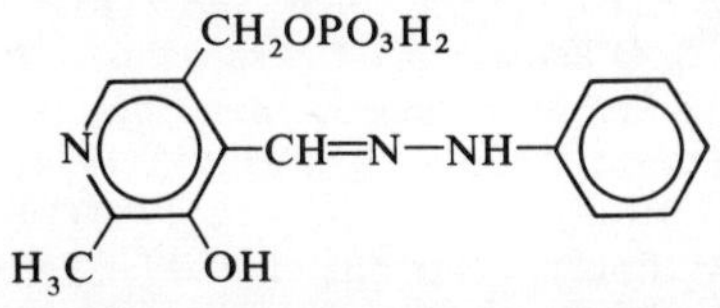

$$CH_2OPO_3H_2$$

$$N \quad -CH=N-NH-$$

$$H_3C \quad OH$$

X

λ_{max} 410, mϵ 25

10 to 20 ng of pyridoxal phosphate can be measured.[55] Since pyridoxal phosphate reacts rapidly with the reagent at room temp while pyridoxal reacts more slowly, the phosphate can be determined in the presence of a moderate excess of pyridoxal.[57] This difference in reactivity is increased by decreasing the temperature and increasing the acidity of the reaction mixture.

Instead of phenylhydrazine, p-nitrophenylhydrazine or 2-hydrazino-benzothiazole can be used. The resultant chromogen would absorb at very much longer wavelength and with much greater intensity in alkaline solution than would the phenylhydrazone.

Semicarbazide might be useful in the direct analysis of pyridoxal phosphate on chromatograms. When paper chromatograms are sprayed with a solution of 0·1 M semicarbazide in a mixture of 0·1 M tris buffer, pH 9, and ethanol (2:3), spots containing pyridoxal and its phosphate emit an intense green fluorescence under ultraviolet light.[58] The fluorescence was stable for weeks and less than 1 µg of phosphate could be detected.

REFERENCES

1. E. A. Peterson and H. A. Sober. *J. Am. Chem. Soc.* **76**, 169 (1954).
2. M. Viscontini, C. Ebnother and P. Karrer. *Helv. Chim. Acta* **34**, 1834 (1951).
3. H. M. Curry and W. A. Bulen. *J. Org. Chem.* **25**, 209 (1960).
4. R. M. Khomutov, M. Y. Karpeiskii and E. S. Severin. *Izvest. Nauk S.S.S.R.* 680 (1964).
5. A. K. Lunn and R. A. Morton. *Analyst* **77**, 718 (1952).
6. D. Heyl, E. Luz, S. A. Harris and K. Folkers. *J. Am. Chem. Soc.* **73**, 3430 (1951).
7. V. R. Williams and J. B. Neilands. *Arch. Biochem.* **53**, 56 (1954).
8. B. E. C. Banks and C. A. Vernon. *J. Chem. Soc.* 1698 (1961).
9. V. Bonavita and V. Scardi. *Experientia* **14**, 7 (1958).
10. V. Bonavita and V. Scardi. *Anal. Chim. Acta* **20**, 47 (1959).
11. V. Bonavita. *Arch. Biochem.* **88**, 366 (1960).
12. R. L. Blakley. *Biochem. J.* **61**, 315 (1955).
13. A. N. Wilson and S. A. Harris. *J. Am. Chem. Soc.* **73**, 4693 (1951).
14. D. Heyl and S. A. Harris. *J. Am. Chem. Soc.* **73**, 3434 (1951).
15. T. L. Hullar. *J. Med. Chem.* **12**, 58 (1969).
16. P. F. Muhlradt, Y. Morino and E. E. Snell. *J. Med. Chem.* **10**, 341 (1967).
17. Kuroda. *Bitamin (Japan).* **28**, 21 (1963).
18. A. L. Morrison and R. F. Long. *J. Chem. Soc.* **211** (1958).
19. W. W. Umbreit, D. J. O'Kane and I. C. Gunsalus. *J. Biol. Chem.* **176**, 629 (1948).
20. D. Heyl, S. A. Harris and K. Folkers. *J. Am. Chem. Soc.* **75**, 653 (1953).
21. J. E. Churchich. *Biochim. Biophys. Acta* **79**, 643 (1964).
22. S. Shinkai and T. C. Bruice. *Biochemistry* **12**, 1750 (1973).
23. A. Gaudiano and M. Polizzi-Sciarrone. *Annali Ist. Sup. Sanitá* **1**, 588 (1965).
24. S. F. Contractor and B. Shane. *Clin. Chim. Acta* **21**, 71 (1968).
25. C. E. Colombini and E. E. McCoy. *Anal. Biochem.* **34**, 451 (1970).
26. H. Kraut and U. Imhoff. *Nahrung* **12**, 29 (1968).
27. Y. H. Loo and L. Badger. *J. Neurochem.* **16**, 801 (1969).
28. S. Takanashi, I. Matsunaga and Z. Tamura. *J. Vitaminol.* **16**, 132 (1970).
29. E. Adams. *Anal. Biochem.* **31**, 118 (1969).
30. M. Yamada, A Saito and Z. Tamura. *Chem. Pharm. Bull.* **14**, 482 (1966).
31. N. Ohishi and S. Fukui. *Arch. Biochem. Biophys.* **128**, 606 (1968).
32. M. Yamada, A. Saito and Z. Tamura. *Chem. Pharm. Bull. Tokyo* **14**, 488 (1966).
33. A. Gaudiano and M. Polizzi-Sciarrone. *Boll. Soc. Ital. Biol. Sper.* **39**, 1874 (1963).
34. J. W. Thanassi and J. S. Fruton. *Biochemistry* **1**, 975 (1962).
35. H. F. Schott and W. G. Clark. *J. Biol. Chem.* **196**, 449 (1952).
36. E. Adams. *Anal. Biochem.* **31**, 484 (1969).
37. K. Soda, A. Novogrodsky and A. Meister. *Biochemistry* **3**, 1450 (1964).
38. D. Cavillini, B. Mondovi and C. DeMarco, in E. E. Snell, P. M. Fasella, A. E. Braunstein and A. Rossi-Fanelli, Eds, "Proceedings of the Symposium on Chemical and Biological Aspects of Pyridoxal Catalysis", Rome 1962, Pergamon Press, New York, 1963, p. 361.
39. H. Maruyama and B. D. Coursin. *Anal. Biochem.* **26**, 720 (1968).
40. C. A. Storvick, E. M. Benson, M. A. Edwards and M. J. Woodring in (D. Glick, Ed.), "Methods of Biochemical Analysis." Interscience, New York, Vol. 12 (1964), p. 183.
41. A. E. Evangelopoulos, I. Karni-Katsadimas and T. G. Kalogerakos. *Enzymologia* **40**, 37 (1971).

42. M. P. Walsh. *Am. J. Clin. Path.* **46**, 282 (1966).
43. B. E. Haskell and E. E. Snell. *Anal. Biochem.* **45**, 567 (1972).
44. A. Hamfelt. *Clin. Chim. Acta* **7**, 746 (1962).
45. G. H. Sloane-Stanley. *Biochem. J.* **44**, 567 (1949).
46. G. Schruber and H. Holzer in H. U. Bergmeyer, Ed. "Methods of Enzymatic Analysis," Academic Press, New York (1965), p. 606.
47. D. B. McCormick, M. E. Gregory and E. E. Snell. *J. Biol. Chem.* **236**, 2076 (1961).
48. W. A. Newton, Y. Morino and E. E. Snell. *J. Biol. Chem.* **240**, 1211 (1965).
49. Y. Morino and E. E. Snell, in H. Tabor and C. W. Tabor, Eds, "Methods in Enzymology," Academic Press, New York, Vol. 17A (1970), p. 439.
50. H. Holzer, U. Gerlach, G. Jacobi and M. Gnoth. *Biochem. Z.* **329**, 529 (1958).
51. S. Gailani. *Anal. Biochem.* **13**, 19 (1965).
52. E. A. Donald and R. F. Ferguson. *Anal. Biochem.* **7**, 335 (1964).
53. K. Soda, T. Yorifuji, H. Misono and M. Moriguchi. *Biochem. J.* **114**, 629 (1969).
54. H. Wada and E. E. Snell. *J. Biol. Chem.* **237**, 133 (1962).
55. G. Rosso, K. Takashima and E. Adams. *Biochem. Biophys. Res. Commun.* **34**, 134 (1969).
56. E. M. Wilson. *Biochim. Biophys. Acta* **67**, 345 (1963).
57. H. Wada and E. E. Snell. *J. Biol. Chem.* **236**, 2089 (1961).
58. R. Häkanson. *J. Chromatog.* **13**, 263 (1964).
59. H. M. Henderson. *Biochem. J.* **95**, 775 (1965).
60. R. S. White and W. B. Dempsey. *Biochemistry* **9**, 4057 (1970).
61. F. Korte and H. Bannuscher. *Angew. Chem.* **69**, 97 (1957).
62. F. Korte and H. Bannuscher. *Biochem. Z.* **329**, 451 (1958).
63. J. W. Huff and W. A. Perlzweig. *J. Biol. Chem.* **155**, 345 (1944).
64. V. Bonavita and V. Scardi. *Arch. Biochem. Biophys.* **82**, 300 (1959).
65. K. M. Grigor, D. von Redlich and D. Glick. *Anal. Biochem.* **50**, 28 (1972).
66. O. Valls, M. Castillo, J. M. Lopez and V. Vilas. *Infcion Quim. Analit. Pura Apl. Ind.* **25**, 188 (1971).
67. M. Castillo, J. M. Lopez, O. Valls and V. Vilas. *Infcion Quim. Analit. Pura Apl. Ind.* **26**, 102 (1972).
68. E. Sawicki, T. R. Hauser, T. W. Stanley, W. C. Elbert and F. T. Fox. *Anal. Chem.* **33**, 1574 (1961).
69. E. Sawicki, T. W. Stanley, T. R. Hauser, W. C. Elbert and J. E. Noe, *Anal. Chem.* **33**, 722 (1961).
70. J. W. Meduski and S. Zamenhof. *Anal. Biochem.* **24**, 202 (1968).
71. E. McEvoy-Bowe. *Analyst* **88**, 893 (1963).
72. T. A. Scott. *Biochem. J.* **80**, 462 (1961).
73. M. Knowlton, F. C. Dohan and H. Sprince. *Anal. Chem.* **32**, 666 (1960).
74. P. Byrom and J. H. Turnbull. *Talanta* **10**, 1217 (1963).
75. M. A. Muhs and F. T. Weiss. *Anal. Chem.* **30**, 259 (1958).
76. B. L. Van Duuren. *J. Org. Chem.* **26**, 2954 (1961).
77. M. Zander. *Chem. Ber.* **97**, 2695 (1964).
78. S. Freed and W. Salmre. *Science* **128**, 1341 (1958).
79. S. Sakai, K. Suzuki, H. Mori and M. Fujino. *Japan Analyst* **9**, 862 (1960).
80. M. Pesez and J. Bartos. *Bull. Soc. Chim. France* 3802 (1966).
81. J. M. Turner. *Biochem. J.* **78**, 790 (1961).
82. A. Karmen, F. Wróblewski and J. S. La Due. *J. Clin. Invest.* **34**, 131 (1955).
83. J. S. La Due, F. Wróblewski and A. Karmen. *Science (Washington)* **120**, 497 (1954).
84. W. T. Jenkins, D. A. Yphantis and I. W. Sizer. *J. Biol. Chem.* **234**, 51 (1959).

85. H. Lis, P. Fasella, C. Turano and P. Vaccini. *Biochim. Biophys. Acta* **45**, 529 (1960).
86. W. T. Jenkins. *J. Biol. Chem.* **236**, 1121 (1961).
87. A. E. Evangelopoulos and I. W. Sizer. *Experientia* **21**, 576 (1965).
88. A. E. Evangelopoulos and I. W. Sizer. *Proc. Natl. Acad. Sci. U.S.* **49**, 638 (1963).
89. C. Turano, A. Giartosio, F. Riva and P. Fasella. *Biochem. Biophys. Res. Commun.* **16**, 331 (1964).
90. H. Wada and E. E. Snell. *J. Biol. Chem.* **237**, 127 (1962).
91. V. Scardi, P. Scotto, M. Iaccarino and E. Scarano. *Biochem. J.* **88**, 172 (1963).

56. PYRUVALDEHYDE (METHYLGLYOXAL)

$$CH_3-\overset{\overset{\displaystyle |}{\|}}{\underset{O}{C}}-CHO$$

I. INTRODUCTION

This compound gives a weak absorption band in water at λ 282·5 nm, $m\varepsilon$ 0·028.[1] Since this band is too weak to use in trace analysis, the aldehyde has been treated with appropriate reagents to form chromogens or fluorogens which can then be assayed. A list of reagents used in this type of analysis is given in Table 48.

II. REAGENTS

A. Anthrone

Fluorimetric anthrone methods for furfural[22] and pentoses[23] have been described. The methods have been modified so as to increase the sensitivity, decrease the analysis time, and render them applicable to pyruvaldehyde and its precursors.[2] It would appear that compounds containing the structure $R-CH_2COCHO$ or their precursors give fluorogens that can be assayed at $F460/505$. Compounds containing the structure

$$-\overset{\displaystyle |}{C}=\overset{\displaystyle |}{C}-CHO$$

react with anthrone in sulphuric acid to give benzanthrone cations fluorescing at $F480/560$. The results and the procedure are given in the glyoxals precursors section. Glyoxal gives negative results.

B. Carbazole

Concentrated sulphuric acid solutions of carbazole, 2-hydroxycarbazole or 6-hydroxychrysene warmed with an aqueous solution of pyruvaldehyde

Table 48. Reagents for the determination of pyruvaldehyde

Reagent	λ_{max} (mε) or $F_{exc/em}$	Ref.
Anthrone	462/505	2
Arsenophosphotungstate	—	3
Carbazole	~625	4
Chromotropic acid	450/505	5
2,3-Diaminophenazine	610, 715	6
2,4-Dinitrophenylhydrazine	575 (25·2)	7–10
2,4-Dinitrophenylhydrazine	555 (44·8)	11
2,4-Dinitrophenylhydrazine	565 (60)	12
Enzymatic	240	13–15
2-Hydrazinobenzothiazole	470/510	
2-Methylindole	540	16
p-Nitrophenylhydrazine	695 (78)	17
Pyrrole	Violet	9
Salicylalhydrazone[a]	Y fluor.	18
Semicarbazide	286	19, 20
Veratrol	—	21

[a]Qualitative.

(or formaldehyde) give an intense blue colour which could be used for the determination of pyruvaldehyde and its precursors.[24]

The following method could also be used for pyruvaldehyde but needs optimization.

Cysteine-carbazole determination of pyruvaldehyde.[3] To 1 ml of aq test solution add 0·2 ml of 2·4% aq L-cysteine hydrochloride monohydrate followed by 6 ml of 75% H_2SO_4 (v/v). Shake vigorously, and immediately add 0·2 ml of 0·1% carbazole in ethanol. Shake vigorously again. When maximum colour is reached, read absorbance at wavelength maximum.

A blue colour is also given by glycolaldehyde, glyceraldehyde, and 2,3-dihydroxyacetone. Ketopentoses give a band at 540 nm, ketohexoses at 560 nm and ketoheptoses at 590 nm.

C. Chromotropic acid

Chromotropic acid can be used for the fluorimetric determination of pyruvaldehyde.[5] In the following modified procedure higher concentrations of chromotropic acid gave higher fluorescence intensities while lower concentrations gave better blanks. A linear relationship through the origin was found between concentration and fluorescence intensity from about 0·02 to 0·4 μg of pyruvaldehyde. Some of the results obtained in the procedure are

Table 49. Chromotropic acid determination of pyruvaldehyde and other compounds

Compound	$F_{exc/em}$	Relative fluor. intensity
Pyruvaldehyde	450/505	100
Glyceraldehyde	450/505	90
Dihydroxyacetone	450/505	40
Methyl vinyl ketone	450/535	5
Acrolein	410, 470/520	2
Isoeugenol methyl ether[a]	400/510	0·6
Isoeugenol[a]	400/520	0·3
Phenylpropargyl aldehyde[a]	410/460	0·3
Crotonaldehyde	450/520	0·3

[a]Test solvent is ethanol.

given in Table 49. Negative results are given by formaldehyde, acetaldehyde, chloral, allyl alcohol, furfural, glycerol, glyoxylic acid, succinaldehyde, 2,4-pentanedione, citral, 2,3-butanedione and glyoxal. Before use, the variables in the procedure should be investigated.

Chromotropic acid determination of pyruvaldehyde. To 2 ml of aq test solution add 5 ml of 1 % chromotropic acid in conc sulphuric acid. Mix well and allow to cool to room temperature. Dilute to 10 ml with conc H_2SO_4 and read the fluorescence intensity at $F450/505$.

D. 2,3-Diaminophenazine

The procedure utilizing 2,3-diaminophenazine for the determination of glyoxal (and pyruvaldehyde and 2,3-butanedione) has been described in the glyoxal section (Chapter 33). With the following procedure the precursors of glyoxal and pyruvaldehyde give negative results. Pyruvaldehyde gives bands at 450, 590s, 610 and 715 nm while glyoxal gives bands at 570 and 600 nm. A brown–yellow 2-methylpyrazino[b]phenazine, **I**, is believed to be formed. This compound has an intense blue colour in sulphuric or acetic acid solution.

I

The appearance of a band at 715 nm indicates the presence of pyruvalde-hyde. The presence of the 450 and 715 nm bands would indicate that the reaction is not as simple as postulated. With the procedure given here pyruvaldehyde gives an mε of 2·1 at λ 610 nm; this should be capable of improvement. The step for removal of the reagent amino groups (and thus materially reducing the colour due to the excess reagent) involving diazotization and treatment with hypophosphorous acid may not be necessary with analysis at very long wavelength.

2,3-Diaminophenazine determination of pyruvaldehyde.[6] Treat 1 ml aq test solution containing less than 0·6 micromole of pyruvaldehyde with 1 ml of 0·021% 2,3-diaminophenazine in glacial acetic acid in a calibrated test tube. Heat at 100° for 10 minutes. Cool in an ice-water bath and add 1 ml of cold 0·02% aq potassium nitrite and 0·5 ml of 50% hypophosphorous acid. Heat at 100° for 20 minutes. Cool and dilute to 4 ml with 0·5 ml of glacial acetic acid. Read the absorbance at 610 or 715 nm.

E. 2,4-Dinitrophenylhydrazine

2,4-Dinitrophenylhydrazine can be used to determine pyruvaldehyde before or after separation dependent on the seriousness of the interference problem. The chromogen, **II**, is formed; it could be analysed in the neutral form or as the anion or the dianion.

II

The thin layer chromatographic separation[25, 26] of the bis-dinitrophenylhydrazones of pyruvaldehyde, α-ketoaldehydes, α-diketones and glyoxal have been discussed in the glyoxal and glyoxals sections. Pure **II** has been shown to absorb at λ 395 and 435 nm with mε 43·5 and 40·7, respectively in chloroform,[12] at λ 565, mε 60 in alcoholic NaOH,[12] at λ 550 nm, mε 69·2 in aq sodium hydroxide solution,[27] at λ 430 and 560 with mε 15 and 47, respectively[28] and at λ 555 nm, mε 44·8 in 5% KOH in 78% methanol.[11]

The mono-2,4-dinitrophenylhydrazone, **III**, absorbs at λ 345 nm, mε 22·9 in chloroform,[29] at λ 230, 270 and 357 nm with mε 10·7, 8·3 and 24·6, respectively,[30] and at λ 490 nm, mε 30·9 in 1 N aq sodium hydroxide solution.[29]

III

Pyruvaldehyde in aq solution can be determined by reaction with 2,4-dinitrophenylhydrazine at 98° for 15 min; at λ_{max} 575 nm an mε of 25·2 is obtained.[7] The colour is stable for at least 30 minutes. The colour due to excess reagent is eliminated by treating the reaction mixture with 2,4-pentanedione to form the colourless pyrazole.

The concentration of pyruvaldehyde in beer can be determined with 2,4-dinitrophenylhydrazine. Beer's law is obeyed from about 1 to 14 µg of pyruvaldehyde in the following procedure.

2,4-Dinitrophenylhydrazine determination of pyruvaldehyde in beer.[8] Mix 10 ml of beer with 25 ml of 0·2% 2,4-dinitrophenylhydrazine in 2 N HCl. After 1 h at room temp evaporate almost to dryness, and extract the formed hydrazones and osazones into 25 ml pyridine. Separate by TLC on silica gel with toluene as solvent. Exposure to diethylamine vapour turns the osazone spots blue. Mix a pyridine extract of the zone corresponding to pyruvaldehyde osazone with 5 ml of 10% diethanolamine, dilute to 25 ml with pyridine and read the absorbance at 585 nm.

F. Diphenylamine

The use of diphenylamine in the determination of pyruvaldehyde, other substituted glyoxals, and precursors of these aldehydes has been discussed.[31] The procedure used is essentially the Dische method for 2-deoxyribose.[32, 33]

G. 2-Hydrazinobenzothiazole

Pyruvaldehyde can also be determined fluorimetrically with 2-hydrazino-benzothiazole. The procedure is given in the glyoxal section. In the absence of glyoxal and dihydroxyacetone, pyruvaldehyde can be determined at $F470/510$ down to about 5 µg of aldehyde. Glyoxal gives about five times as intense spectral bands at $F470/525$. Negative results are obtained with formaldehyde, acetaldehyde, acrolein, crotonaldehyde, methylvinyl ketone, glycerol, 1,1,3-trimethoxypropene, 2-butanone, glyoxylic acid and glycol-aldehyde.

H. 2-Methylindole

In the determination of pyruvaldehyde with 2-methylindole the following procedure was used. It was not optimized for use in this type of assay.

2-Methylindole determination of pyruvaldehyde.[16] To 1 ml of aq test solution add 1 ml of conc HCl and 0·5 ml of 0·2% 2-methylindole in alcohol. Mix, let stand for 1 h, and read absorbance at 540 nm.

The procedure has been applied to the determination of pyruvaldehyde in beer.[34] The calibration graph is rectilinear up to 10 ppm of pyruvaldehyde.

2-Methylindole determination of pyruvaldehyde in beer.[34] Add 25 ml of degassed beer to 7·5 g of salt in a distilling flask and evaporate under reduced pressure at < 40° to dryness. Adjust volume of distillate to 20 ml. To a 4 ml aliquot add 1 ml of conc HCl and 1 ml of fresh 0·2 % alcoholic 2-methylindole. After 1 h read the absorbance at 540 nm.

I. Hydrazines

The 4-nitrophenylhydrazone of pyruvaldehyde, **IV**, absorbs in alcohol at λ 241, 295 and 379 nm with $m\varepsilon$ 7·6, 3·7 and 35·5, respectively.[30]

$$O_2N-\bigcirc-NH-N=CH-\underset{\underset{CH_3}{|}}{C}=O$$

IV

However, analysis through the bis-*p*-nitrophenylhydrazone, **V**, gives much greater sensitivity. This type of chromogen can be analysed as the neutral compound, the anion, the di-anion or as an oxidized derivative. Pyruvaldehyde gives a band at 695 nm, $m\varepsilon$ 78 by a procedure described in the glyoxal

$$O_2N-\bigcirc-NH-N=CH-\underset{\underset{CH_3}{|}}{C}=N-NH-\bigcirc-NO_2$$

V

section. This band is derived from the di-anion of **V**. Glyoxal and 2,3-butanedione also react in the procedure.

Pyruvaldehyde gives a yellow fluorescent derivative with salicylalhydrazone, Fig. 89.[18] The reaction needs study before it could be applied quantitatively.

Pyruvaldehyde reacts rapidly and quantititatively with semicarbazide at room temp to form a di-semicarbazone that absorbs at 286 nm, $m\varepsilon$ 32.[19, 20] Essentially, the aldehyde is treated with 0·067 M semicarbazide HCl in 0·1 M, pH 7·4, sodium phosphate and after 15 min the absorbance is read at 286 nm. This reaction has been coupled with the reaction of pyruvaldehyde with glutathione to measure the catalyzing enzymes, glyoxalase **I** and glyoxalase **II**.[19]

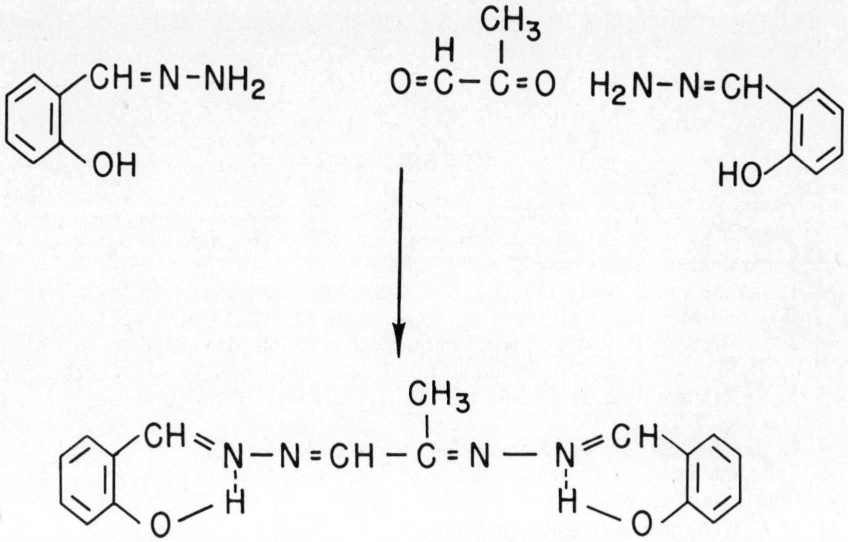

FIG. 89. Reaction of pyruvaldehyde with salicylhydrazone.

J. Glutathione

Pyruvaldehyde can also be determined through the reaction with glutathione as catalysed by glyoxalase I or lactoyl-glutathione lyase (s-lactoyl-
glutathione methylglyoxal-lyase (isomerizing), EC 4.4.1.5).[13, 14, 15] The final
chromogen is measured at 240 nm.

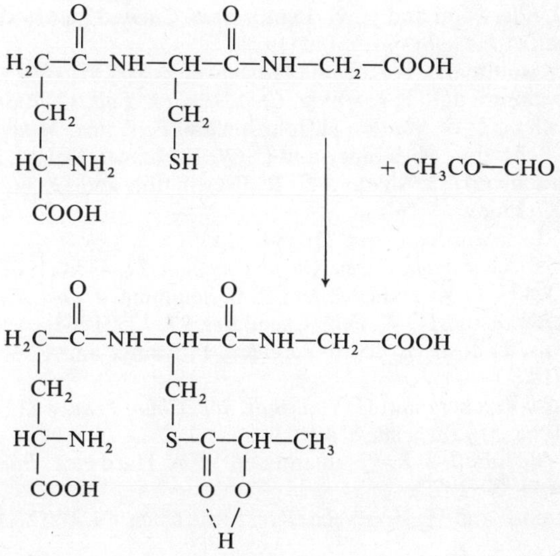

A band is obtained at 240 nm, mɛ 3·37 which is derived from the —S—C=O chromophore. s-Ethyl thioacetate, C_2H_5S—CO—CH_3 contains this grouping and absorbs at λ 233, mɛ 5·2 in water or 0·01 N HCl.[35]

REFERENCES

1. G. Mackinney and O. Temmer. *J. Am. Chem. Soc.* **70**, 3586 (1948).
2. E. Sawicki, R. A. Carnes and R. Schumacher. *Mikrochim. Acta* 929 (1967).
3. N. Aryama. *J. Biol. Chem.* **77**, 359 (1928).
4. Z. Dische and E. Borenfreund. *J. Biol. Chem.* **192**, 583 (1951).
5. B. J. Thornton and J. C. Speck. Jr., *Anal. Chem.* **22**, 899 (1950).
6. J. M. Dechary, E. Kun and H. C. Pitot. *Anal. Chem.* **26**, 449 (1954).
7. D. P. Johnson, F. E. Critchfield and J. E. Ruch. *Anal. Chem.* **34**, 1389 (1962).
8. S. R. Palamand, G. D. Nelson and W. A. Hardwick. *Tech. Q. Master Brewers Ass. Am.* **7**, 111 (1970).
9. H. Barrensheen and M. Dregnus. *Biochem. Z.* **233**, 296 (1932).
10. S. R. Palamand, G. D. Nelson and W. A. Hardwick. *Proc. Am. Soc. Brew. Chem.* 186 (1970).
11. C. F. Wells, *Tetrahedron* **22**, 2685 (1966).
12. L. A. Jones and C. K. Hancock. *J. Am. Chem. Soc.* **82**, 105 (1960).
13. E. Racker. *J. Biol. Chem.* **190**, 685 (1951).
14. E. Racker in S. P. Colowick and N. O. Kaplan, Eds, "Methods in Enzymology", Academic Press, New York, Volume 3 (1957), p. 296.
15. H. Klotzsch and H. U. Bergmeyer in H. U. Bergmeyer, Ed., "Methods of Enzymatic Analysis", Academic Press, New York (1963), p. 283.
16. Z. Dische and S. Robbins. *Biochem. Z.* **271**, 304 (1934).
17. E. Sawicki, T. R. Hauser and R. Wilson. *Anal. Chem.* **34**, 505 (1962).
18. E. Sawicki and T. W. Stanley. *Chemist Analyst* **49**, 107 (1960).
19. N. M. Alexander and J. L. Boyer. *Anal. Biochem.* **41**, 29 (1971).
20. J. C. Underwood and H. G. Lento. *Anal. Chem.* **32**, 1656 (1960).
21. E. Baer. *Arbeitsphysiol.* **1**, 130 (1928).
22. R. Sawamura and T. Koyama. *Yakugaku Zasshi* **81**, 1689 (1961).
23. R. Sawamura and T. Koyama. *Chem. Pharm. Bull.* **12**, 706 (1964).
24. E. Sawicki, T. W. Stanley, H. Johnson and F. T. Fox. *Mikrochim. Acta* 741 (1962).
25. D. P. Schwartz, M. Keeney and O. W. Parks. *Microchem. J.* **8**, 176 (1964).
26. D. P. Schwartz, J. Shamey, C. R. Brewington and O. W. Parks. *Microchem. J.* **13**, 407 (1968).
27. W. S. Beck. *J. Biol. Chem.* **212**, 847 (1955).
28. Z. Holzbecher. *Coll. Czech. Chem. Commun.* **32**, 4393 (1967).
29. L. A. Jones, C. K. Hancock and R. B. Seligman. *J. Org. Chem.* **26**, 228 (1961).
30. G. Henseke and H.-W. Pelz. *Chem. Ber.* **97**, 725 (1964).
31. C. Rioux-Lacoste, C. Izard-Verchére, P. Rumpf and C. Viel. *Compt. Rend.* **274**, 1621 (1972).
32. C. Izard-Verchére and C. Viel. *Bull. Soc. Chim. France* 2122, 3092 (1971).
33. Z. Dische. *Mikrochemie* **8**, 4 (1930).
34. J. M. Aldenhoff, S. R. Palamand and W. A. Hardwick. *Bull. Ass. r. Anciens Etud. Brass.* **68**, 61 (1972).
35. W. Drenth and H. Hogeveen. *Rec. Trav. Chim.* **79**, 1002 (1960).

57. RETINAL

I. INTRODUCTION

The various structures of interest are shown in Fig. 90. All-*trans*-retinal or vitamin A_1 aldehyde or retinene exists in dimorphic forms, with m.p. 57 and 63°,[1] and is soluble in most organic solvents, fats and oils and practically insoluble in water. The many conformations of retinal, the binding site of retinal in native rhodopsin and background information on rhodopsin and isorhodopsin have been reviewed.[2]

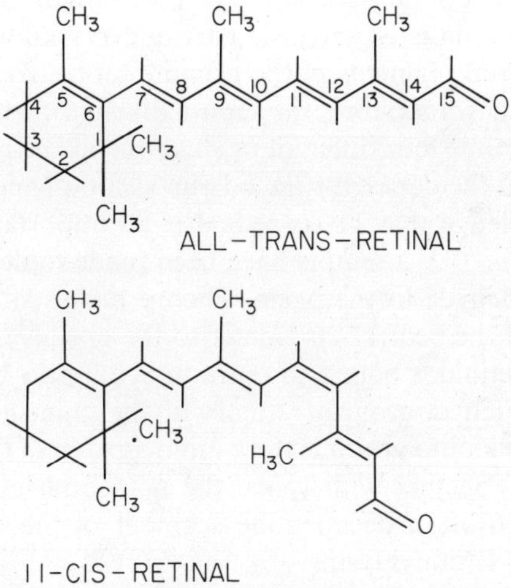

FIG. 90. Structures of all-*trans*-retinal and 11-*cis*-retinal.

A 3-dehydroretinal is available in which there is a double bond in the 3,4-position of retinal. It is also called vitamin A_2 aldehyde or 3-dehydro-retinene. This aldehyde may exist in three different crystalline forms.[1]

The eyes of most vertebrates contain two kind of light receptors: rods, for vision in dim light, and cones, for vision in bright light and colour vision.

233

These photoreceptors contain photosensitive pigments that bleach on exposure to light. Some aspect of these series of chemical reactions triggers a nervous excitation which, transmitted from neuron to neuron along the optic pathways to the brain, ends in exciting visual sensations.[3] Direct microspectrophotometry of human foveas and single human cones has revealed that primary retinas possess, in addition to rods with their rhodopsin, three kinds of cones: blue-, green- and red-sensitive, each containing predominantly or exclusively one of three colour-vision pigments, with wavelength maxima at about 435, 540 and 565 nm.[4, 5]

Light-bleached red- and green-sensitive pigments are regenerated by adding 11-*cis* retinal in the dark.[6] The same seems to be true of the blue-sensitive pigment. The only action of the light is to isomerize the chromophore of a visual pigment from the 11-*cis* to the all-*trans* configuration.[7] Everything else that happens—chemically, physiologically and psychologically—represents "dark" consequences of this one light reaction.[3]

All known visual pigments contain 11-*cis*-retinal or 11-*cis*-3-dehydroretinal as the chromophore. When a visual pigment is bleached by light, the all-*trans*-retinal results. Before it can take part again in regenerating the visual pigment, it must be reisomerized to the 11-*cis* configuration. Thus, a cycle of *cis–trans* isomerization is an intrinsic part of every known visual system.[3]

Since all the visual pigments of the primate retina, rod and cone, contain the 11-*cis*-retinal chromophore, they must differ in their opsins.[3] Normal human vision requires four different opsins: one in the rods, to make rhodopsin, and three in the cones, for the colour-vision pigments.

With the knowledge that 11-*cis*-retinal is an important chromophore in the visual pigments[7–12] attempts have been made to determine the type of linkage of this aldehyde to the opsin. Theory has usually involved a "lock and key" fitting of the bent 11-*cis* isomer to the opsin.[13, 14]

In rhodopsin, retinal is bound to opsin in Schiff base linkage, by the condensation of the aldehyde group of retinal with the amino group of opsin.[15, 16] In cattle opsin the amino group is the ε-amino group of the lysine portion of the molecule.[17] Together with lysine the neighbouring covalently bound amino acids constitute a decapeptide segment of the composition: Ala_3-Phe_3ThrProIle-ε-N-retinyl lysine.

Generally in vertebrates the chromophore in the native pigment is believed to be bound to the ε-amino group of the amino acid lysine.[18, 19] However, in native bovine rhodopsin, the 11-*cis* retinylidene chromophore is bound to the lipid phosphatidyl ethanolamine through a Schiffs base linkage which is probably protonated *in situ*.[20] Since this cation absorbs at 435 nm, the additional and often large red shift required to fit the pigment to its physiological function must arise from a unique type of perturbation controlled by its lipid and/or protein environment.[21] Molecular orbital calculations are stated to be consistent with the visual pigment model of a protonated Schiff's base of retinal perturbed by a charge group in its environment. These various factors will be discussed more fully in the amino portion of this section.

II. SPECTRAL PROPERTIES

First we will discuss the spectra of the retinals and dehydroretinals, Table 50.

Table 50. Absorption spectra of retinal and dehydroretinal

Compound	Solvent	λ_{max}	(mε)	Ref.
All-*trans*-retinal	Pet. ether	245	(4·4)	22
		369·5	(47·9)	
	C_6H_{12}[a]	245	(4·6)	22
		373	(43·7)	
	CCl_4	384[b]		23
	Ethanol	250	(7·1)	22
		385·5	(39·8)	
	Ethanol	381	(43·7)	1
	Ethanol	254	(7·9)	
		381	(42·7)	24
	Ethanol	375	(30·9)	25
	EtOH–ether–isopentane	373	(47·9)	26
	$CHCl_3$	255	(4·0)	22
		389	(37·2)	
	$CHCl_3$	385	(38·0)	27
	H_3PO_4	410	(31·6)	28
		460	(20)	
		560	(39·8)	
9-*cis*-Retinal	Ethanol	373	(36·3)	1
	Ethanol	254	(8·9)	
		376	(36·3)	24
	EtOH–ether–isopentane	366	(39·8)	26
11-*cis*-Retinal[c]	EtOH–ether–isopentane	369	(26·3)	26
13-*cis*-Retinal	EtOH–ether–isopentane	366	(38·9)	26
	Ethanol	257	(9·6)	1
		375	(35·5)	
9,13-di-*cis*-Retinal	EtOH–ether–isopentane	360	(35·5)	26
	Ethanol	368	(32·4)	1
11,13-di-*cis*-Retinal	Ethanol	254	(17·0)	1
		376	(24·6)	
	Ethanol	255	(16·6)	30
		285s	(10)	
		376	(24·6)	

Table 50—*continued*

Compound	Solvent	λ_{max}	(mε)	Ref.
3-Dehydroretinal	Pet. ether	385	(41·7)	32
	C_6H_{12}	386	(40·7)	32
	C_6H_{12}	385	(41·7)	33
	C_5H_{12}	388	(40·7)	34
	Isopropanol	396	(40·7)	32
	Ethanol	397	(39·8)	32
	Ethanol	390	(35·5)	33
		400	(39·8)	
	Ethanol	315s	(11·8)	34
		400	(38·0)	
	Chloroform	405	(40·7)	33
		408	(35·5)	
	Chloroform	407	(38·0)	32
	Chloroform	407	(36·3)	34
9-*cis*-3-Dehydroretinal	Ethanol	315	(19·1)	35
		391	(33·9)	
11-*cis*-3-Dehydroretinal	Ethanol	252	(12·9)	36
		321s	(14·5)	
		393	(25·1)	
13-*cis*-3-Dehydroretinal	Ethanol	314s	(11·8)	35
		395	(33·1)	
11,13-di-*cis*-3-dehydro-retinal	Ethanol	261	(11·0)	35
		269	(11·0)	
		386	(26·9)	

[a] λ_{max} 376 in cyclohexane and 415 nm on silica gel; λ_{max} 373 nm in 3-methylpentane and λ515 at 77°K in 3-methylpentane and HCl.[23]

[b] λ_{max} 412 on silica gel at $2·5 \times 10^{-6}$ to $2·5 \times 10^{-5}$ mol/g silica gel and λ_{max} 415 and 465 at 5×10^{-5} mol/g silica gel.

[c] Photoisomerism of 11-*cis*-retinal studied in solution.[29] The first 3 (π, π^*) singlet states of 11-*cis*-retinal have λ_{max} 255, 290 and 360 nm, respectively.[30, 31]

All-*trans*-retinal absorbs at shortest wavelength in hydrocarbon solvents and at longest wavelength in chloroform. It absorbs at longer wavelength when adsorbed on silica gel and at even longer wavelength at 77° in acidic media. Its spectra in strong acids need more thorough examination. It can be estimated with the help of its ultraviolet absorption maxima.[37] It has been reported to fluoresce.[38] Attempts to reproduce this emission spectrum with fresh retinal have failed.[23] Aging of the retinal does give the reported fluorescence. It would appear that fluorescence of retinal is an artifact of autooxidation.

All-*trans*-retinal (or 3-dehydroretinal) absorbs at longer wavelength and with a greater intensity than any of its isomers. The effect of solvent

on the absorption spectrum of 3-dehydroretinal is somewhat similar to
that obtained with retinal. The absorbance of 3-dehydroretinal at longer
wavelengths than retinal is derived from its longer chain of conjugation.

III. SPECTRA OF SCHIFF BASES

The growing importance of the reaction of the retinals and dehydroretinals with amines stems from the discovery that N-retinylideneopsin
is a Schiffs base,[39] and that the visual pigment rhodopsin is comprised of
11-*cis*-retinal bound to the protein opsin as an ε-lysine Schiff base.[40]
Although the visual pigments contain as their main common chromophore
11-*cis*-retinal, their absorption maxima vary from λ 433 to 562 nm.[41] Because
of this wide variance in wavelength maximum, it would appear that the re-
mainder of the molecule is of considerable importance in its influence on the
absorption spectrum.

The wide range in wavelength maxima of the Schiff base cations of retinal
and dehydroretinal are of interest from the viewpoints of analytical usage
and in understanding colour vision. The wavelength maximum values of the
visual pigments of a large series of fish species[42, 43] and other animals[42]
tend to cluster in the wavelength regions: 512, 523·5, 534 and 543 nm for
dehydroretinal-based fish pigments, at 478·5, 486·5, 494, 500·5, 506, 511·5
and 519 nm for retinal-based fish pigments, and at 492, 501·5, 519 and 528 nm
for retinal-based pigments from other animals. These wavelength changes
could be the result of extraconjugation at the N group or an interaction of
non-conjugated groups with the cationic resonance structures. For the study
of this red shift-effect the spectral absorption properties of some model
Schiff base hydrochlorides have been investigated.[23, 44–46]

The effect of solvent on the long wavelength maximum of N-all-*trans*-
retinylidine-*n*-butylamine, **I**, is shown in Table 51.[23]

I

The cation formed by protonation at the nitrogen atom absorbs at approximately 85 nm longer wavelength than **I** in the various solvents. The cation is
also formed on silica gel. **I** (10^{-4} M) is stated to fluoresce in EPA and 3-methyl-
pentane at 77°K at F350/485, Fig. 91.[23] The addition of a trace of acetic

Table 51. Absorption spectra of N-all-*trans*-retinylidene-*n*-butylamine in various solvents.[23]

Solvent	λ_{max}	λ_{max}	
		Solvent + acid	Solvent + SiO_2
Cyclohexane	361		398
Methanol	364[a]	448	
Benzene	366	459	438
CCl_4	368[b]	451	415[c]
Chloroform	371	461	470[c]
40 % aq. sodium xylene sulphonate	405	—	—

[a] λ 450 at $-68°$.
[b] λ 368 at $-70°$.
[c] At 2.09×10^{-6}. However, at 3.92×10^{-5} mol/g silica gel λ_{max} 415 and 485 nm.

Spectroscopic behaviour of retinal

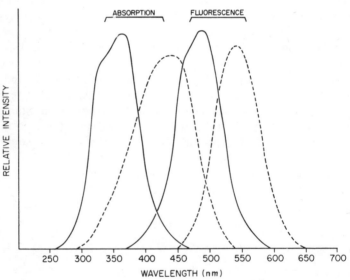

FIG. 91. Fluorescence emission spectra at 77°K of N-all-*trans*-retinylidene-*n*-butylamine (I) in : (———) 3-methylpentane; (– – – –) 3-methylpentane/silica gel.[23] Absorption spectra at room temperature.

acid shifts the fluorescence maximum to 540 nm. In the methylpentane/silica gel matrix (no added acid) **I** also shows a fluorescence maximum near 540 nm. However, the authors caution that this fluorescence could be an artifact of autooxidation.

The effect of hydroxylic solvents on the absorption spectra of some retinal Schiff bases has been investigated.[47–52] Schiff bases formed between retinal and aliphatic amines absorb in the range of 360 to 370 nm in aqueous solvents.[44] Upon acidification this maximum shifts to about 450 nm. The Schiff base of retinal and ethanolamine phosphoglyceride appears to be unique since it absorbs at 336 nm in chloroform–methanol.[47] It is believed that the propinquity of the phosphate group disturbs the electronic configuration at the C=N position sufficiently to favour the methanol over the C=N in the competition to hydrogen bond to water. It has been demonstrated that only in the presence of methanol are the spectra of the retinal Schiff bases consistent, even when protonated.[52] However, the unprotonated Schiff base formed by retinal and ethanolamine phosphoglyceride absorbs at 365 nm and, after protonation, at 450 nm in anhydrous chloroform. Addition of methanol shifts the long wavelength maximum to 500 nm. This chromogen appears to be the product of a $\pi \rightarrow \pi$ interaction between an unsaturated fatty acid component of ethanolamine phosphoglyceride and the retinal chain. The reaction does not occur unless methanol is present in the solvent.[50] The mε value of the chromogen absorbing at 500 nm is about twice that of the one absorbing near 338 nm.

The spectral shifts in the retinal Schiff base complexes with aniline derivatives have been investigated.[45] The absorption spectra of one of the Schiff base cations and of the starting products are shown in Fig. 92. It would appear that the extraconjugative effect of the phenyl grouping shifts the long wavelength band to the red with increasing electronegativity of the meta and para substituents in the phenyl group, Table 52. Or, as stated in the authors' words, "the λ_{max} values in the protonated Schiff bases are red shifted as the positive charge on the nitrogen increases due to the inductive effect of substituents in the meta and para positions".[45] The authors conclude that

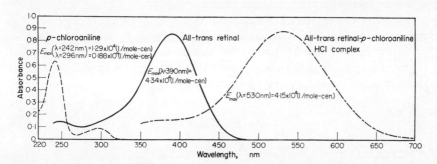

FIG. 92. Ultraviolet–visible absorption spectra of p-chloroaniline in hexane (-----), all-trans-retinal in chloroform (———), and the p-chloroaniline retinal hydrogen chloride Schiff's base complex in chloroform (—---—).[45]

Table 52. Effect of electron–acceptor strength of substituents in retinal Schiff base complexes.[45]

Aniline substituent	Para position in EtOH λ_{max}	in CHCl$_3$ λ_{max}	Meta position in EtOH λ_{max}
—CH$_3$	499[a]	517	505
—OH	500	520	506
—OCH$_3$	505	522	508
—H	504[b]	522	504
—Cl	512	530	514
—CO$_2$H	523[c]	542	510
—COCH$_3$	524	550	511
—CH	533	564	—
—NO$_2$	543	574	523

[a] λ 500 in aq ethanol acidified with HCl.[44]   [c] λ 530 in the above solvent.[44]
[b] λ 490 to 500 in the above solvent.[44]

the discontinuous spectra reported for the natural pigments may be the result of a discrete number of substituents near the protein chromophore which by inductive or field effects can change the positive charge on the nitrogen atom of the chromophore and shift the λ_{max} value. In analogy with rhodopsins these compounds absorb near λ_{max} 500 nm with an mε of approximately 50 l mol^{-1} cm^{-1}. Enamine compounds of retinal and secondary amines show a red shift in their absorption spectra of 75 to 100 nm merely by addition of HCl.[16, 39, 44]

Naturally occurring visual pigments based on retinal show absorption maxima over the range 440 to 620 nm. In a similar fashion the cationic resonance structures of the reaction products from retinal and a series of imines had absorption maxima ranging from 440 to 655 nm, Table 53.[46]

Like the 11-*cis* isomer, 9-*cis*-retinal reacts with various opsins; isopigments are formed. The wavelength maximum of a solution of 9-*cis* retinal in carbon tetrachloride is 372 nm. In the presence of indole and anhydrous HCl the maximum shifts to 585 nm with mε 16.[46] The mechanism of these various reactions with secondary amines is shown in Fig. 93.

IV. REAGENTS

A. Amines

Since amines give such vivid coloured chromogens with the retinals, they have been used in their analysis. p-Aminobenzoic acid and p-aminosalicylic acid have been used in the assay.[53] In the p-aminobenzoic acid method

Table 53. Spectral bands obtained from reaction of retinal
with secondary amines.[46]

Secondary amine	λ_{max} (neutral compound)[a]	λ_{max} (cation)
Piperidine	342	440
Pyrrolidine	357	445
Piperazine	350	470
Indoline	376	510, 570s
3-Pyrroline	330	475[b]
Diphenylamine	380	530
Indole	380	610
Carbazole	360, 380	620
Pyrrole	380	655

[a] Peaks typical of the secondary amine are not included.
[b] Subsidiary peaks at 378, 397 and 424 nm.

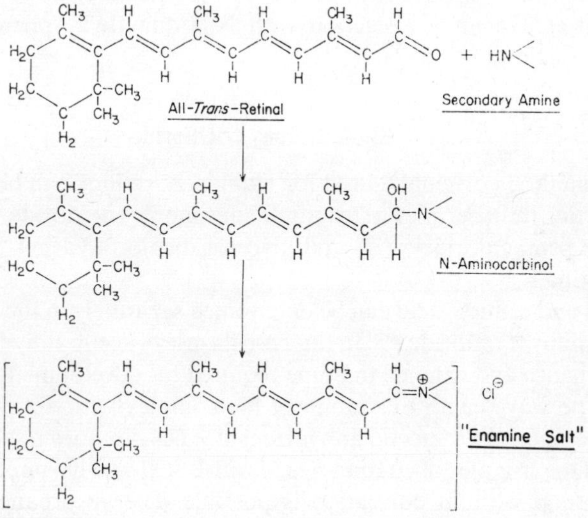

FIG. 93. Proposed reaction scheme of retinal with secondary amines to form an intermediate N-aminocarbinol which, upon protonation with HCl. forms an enamine salt.[46]

Beer's law is obeyed for 3–30 μg of retinal and 4–30 μg of 3-dehydroretinal, 5,6-monoepoxy-3-dehydroretinal or 5,6-monoepoxyretinal. Retinal gives an intense pink coloration, λ_{max} 530 nm, mε 47; 3-dehydroretinal an intense pink, λ_{max} 550 nm, mε 41; 5,6-epoxyretinal a yellow coloured derivative, λ_{max} 450 nm, mε 42; and 5,6-epoxy-3-dehydroretinal an intense pink coloration, λ_{max} 500 nm, mε 35. This colour is stable for 15 minutes. After 45 min in the dark there is a 10% loss in colour. The acetate, alcohol, acid and epoxy derivatives of vitamin A do not react. In the thiobarbituric acid method the absorbance reaches a maximum after 30 min whereas in this method only 10 min is necessary. Somewhat similar results are obtained with p-amino-salicylic acid as the reagent, except that millimolar absorptivities are a little lower.

Estimation of retinal. 3-dehydroretinal, 5,6-epoxyretinal, and 5,6-epoxy-3-dehydroretinal with p-*aminobenzoic acid or* p-*aminosalicylic acid.*[53] To 3 ml of ethanolic test solution add 1 ml of a 1% ethanolic solution of the amine followed by 1 ml of 2 N HCl. Shake and let stand in the dark for 10 minutes. Read the absorbance at the wavelength maximum.

A chloroform solution of retinal and excess o-aminophenol heated on the boiling water bath for about 10 s and then treated with a few drops of concentrated HCl gives a bright red colour which can be extracted into chloroform.[54]

The absorption spectrum of retinal in cyclohexane shows a wavelength maximum at 376 nm;[55] reaction with N,N-dimethyl-p-phenylenediamine shifts the maximum to 557 nm.[56]

B. Antimony trichloride

Many methods originally used for vitamin A, retinol, can be modified for use with the retinals.[57] For example, antimony trichloride,[1, 31, 32, 58–66] antimony pentachloride[27, 58] and glycerol dichlorohydrin[58] can be used for the retinals.

Retinal and retinoic acid can be determined separately in the same mixture with antimony trichloride.[65] In this case the use of acetic anhydride increases the absorbance and extends the time required for development of maximum colour. The wavelength maximum of the complex with antimony chloride (in the presence of 2% acetic anhydride) at λ 664 nm does not interfere with the λ_{max} of the complex of vitamin A acid with $SbCl_3$ at λ 474 nm. Simultaneous determination without correction is possible. The absorbances for retinal and retinoic acid are measured during the periods 2·3–4 s and 4–8 s, respectively, after the start of the reaction. With a microcell it is possible to measure 25 to 200 ng of retinal by reacting 0·05 ml of test solution with 0·2 ml of the antimony chloride reagent.[65]

The antimony chloride probably adds to the retinoic acid to form a zwitterion with a 9-C atom cationic resonance structure absorbing at λ 474 nm and adds to the retinal to form a zwitterion with a 12-C atom cationic resonance structure absorbing at 664 nm. The instability of these chromogens indicates that further reactions take place readily. Postulated

mechanisms for the reactions of retinal,[27] retinol,[66–68] aliphatic polyenes[69–72] and vitamin A related polyenes[73, 74] with various types of acids
are consistent with a carbonium ion explanation.

Another mechanism which has been postulated involves the reaction of
retinal with $SbCl_5$ (with and without acetyl chloride).[27] In chloroform the
aldehyde gave a band at λ_{max} 385 nm, mε 38·2. With the addition of $SbCl_3$
(containing small amounts of $SbCl_5$) and acetyl chloride the band shifted to
λ_{max} 660 nm, mε 95. The authors postulate the formation of a low energy
zwitterionic resonance structure stabilized as shown in II.

II

The reaction of 3-dehydroretinal with antimony trichloride has also been
investigated.[58] With purified antimony trichloride, 14% (w/w) in chloroform containing 2% (v/v) acetic anhydride the intensity of the long wavelength band of the green–blue colour produced with dehydroretinal increased
with concentration of the aldehyde and decreased with time. In the absence of
acetic anhydride, the long wavelength band of the chromogen was steady at
741 nm and did not fade for about 15 s. Beer's law was obeyed and $E_{1\,cm}^{1\%}$
at 741 nm was 4200.

Antimony chloride determination of 3-dehydroretinal.[58] Add 2 ml of 14%
$SbCl_3$ in chloroform to 0·5 ml of the chloroform test solution in a cuvette.
Immediately read the absorbance at 741 nm.

Antimony pentachloride in chloroform gave no colour reaction with
dehydroretinal. However, in the presence of acetic anhydride a band was
obtained near 700 nm but the $E_{1\,cm}^{1\%}$ was less than obtained with $SbCl_3$ and
the fading was much more rapid.

With the help of $SbCl_3$, retinal and 3-dehydroretinal can be determined in
the presence of each other.[75]

C. Glycerol dichlorohydrin

3-Dehydroretinal gives a blue–green colour with glycerol dichlorohydrin
(e.g. 1,3-dichloropropan-2-ol) which reaches maximum intensity in about
2 min and then begins to fade a few seconds later. With concentrations of the

aldehyde in the range of 0.27–$4.33\,\mu g\,ml^{-1}$, Beer's law is obeyed and the absorption maximum is constant at 618 nm. The average $E_{1\,cm}^{1\%}$ at 618 nm is 1340. Retinal reacted with glycerol dichlorohydrin gave a coloured product with λ_{max} 653 nm and a shoulder at 610 nm.

Glycerol dichlorohydrin determination of retinals.[58] To 2 ml of glycerol dichlorohydrin (distilled from its solution containing 2% $SbCl_3$) add 0·5 ml of chloroform test solution. Mix with a polythene rod. Read absorbance at wavelength maximum after standing for 2 minutes.

Carotenes and other polyenes react in these methods. This last method is less sensitive than the $SbCl_3$ methods.[76] In spite of these shortcomings retinal and retinol can be readily distinguished by the glycerol dichlorohydrin method since retinal gives a band at 660 nm while retinol has a band at 550 nm.[77]

D. 2,4-Dinitrophenylhydrazine

Retinal and 3-dehydroretinal can also be determined with 2,4-dinitrophenylhydrazine (DNPH) in the presence of retinol, retinyl acetate, retinoic acid and β-carotene. Other aldehydes would interfere.

DNPH determination of retinals.[78] To 1 ml of methanolic test solution containing 1 to 25 μg of the retinal add 1 ml of reagent (dissolve 200 mg of DNPH in 50 ml of carbonyl-free methanol, 8 ml of conc HCl and water to 100 ml). After reaction in the dark for 30 min add 1 ml each of pyridine–water (4:1) and 33% methanolic KOH. Read the absorbance at 525 nm.

p-Nitrophenylhydrazine could be used instead of DNPH. The consequent hydrazone would absorb at much longer wavelength and with greater intensity. In addition the hydrazone could be phosphorescent.

E. Hydroxylamine

Hydroxylamine has also been used in the analysis of the retinals. The absorption spectra of these oximes have been reported, Table 54.

Partial bleaching analyses of visual pigments are frequently carried out in the presence of hydroxylamine.[80–83] The unbleached pigment does not react with the hydroxylamine while the retinal or 3-dehydroretinal formed during the bleaching does react to form an oxime. These oximes have sharper bands than those of the direct photoproduct in alkaline solution. Consequently difference spectra obtained in this way involve less interference between pigment and photoproduct bands, thus giving more reliable indications of the wavelength maximum of the pigment.[80]

Table 54. Absorption spectra of retinal (A) and dehydroretinal (B) oximes[a]

Oxime	Solvent	λ_{max}	$m\varepsilon$	Ref.
A	2% Aq digitonin	367	(51·3)	79
A	Ethanol	358	(60·3)	39
		359	(57·5)	59
A[b]	n-Hexane	342s	(63)	29
		356	(63)	
A	Pet. ether	356	(58·9)	39
B	Ethanol	308	(16·2)	59
		377·5	(53·7)	

[a] Probably all-*trans*.
[b] And also spectra of 3-isomers.

F. Hydrazides

Hydrazides can also be used in the analysis of retinal. Thus, the iso-nicotinoyl- and nicotinoylhydrazides of retinal absorb at λ_{max} 396, $m\varepsilon$ 49 and λ_{max} 395, $m\varepsilon$ 53·7, respectively.[84]

G. Opsin

Several methods utilizing opsin (a protein of the retina) have been proposed for the determination of 9-*cis* and 9,13-di-*cis*-retinals.[31, 85, 86] Essentially, isorhodopsin, λ_{max} 487 nm, is formed. The only other isomer which reacts to any extent with opsin is the 11-*cis* isomer, which has been found only in the eye.[86]

In the procedure recoveries of 9-*cis*-retinal averaged $99 \pm 4\%$ within 2 h and with concentrations ranging from $0.222-0.909\,\mu g\,ml^{-1}$ of the final solution.[85] Recoveries of amounts less than $0.222\,\mu g\,ml^{-1}$ were high. Addition to the cell of all-*trans*-retinal or 13-*cis*-retinal had no effect on the analysis. About $29 \pm 3\%$ of 9,13-di-*cis*-retinal isomerized to 9-*cis*-retinal and formed isorhodopsin within 2 h; the formation of isorhodopsin was complete $(98 \pm 2\%)$ in 5–7 h. The average total recovery of $96 \pm 7\%$ for all known mixtures of the 9-*cis*- and 9,13-di-*cis*-retinals indicates the value of the technique for measuring total 9-*cis* isomers. The per cent of 9-*cis* isomers in a mixture can then be determined in conjunction with a determination of total retinal by reaction with antimony trichloride.

In the following procedure opsin is prepared from cattle retinas and is pretested with 11-*cis*-retinal. A solution of 2% digitonin dissolved in pH 6·8 phosphate buffer is used.

Opsin determination of 9-cis-*retinals*.[85] Work in red light. To 0·5 ml portions of excess opsin in the 2% digitonin solution contained in 2 cells add 0·5 ml of a test solution of the 9-*cis* retinals (0·12–0·45 µg) in the 2% digitonin solution. Mix and incubate in the dark for 2 h at 20–25°. Stop the reaction in cell I by adding 0·1 ml of freshly neutralized hydroxylamine (6·95% hydroxylamine hydrochloride in water). Add hydroxylamine to the control cell. After 15 min, read absorbance (*A*) of cell I at 487 nm. Remove control cell and cell I from spectrophotometer and bleach for 15 min in the light of a 160-watt tungsten lamp passed through Jena GG3 and Corning 3962 filter glasses to decrease ultraviolet and infrared radiation, respectively. Read absorbance (*A*) of cell I at 487 nm. The difference in *A* before and after bleaching cell I is called A_I. Follow same procedure for cell II after incubating for six hours. The difference in *A* before and after bleaching cell II is called A_{II}. Calculate the content of 9-*cis* isomers by assuming 100% reaction of 9-*cis*-retinal and 21% reaction of 9,13-di-*cis*-retinal (by isomerization to 9-*cis*-retinal)[86] in 2 h and 100% reaction of both isomers in 6 h:

$$\mu g\ 9,13\text{-di-}cis\text{-retinal} = \frac{1\cdot1 \times 10^4 (A_{II} - A_I)}{0\cdot79 \times 1\cdot25 \times 1017}$$

$$\mu g\ 9\text{-}cis\text{-retinal} = \frac{1\cdot1 \times 10^4 [(A_I) - [1\cdot27(A_{II} - A_I) - (A_{II} - A_I)]]}{1\cdot25 \times 1150}$$

where 0·79 is a correction for the fact that the equivalent of 21% of the 9,13-di-*cis*-retinal results in isorhodopsin after 2 h, 1·25 is the correction for the 25% increase in mε of isorhodopsin relative to that of the 9-cis isomers, 1017 is the $E_{1\,cm}^{1\%}$ at 377 nm of 9,13-di-*cis*-retinal in 2% digitonin solution, and 1150 is the $E_{1\,cm}^{1\%}$ of 9-*cis*-retinal.

The latter equation can be simplified to the following:

$$\mu g\ 9\text{-}cis\text{-retinal} = \frac{1\cdot1 \times 10^4 (1\cdot27 A_I - 0\cdot27 A_{II})}{1\cdot25 \times 1150}$$

No correction is made for the small apparent reaction of opsin with the all-*trans*- and 13-*cis*-retinals (about 0·5 to 1% with up to 80 µg in the cell).

MBTH or HBT could also prove useful in the analysis of the various retinals.

H. 2-Thiobarbituric acid

2-Thiobarbituric (TBA) acid has been used for the estimation of retinal in the presence of retinyl acetate, retinol, retinoic acid or β-carotene[87] as well as for the estimation of 3-dehydroretinal, 5,6-epoxyretinal and 5,6-epoxy-3-dehydroretinal.[88–90] The methods are stated to be capable of being directly employed for the estimation of the various aldehydes of vitamin A and epoxyvitamin A in ethanol extracts of tissues.

In the following procedure Beer's law is obeyed from 1 to 28 μg retinal. All-*trans*-, 9-*cis*- or 13-*cis*-retinal react with TBA to give λ_{max} 530 nm, mε 58.[87] The chromogen, **III**, is formed with all-*trans*-retinal. Colour development is retarded by the presence of water. In addition the absorption maximum

III

can shift up to 18 nm and fading will be greatly accelerated. When less than 1 ml of water is present in the final mixture, the wavelength maximum is around 528 to 536 nm and the error introduced by measurement at 530 nm is negligible. Ethanol is used in extraction of retinal from the retina because it is effective and the aldehyde is relatively stable in refrigerated ethanol extracts. Acetic acid is necessary to obtain quantitative extraction of the retinal. The use of thiourea helps to lessen the deleterious effects of water on colour development and greatly decreases the rate of fading in light. One milligram of retinol does not interfere with the formation of the chromogen from 10 μg of retinal. β-Carotene (100 μg) does not form a chromogen with TBA and does not hinder development of the colour from 10 μg of retinal. However, β-carotene has an mε of 0·85 at 530 nm. The TBA reagent may be used to analyse retinal on paper chromatograms (ascending, ethanol–water, 40:60). Spraying gave a violet spot with detection limit of 0·4 μg. The spot faded rapidly in light but was stable for several weeks in darkness. Ethanolic extracts of the calf, rat or rabbit could be assayed. No colour was obtained with extracts of skin, liver, intestine, kidney, brain, urine or blood from the rat or rabbit.

In some respects the TBA method is superior to the $SbCl_3$ method wherein a transitory blue colour is produced and corrections may be necessary for retinol,[31, 63, 64] the 1,3-dichloro-2-propanol method[91] wherein a fading green colour is obtained and a correction may be necessary for retinol[76] and the ultraviolet absorption method[31, 37] which is complicated by differences in the spectral properties of the various *cis* and *trans* isomers.

2-Thiobarbituric acid estimation of retinal.[87] To 3 ml of 90% ethanolic test solution (containing 2 to 20 μg of retinal) add 1 ml of 4% thiourea in glacial acetic acid, 1 ml of 0·6% TBA in absolute ethanol and mix well. Let stand in the dark at room temp for 30 minutes. Read absorbance at 530 nm.

Other reagents that could be used in the determination of the retinals include azulenes, carbazoles, indoles, pyrroles, lepidinium and quinaldinium salts, and polynuclear hydrocarbons.

REFERENCES

1. C. D. Robeson et al. J. Am. Chem. Soc. 77, 4120 (1955).
2. H. Langer, Ed., "Biochemistry and Physiology of Visual Pigments," Springer-Verlag, 1973.
3. G. Wald. Science 162, 230 (1968).
4. P. K. Brown and G. Wald. Science 144, 45 (1964).
5. W. B. Marks, W. H. Dobelle, E. F. MacNichol. Science 143, 1181 (1964).
6. P. K. Brown and G. Wald. Nature 200, 37 (1963).
7. P. A. Plack, S. K. Kon and S. Y. Thompson. Biochem. J. 71, 467 (1959).
8. G. Wald, P. K. Brown and P. H. Smith. J. Gen. Physiol. 38, 623 (1955).
9. G. Wald. J. Gen. Physiol. 19, 35 (1935).
10. R. A. Morton and T. W. Goodwin. Nature (London) 153, 405 (1944).
11. P. K. Brown and G. Wald. J. Biol. Chem. 222, 865 (1956).
12. R. Hubbard and R. C. C. St. George. J. Gen. Physiol. 41, 501 (1957–58).
13. H. J. A. Dartnall. The Visual Pigments , Wiley, New York (1957), pp. 122–123.
14. R. Hubbard and A. Kropf. Ann. N.Y. Acad. Sci. 81, 388 (1959).
15. F. D. Collins. Nature 171, 469 (1953).
16. R. A. Morton and G. A. J. Pitt. Biochem. J. 59, 128 (1955).
17. D. Bownds. Nature 216, 1178 (1967).
18. M. Akhtar, P. T. Blosse and P. B. Dewhurst. Chem. Comm. No. 450, 631 (1967).
19. D. Bownds. Federation Proc. 25, 787 (1966).
20. E. W. Abrahamson and J. R. Wiesenfeld, Presented at the 2nd International Symposium on the Biochemistry of the Eye, Nijmegen, Netherlands (1968).
21. J. R. Wiesenfeld and E. W. Abrahamson. Photochem. Photobiol. 8, 487 (1968).
22. S. Ball, T. W. Goodwin and R. A. Morton. Biochem. J. 42, 516 (1948).
23. C. S. Irving and P. A. Leermakers. Photochem. Photobiol. 7, 655 (1968).
24. H. A. M. Jacobs et al. Rec. Trav. Chim. 84, 1113 (1965).
25. W. Graham, D. A. van Dorp and J. F. Arens. Rec. Trav. Chim. 68, 609 (1949).
26. L. Jurkowitz. Nature 184, 614 (1959).
27. W. Krauss and H. Grund. Z. Elektrochem. 58, 142 (1954).
28. S. Ball and R. A. Morton. Biochem. J. 45, 298 (1949).
29. R. Hubbard. J. Am. Chem. Soc. 78, 4662 (1956).
30. J. M. Dieterle and C. D. Robeson. Science 120, 219 (1954).
31. R. Hubbard, R. Gregerman and G. Wald. J. Gen. Physiol. 36, 415 (1953).
32. H. R. Cama, P. D. Dalvi, R. A. Morton, M. K. Salah, G. H. Steinberg and A. L. Stubbs. Biochem. J. 52, 535 (1952).
33. M. K. Salah and R. A. Morton. Biochem. J. 43, LVI (1948).
34. K. R. Farrar, J. C. Hamlet, H. B. Jones. J. Chem. Soc. 2657 (1952).
35. U. Schwieter et al. Helv. Chim. Acta 45, 528 (1962).
36. U. Schwieter et al. Helv. Chim. Acta 45, 517 (1962).
37. O. R. Braekkan, H. Myklestad and L. R. Njaa. Acta Chem. Scand. 14, 779 (1960).
38. D. E. Balke and R. S. Becker. J. Am. Chem. Soc. 89, 5061 (1967).

39. G. A. J. Pitt, F. D. Collins, R. A. Morton and P. Stok. *Biochem. J.* **59**, 122 (1955).
40. M. Akhtar, P. T. Blosse and P. B. Dewhurst. *Chem. Commun.* **631** (1967).
41. C. D. B. Bridges. *Nature* **203**, 303 (1964).
42. H. J. A. Dartnall and J. N. Lythgoe. *Vision Research* **5**, 81 (1965).
43. C. D. B. Bridges. *Cold Spring Harbor Symposia Quant. Biol.* **30**, 317 (1965).
44. S. Ball, F. D. Collins, P. D. Dalvi and R. A. Morton. *Biochem. J.* **45**, 304 (1949).
45. B. Rosenberg and T. M. Krigas. *Photochem. Photobiol.* **6**, 769 (1967).
46. J. Troth and B. Rosenberg. *Vision Res.* **8**, 1471 (1968).
47. N. E. Sharpless, R. G. Adams and W. H. Jennings. *Trans. N.Y. Acad. Sci.* **35**, 547 (1973).
48. F. J. M. Dalmen and S. L. Bonting. *Nature* **222**, 879 (1969).
49. R. G. Adams, W. H. Jennings and N. E. Sharpless, *Nature* **226**, 270 (1970).
50. N. E. Sharpless, R. G. Adams and W. H. Jennings. *Photochem. Photobiol.* **13**, 21 (1971).
51. P. A. Plack and D. J. Pritchard. *Biochem. J.* **115**, 927 (1969).
52. P. E. Blatz, N. Baumgardner, V. Balasubramaniyan, P. Balasubramaniyan and E. Stedman. *Photochem. Photobiol.* **14**, 531 (1971).
53. A. K. Mallia and H. R. Cama. *Anal. Biochem.* **30**, 86 (1969).
54. S. Thabet and O. Tabibian. *Clin. Chim. Acta* **13**, 393 (1966).
55. N. L. Wendler, C. Rosenblum and M. Tishler. *J. Am. Chem. Soc.* **72**, 234 (1950).
56. S. Hunig and J. Utermann. *Chem. Ber.* **88**, 1201 (1955).
57. N. D. Embree, S. R. Ames, R. W. Lehman and P. L. Harris in D. Glick, Ed., Methods of Biochemical Analysis, Vol. 4, Interscience Publishers Inc., New York, 1957, p. 43.
58. P. A. Plack. *Biochem. J.* **81**, 556 (1961).
59. K. R. Farrar, J. C. Hamlet, H. B. Henbest and E. R. H. Jones. *J. Chem. Soc.* 2657 (1952).
60. J. Bruggemann, N. Kraus and J. Tiews. *Z. Anal. Chem.* **135**, 241 (1952).
61. G. Wald. *J. Gen. Physiol.* **22**, 391 (1938–1939).
62. F. H. Wilt. *Developmental Biol.* **1**, 199 (1959).
63. N. I. Krinsky. *J. Biol. Chem.* **232**, 881 (1958).
64. J. E. Dowling. *Nature* **188**, 114 (1960).
65. A. A. Dmitrovskiĭ and G. V. Eremina. *Biochimiya* **32**, 1209 (1967).
66. P. E. Blatz and A. Estrada. *Anal. Chem.* **44**, 570 (1972).
67. P. E. Blatz, N. Baumgardner, V. Balasubramaniyan, P. Balasubramaniyan and E. Stedman. *Photochem. Photobiol.* **14**, 49 (1971).
68. P. E. Blatz and D. L. Pippert. *J. Am. Chem. Soc.* **90**, 1296 (1968).
69. T. S. Sorenson. *Can. J. Chem.* **42**, 2768 (1964).
70. T. S. Sorenson. *J. Am. Chem. Soc.* **87**, 5075 (1965).
71. N. C. Deno, C. U. Pittman, Jr. and J. O. Turner. *J. Am. Chem. Soc.* **87**, 2153 (1965).
72. N. C. Deno, H. G. Richey, Jr., N. Friedman, J. D. Hodge, J. J. Houser and C. U. Pittman, Jr. *J. Am. Chem. Soc.* **85**, 2991 (1963).
73. P. E. Blatz, D. L. Pippert and V. Balasubramaniyan. *Photochem. Photobiol.* **8**, 209 (1968).
74. P. E. Blatz, D. L. Pippert, L. Sherman and V. Balasubramaniyan. *J. Chem. Educ.* **46**, 512 (1969).
75. P. A. Plack and S. K. Kon. *Biochem. J.* **81**, 561 (1961).
76. C. J. Pollard and J. G. Bieri. *Biochim. Biophys. Acta* **31**, 558 (1959).
77. S. R. Ames, W. J. Swanson, H. A. Risley and P. L. Harris. *Federation Proc.* **13**, 174 (1954).

78. J. John, A. K. Mallia and H. R. Cama. *Indian J. Biochem.* **7**, 138 (1970).
79. G. Wald and P. K. Brown. *Science* **127**, 222 (1958).
80. H. J. A. Dartnall. *Vision Res.* **7**, 1 (1967).
81. F. Crescitelli. *J. Gen. Physiol.* **39**, 423 (1956).
82. F. Crescitelli. *J. Gen. Physiol.* **40**, 217 (1956).
83. F. Munz. *J. Gen. Physiol.* **40**, 233 (1956).
84. T. Miki and Y. Hara. *Chem. Pharm. Bull.* (*Japan*) **10**, 922 (1962).
85. D. C. Herting, E. E. Drury and P. L. Harris. *Anal. Biochem.* **4**, 459 (1962).
86. P. S. Brown, W. P. Blum and M. H. Stern. *Nature* **184**, 1377 (1959).
87. S. Futterman and L. D. Saslaw. *J. Biol. Chem.* **236**, 1652 (1961).
88. A. K. Mallia, M. R. Lakshmanan, K. V. John and H. R. Cama. *Biochem. J.* **111**, 23 (1969).
89. M. R. Lakshmanan, F. B. Jungalwala and H. R. Cama. *Biochem. J.* **95**, 27 (1965).
90. M. R. Lakshmanan, C. S. Vaidyanathan and H. R. Cama. *Biochem. J.* **90**, 569 (1964).
91. A. E. Sobel and S. D. Snow. *J. Biol. Chem.* **171**, 617 (1947).

58. SALICYLALDEHYDE

I. PHYSICAL PROPERTIES

M.p. 1·6, b.p. 197°, $D_{20}^{20} = 1·1690$, $n_D{}^{20} = 1·574$, $n_D{}^{25} = 1·5017$. Volatile in steam. Slightly soluble in water and soluble in alcohol and ether.

II. ABSORPTIOMETRIC PROPERTIES

Since salicylaldehyde has a hydroxyl group conjugated to a formyl group and bound to it by an intramolecular hydrogen bond, its photometric properties can be very useful in characterization and assay. In Table 55 are shown the absorption spectra of salicylaldehyde in various solvents. The spectra are characteristic of salicylaldehyde showing three to four bands in neutral solution dependent on the polarity of the solvent. The anion absorbs approximately 50 nm further into the visible than does the neutral compound. With increasing basicity of the solvent the anion absorbs at ever longer wavelengths with increasing intensity. Examples of these large shifts in wavelength and intensity are shown by the long wavelength band of salicylaldehyde in a non-polar solvent and a highly basic mixture, Fig. 94.

III. FLUORESCENCE PROPERTIES

The fluorescent properties of the salicylaldehyde anion can be used in the analysis of this aldehyde. The determination limit for salicylaldehyde in alkaline dimethylformamide is 3 ng, Fig. 95. In the same solvent mixture m- and p-hydroxybenzaldehyde, m- and p-hydroxyacetophenone and o-, m- and p-hydroxybenzophenone are non-fluorescent. Salicylic acid, m-hydroxy-

251

benzoic acid, and *o*-hydroxyacetophenone are fluorescent in the same solvent. Salicylaldehyde is also fluorescent in alkaline solutions of methanol and dioxane. The fluorescence excitation and emission spectra of 5 ng of salicylaldehyde anion, 10 ng of *o*-hydroxyacetophenone anion and 100 ng of 2-hydroxy-1-naphthaldehyde can be obtained on paper.

Table 55. Ultraviolet absorption spectra of salicylaldehyde in various solvents.

Solvent	λ_{max}	mε			Ref.
Water	255, 323				1
0·1 N HCl	221, 256, 324	19·1, 12·6,	3·4		2
Aqueous acid[a]	210, 255, 324	17·4, 11·2,	3·0		3
Ethanol	255, 276, 325	10,	0·63, 3·0		4–6
Ethanol[b]	255, 325	12,	3·6		7
Dioxane	256, 326	11·5,	3·6		11
Ether	218, 251s, 256, 325	15·1, 10·5, 10·7,	3·5		12
n-Hexane	215, 250, 257, 325	17, 11, 11·8,	3·6		12–14
Hexane	255, 270, 328	10,	0·11, 3·2		6
Hexane[c]	255, 259, 330	12·6, 12·6,	4·0		15
Pentane	251, 257, 328	11·0, 12·0,	3·8		d
Dimethylformamide	265, 330	—,	3·5		
0·1 N NaOH	226, 265, 377[e]	18·2, 7·6,	6·8		2
pH 13	265, 376	8·3,	6·2		18
Ethanolic KOH	230, 265, 382	18·6, 7·2,	6·9		7
DMF–TEA[f]	265, 407	8·7,	9·0		d

[a] The isomer 4-hydroxybenzaldehyde absorbs at λ 221 and 283 nm with mε 11·5 and 15·9, respectively, in aq acid.[3]

[b] Salicylaldehyde recommended as a standard to calibrate ultraviolet spectrophotometers with an mε of 3·662 at λ 326 nm in ethanol.[8] Unfortunately, values ranging from λ 254, 324·5 with mε 12·3, 4·4, respectively,[9] to λ 260, 330 with mε 7·9, 3·2, respectively,[10] in ethanol have been reported.

[c] Salicylaldehyde in hexane λ_{max} 328·5 nm, mε 3·23 while 2-methoxybenzaldehyde has λ_{max} 310 nm, mε 5·6.[16]

[d] See Fig. 94.

[e] λ 382 nm, mε 7·1 in 0·1 N NaOH[17] and λ 378 nm, mε 5·5 in aq alkali[4] also reported.

[f] Dimethylformamide containing 2% of 10% aq tetraethylammonium hydroxide.

In the fluorimetric analysis of salicylaldehyde anion and other fluorescent anions, concentration and quenching effects and the effect of solvent basicity on fluorescence intensities and wavelength positions of the excitation and emission maxima must be appreciated for proper use of this technique. For example, consider the concentration effect on the excitation spectrum of salicylaldehyde in Fig. 96. The bands at 363 and 450 nm are spurious. The minimum at 410 nm actually is the excitation band inverted.

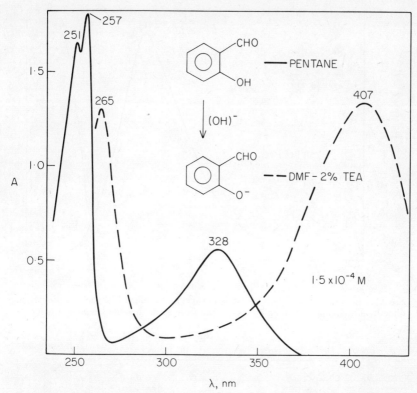

FIG. 94. Absorption spectra of salicylaldehyde ($1\cdot5 \times 10^{-4}$ M) in pentane (———) and in dimethylformamide containing 2% of 10% aqueous tetraethylammonium hydroxide.

IV. QUENCHOFLUORIMETRY

Quenching phenomenon can also prove useful in the analysis of salicyl-aldehyde and analogous molecules. Thus, in methanol–nitromethane (1:1) containing a few per cent of 29% tetraethylammonium hydroxide, salicyl-aldehyde and its 5-methyl-, 5-bromo- and 6-methoxy- derivatives fluoresce under ultraviolet light with a brilliant green colour. o-Methoxybenzalde-hyde and benzanthrone have green and blue–green fluorescences, respectively, while o-hydroxyacetophenone fluoresces with a light green intensity. The following usually fluorescent compounds do not fluoresce in this alkaline solvent : salicylic acid and its isomers, 1-hydroxy-2-naphthoic acid, 2-hydroxy-1-naphthoic acid, 4-hydroxyxanthone, 1-aminopyrene, carbazole, acridine, benzo[a]pyrene, benzo[e]pyrene, and perylene.

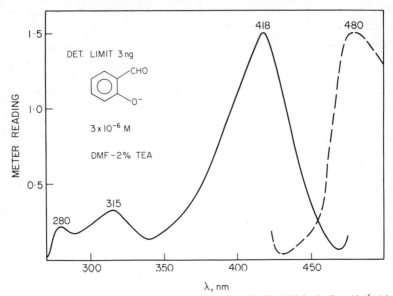

FIG. 95. Fluorescence excitation and emission spectra of salicylaldehyde (3×10^{-6} M) in dimethylformamide containing 2% of 10% aqueous tetraethylammonium hydroxide.

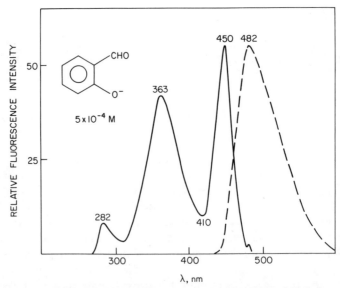

FIG. 96. Fluorescence excitation (spurious) and emission spectra of salicylaldehyde (5×10^{-4} M) in dimethylformamide containing 1% of 29% methanolic tetraethylammonium hydroxide. Concentration effect causes inversion of excitation spectra.

On the other hand, in 1,1-dimethylhydrazine containing about 1% of 29% methanolic tetraethylammonium hydroxide the fluorescences of sali-cylaldehyde as well as those of 6-methoxysalicylaldehyde, acridine, anthra-cene, pyrene, fluoranthene, benzo[a]pyrene, benzo[e]pyrene, carbazole and perylene are quenched. The following compounds are still fluorescent in this media: 5-bromosalicylaldehyde, o-hydroxyacetophenone, salicylic acid and the 1,2-hydroxynaphthoic acids.

Examination of the results obtained with just these two solvent systems shows the exciting possibilities of expanded use of quenchofluorimetry in trace analysis. Particularly striking is the non-fluorescence of salicylic acid and the fluorescence of salicylaldehyde in the alkaline nitromethane solution and the non-fluorescence of salicylaldehyde and the fluorescence of salicylic acid in the alkaline dimethylhydrazine solution. The lack of fluorescence of salicylaldehyde in dimethylhydrazine solution is probably due to the forma-tion of non-fluorescent **I**.

I

$$\text{CH}=\text{N}-\text{N(CH}_3)_2$$
(with O⁻ group)

V. PHOSPHORESCENCE

Salicylaldehyde and its derivatives and isomers can also phosphoresce. Thus in EPA at 77°K salicylaldehyde can be determined at $P330/435$. The compound has excitation and emission bands at $P260$, 285s, 330/410, 435, 455s. The determination limit is about 1 ng of salicylaldehyde. The phos-phorescent method of analysis is probably not as selective as is the fluorescence procedure since hydroxybenzoic acids and a large number of hydroxy-phenylcarbonyl compounds phosphoresce.

VI. REAGENTS

A. Aluminium salts

Analytical use can be made of the known chelating effect of aluminium with compounds containing ortho-hydroxycarbonyl groups.[19] When 0·5 ml of 0·6% ethanolic aluminium chloride is added to 2·5 ml of an alcoholic test solution containing salicylaldehyde, the wavelength shifts from 323 nm to 376 nm. Hydroxybenzoic acids and other hydroxybenzaldehydes show minor shifts in wavelength.

Salicylaldehyde can also be determined through the fluorescence obtained by treatment with aluminium chloroisopropylate in ethanol.[20] Salicylate and methyl salicylate interfere since they also fluoresce, but with an appropriate quenching agent this interference could be cancelled.

B. Boric acid

Boric acid is a reagent which can be used in the fluorimetric analysis of salicylaldehyde and other o-hydroxyphenylketones.[21] These compounds reacted with boric acid in acetic anhydride form a fluorogen consisting of ligand–boric acid (molar ratio 1:1). The relative fluorescence intensities obtained with some of these compounds by the following procedure are given in Table 56.

Table 56. Fluorescence characteristics of the chelates of salicylaldehydes and o-hydroxyphenylketones with boric acid.[21]

$$\underset{R_1}{\overset{OH}{\bigcirc}} \overset{\displaystyle C-R_2}{\underset{\displaystyle O}{\|}}$$

| Substituent | | $Conc = 2 \times 10^{-6}$ M | |
R_1	R_2	$F_{exc/em}$	RFI[a]
H	H	388/495	43
4-OH	H	310/446	231
		360/466	48
5-OH	H	403/525	15
3-OCH$_3$	H	428[b]	0
3,5-di Br	H	426[b]	0
4-OH	—CH$_2$C$_6$H$_5$	314/455	673[c]
		358/455	241
4-OH	—CH$_3$	305/447	662
		355/447	214
H	—C$_2$H$_5$	380/473	289
H	—CH$_3$	380/473	256
4-OCH$_3$	—C$_6$H$_5$	328/530	142
		375s/530	31

[a] Relative fluorescence intensity. Quinine sulphate = 1000 at $F347/452$.
[b] Ultraviolet wavelength maxima.
[c] Medium consisted of 8 volumes of acetic anhydride and 2 volumes of 5% boric acid in acetic anhydride (w/v).

Boric acid determination of salicylaldehyde and other o-hydroxyphenyl-ketones.[21] To 9 ml of the acetic anhydride test solution add 1 ml of 5% boric acid in acetic anhydride. Allow the mixture to react for 30 min at 20 to 25°.

Read the fluorescence intensity (for salicylaldehyde) at $F390/490$. Beer's law is obeyed from 10^{-7} to 4×10^{-6} M salicylaldehyde.

C. Nitrophenylhydrazines

Salicylaldehyde could also be characterized and determined by 2,4-dinitrophenylhydrazine or other nitrophenylhydrazines. Thus, the pure dinitrophenylhydrazone of salicylaldehyde absorbs at λ 381 nm. mε 29·5,[22] mε 27·5[23] in chloroform, at λ 387 nm, mε 29·5 in ethanol,[24] and at λ 475 nm, mε 35·5 in ethanolic chloroform containing sodium ethoxide.[22] This dinitrophenylhydrazone would have to be separated from other dinitrophenylhydrazones because of their interference, as can be seen from the spectral data for the dinitrophenylhydrazone of 4-hydroxybenzaldehyde: λ 395 nm, mε 28·8 in ethanol and λ 482 nm, mε 32·4 in ethanolic 0·12 N KOH.[24]

The nitrophenylhydrazones of salicylaldehyde could also prove to be of some value. Their spectral data in ethanol has been reported, e.g. o-nitrophenylhydrazone, λ_{max} 340, 435 and mε 12·6, 10, respectively; m-nitrophenylhydrazone, λ_{max} 242, 340, 430s and mε 15·9, 20, 1, respectively; and p-nitrophenylhydrazone, λ_{max} 300, 322, 408 and mε 6·3, 6·3, 15·9, respectively.[25]

D. Hydrazines

Hydrazine reacts with salicylaldehyde in alkaline solution to form a green–yellow fluorescent azine, **II**.

II

This compound fluoresces at $F350/465$ in ethanol containing about 1% of 29% methanolic tetraethylammonium hydroxide. About 2 ng of the azine can be determined fluorimetrically. It has been reported to fluoresce at $F394/493$ in methanolic 0·15 M HClO$_3$ and at $F362/362/535$ in toluene.[26] The azines of salicylaldehyde and its derivatives and analogues have been shown to fluoresce yellow to orange in the solid state.[27] This property could be made use of in direct fluorimetric analysis of spots on chromatograms. It has been shown that trace amounts of salicylaldehyde and other o-hydroxyarylcarbonyl compounds give intense yellow orange fluorescent spots with hydrazine.[28] An aqueous solution containing 5% hydrazine sulphate and 10% sodium acetate is used as the reagent.

Another hydrazine derivative that could be used to determine salicylaldehyde spectrophotometrically and probably fluorimetrically is MBTH.

E. Picolinium and analogous salts

Picolinium, lepidinium and quinolium salts could also be used to determine salicylaldehyde. For example, with 1-methyl-2-picolinium iodide the chromogen, III, would be obtained.

III

Pure III absorbs at λ 598, mε 30·0 in benzene, λ 586, mε 36·3 in chloroform, and λ 494, mε 20·0 in ethanol.[29] Proton addition to the oxygen shifts these bands to much shorter wavelengths, e.g. in acidic ethanol λ_{max} 359 nm, mε 9·6.

F. Salicyloylhydrazide

Salicylaldehyde forms a salicyloylhydrazone, IV, which fluoresces at $F$390/470.[30]

IV

The salicyloylhydrazone of p-hydroxybenzaldehyde and p-dimethylaminobenzaldehyde also fluoresced at $F$390/470. The reagent, salicyloylhydrazide· fluoresces maximally at $F$350/425. The aldehyde can be treated with the reagent in 0·1 M carbonate–bicarbonate buffer at pH 10.

The fluorescence of IV was sufficiently different from that of the reagent so that its fluorescence spectrum could be obtained directly in a reaction mixture after adjustment of pH, without interference from excess reagent. If necessary, IV could be separated from the reagent by partition between purified methylene chloride and 20% ethanol, 0·1 M in HCl. The reagent remains in the aqueous phase.

REFERENCES

1. P. W. Alexander and R. J. Sleet. *Aust. J. Chem.* **23**, 1183 (1970).
2. L. Doub and J. M. Vandenbelt. *J. Am. Chem. Soc.* **71**, 2414 (1949).
3. C. Postmus, Jr. *et al. J. Org. Chem.* **29**, 2693 (1964).
4. R. A. Morton and A. L. Stubbs. *J. Chem. Soc.* 1347 (1940).
5. N. J. Leonard, R. T. Rapala, H. L. Herzog and E. R. Blout. *J. Am. Chem. Soc.* **71**, 2997 (1949).
6. N. A. Valyashko and N. N. Valyashko. *Zhur. Obshchei Khim.* **18**, 1113 (1948).
7. H. W. Lemon. *J. Am. Chem. Soc.* **69**, 2998 (1947).
8. J. M. Vandenbelt, J. Forsyth and A. Garrett. *Ind. Eng. Chem., Anal. Ed.* **17**, 235 (1945).
9. A. Burawoy and J. T. Chamberlain. *J. Chem. Soc.* 2310 (1952).
10. P. Grammaticakis. *Bull. Soc. Chim. France* **20**, 821 (1953).
11. D. Heinert and A. E. Martell. *J. Am. Chem. Soc.* **85**, 183 (1963).
12. J. C. Dearden and W. F. Forbes. *Can. J. Chem.* **38**, 1837 (1960).
13. J. C. Dearden and W. F. Forbes. *Can. J. Chem.* **38**, 896 (1960).
14. J. C. Dearden and W. F. Forbes. *Can. J. Chem.* **37**, 1294 (1959).
15. A. Bertoluzza and A. M. Marinangeli. *Ann. Chim. (Rome)* **52**, 731 (1962).
16. A. Burawoy and J. T. Chamberlain. *J. Chem. Soc.* 3734 (1952).
17. N. Melchior. *J. Am. Chem. Soc.* **71**, 3647 (1949).
18. B. E. Dawson and T. Henshall. *J. Phys. Chem.* **67**, 1187 (1963).
19. T. Swain. *Chem. Ind.* 1480 (1954).
20. I. Simonyi and G. Tokár. *Magyar Kém. Folyóirat.* **63**, 210 (1957).
21. T. Shibazaki and T. Nishimura. *Yakugaku Zasshi* **90**, 413 (1970).
22. L. A. Jones, J. C. Holmes and R. B. Seligman. *Anal. Chem.* **28**, 191 (1956).
23. G. D. Johnson. *J. Am. Chem. Soc.* **75**, 2720 (1953).
24. J. D. Roberts and C. Green. *J. Am. Chem. Soc.* **68**, 214 (1946).
25. P. Grammaticakis. *Bull. Soc. Chim. France* **21**, 1372 (1954).
26. A. Weller and H. Wolf. *Ann.* **657**, 64 (1962).
27. H. Wolf and O. Westphal. *Ann.* **657**, 39, 52 (1962).
28. F. Feigl and V. Anger. "Spot Tests in Organic Analysis," 7th ed., Elsevier Publishing Co., Amsterdam, 1966, p. 341.
29. J. P. Saxena, B. K. Tak and T. N. Agrawal. *J. Indian Chem. Soc.* **49**, 255 (1972).
30. P. S. Chen, Jr. *Anal. Chem.* **31**, 296 (1959).

59. STREPTOMYCIN

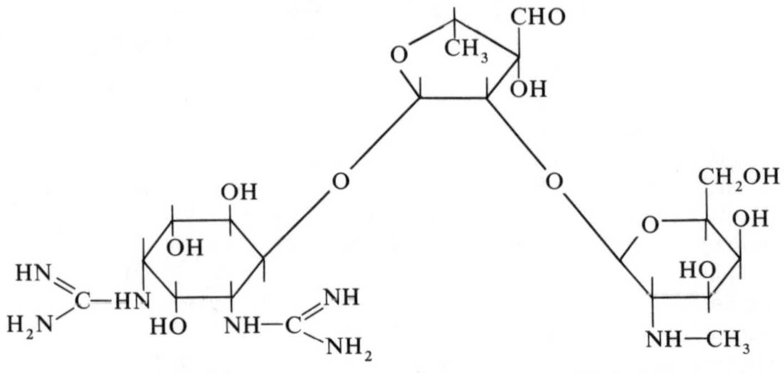

Streptidine   Streptose   Methylglucosamine

I. INTRODUCTION

Streptomycin, an antibiotic obtained from *Streptomyces griseus*, is composed of 3 components as shown above. Its pharmacological properties have been discussed.[1]

In 0·1 N alkali streptomycin absorbs at λ 325, mϵ 5·0.[2]

Methods have been developed for streptomycin based on it being a monosubstituted guanidine.[3-5] However compounds containing other guanidino groups would react. Chemicals like tris(hydroxymethyl)amino-methane, glycylglycine and some amino acids also interfere even in very low concentrations.

Since streptomycin is an aldehyde it can undergo many of the reactions described in the aliphatic aldehyde sections.

II. REAGENTS

A. Hydrazines

Some of the reagents which have been used to determine this aldehyde include 4-[4-(p-chlorophenylazo)-1-naphthyl]semicarbazide, **I**,[6] 2,4-di-nitrophenylhydrazine,[7] 9-hydrazinoacridine, **II**,[8] and 2-thiobarbituric acid.[9]

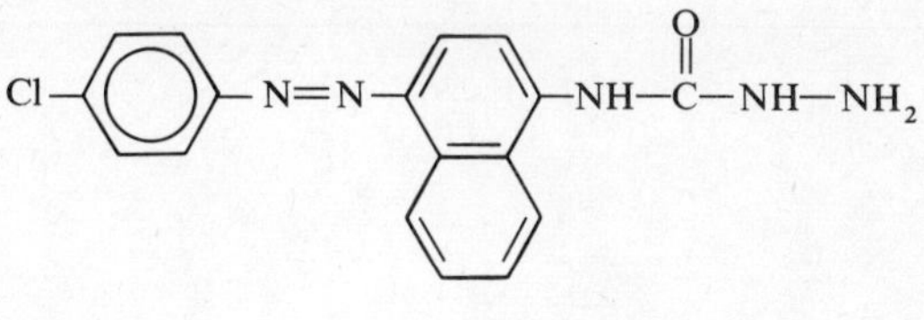

$$Cl-\langle\bigcirc\rangle-N{=}N-\bigcirc{-}NH{-}\overset{\displaystyle O}{\underset{\displaystyle \|}{C}}{-}NH{-}NH_2$$

I

$$\overset{\displaystyle NH{-}NH_2}{\bigcirc}$$

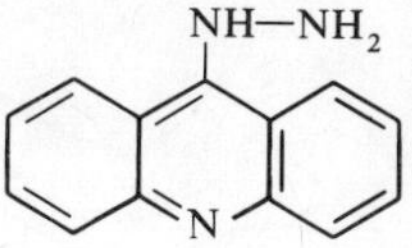

II

In the semicarbazide procedure the excess reagent is extracted with chloroform, hydrochloric acid is added to the remaining solution, and the colour, which develops immediately and is stable for 1 h, is read at 580 nm. Dihydrostreptomycin and streptobiosamine do not interfere.

Streptomycin forms a yellow hydrazone in acid solution upon reaction with 2,4-dinitrophenylhydrazine.[7] Excess reagent is extracted with butyl acetate and the absorbance is determined at 430 nm. While other aldehydes interfere, sugars and amino sugars do not. 4-Nitrophenylhydrazine could also be used here; the final chromogen would absorb at longer wavelengths and with greater intensity than the dinitrophenylhydrazone.

Hydrazone formation can also be the basis of a fluorimetric assay.[8] The fluorogen is the 9-acridinehydrazone of streptomycin formed from 9-hydrazinoacridine. The reagent is also fluorescent and has to be separated from the fluorogen. The excess reagent, in addition to the hydrazones of acidic, neutral and weakly basic compounds, is separated from the strongly basic streptomycin hydrazone by extraction from acid solution with benzyl alcohol. The solution is then assayed fluorimetrically.

B. 2-Thiobarbituric acid

The oxidation product of streptomycin reacts with TBA to give a chromogen absorbing at λ 415.[9] This maximum is absent from spectra of other compounds tested, including deoxy sugars, streptidin, N-acetylglucosamine, sucrose and ribose, Fig. 97.

Reproducibility results are claimed in the following method. The colour is stable for at least an hour. Beer's law is followed from 15 to 200 $\mu g\,ml^{-1}$.

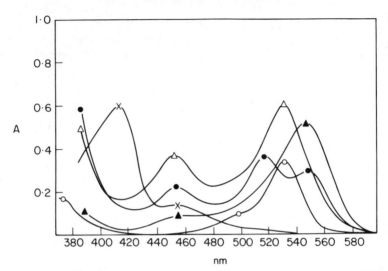

FIG. 97. Spectra of the chromogens arising from streptomycin and from some other compounds by the thiobarbituric acid method. Streptomycin, $100 \mu g \, ml^{-1}$ (— × —); 2-deoxy-D-glucose, $100 \mu g \, ml^{-1}$ (—○—); N-acetylglucosamine, $100 \mu g \, ml^{-1}$ (▲); streptidine, $100 \mu g \, ml^{-1}$ (no colour); sucrose, $10 \, mg \, ml^{-1}$ (△); ribose, $1 \, mg \, ml^{-1}$ (●).[9]

TBA determination of streptomycin.[9] *Reagent:* Dissolve 3 g of thiobarbituric acid in about 700 ml of water and 30 ml of 1 N NaOH, adjust pH to 2 with 1 N HCl, and dilute to 1 l with water.

Procedure. Mix 1·5 ml of test solution containing 15 to 300 μg streptomycin with 0·05 ml of 0·1 M potassium metaperiodate in 1 N H_2SO_4. After 15 min incubation at 37°, add with shaking 0·5 ml of 2% sodium arsenite in 0·5 N HCl. After disappearance of the brownish colour add 1 ml of 0·3% TBA reagent. Heat at 100° for 10 minutes. Cool and read absorbance at 415 nm. The milli-molar absorptivity obtained for streptomycin is 17·6.

REFERENCES

1. W. C. Cutting. "Handbook of Pharmacology," Appleton-Century-Crofts, New York, 1969, p. 53.
2. J. Fried and E. Titus. *J. Am. Chem. Soc* **70**, 3615 (1948).
3. S. Sakaguchi. *J. Biochem. Tokyo* **5**, 25 (1925).
4. H. Rosenberg, H. Ennor and J. F. Morrison. *Biochem. J.* **63**, 153 (1956).
5. I. Szilagyi and I. Szabo. *Nature (London)* **181**, 52 (1958).
6. E. K. Marshall, Jr., K. C. Blanchard and E. L. Buhle. *J. Pharmacol. Exp. Therapy* **90**, 367 (1947).

7. E. M. Savitskaya and V. I. Kartseva. *Zhur. Anal. Khim.* **8**, (1953); through *Chem. Abstr.* **47**, 5070 (1953).
8. G. E. Boxer and V. C. Jelinek. *J. Biol. Chem.* **170**, 491 (1947).
9. E. Duda. *Anal. Biochem.* **51**, 651 (1973).

60. SUCCINALDEHYDE

$$OHC—CH_2—CH_2—CHO$$

I. PHYSICAL PROPERTIES

B.p. 169–170° dec, 56·5° at 9 mm; D_4^{18} 1·069; n_D^{18} 1·42617. Polymerizes readily.

II. PREPARATION

Microamounts of this aldchyde could be prepared through the hydrolysis of furan.[1] However, for calibration purposes succinaldehyde is best prepared in excellent yield during or just before analysis through the complete hydrolysis within 30 min of pure 2,5-dimethoxytetrahydrofuran in aq 0·1 N sulphuric acid.

Since the treatment of 1,2-*cis*-cyclododecanediol with MnO_2 in methylene chloride for 4 h gives an 85% yield of 1,12-dodecanedial,[2] succinaldehyde could probably be obtained from 1,2-*cis*-cyclobutanediol.

III. REAGENTS

A. 4-Dimethylaminobenzaldehydes

A colorimetric[3] and a fluorimetric[3] method are available for the determination of succinaldehyde and its precursors. In the colorimetric method a standard deviation of $\pm 2·5\%$ is obtained. The colour fades by approximately 8% in 18 minutes. The calibration curve deviates slightly from Beer's law. The specificity of the method is shown in Table 57. Although pyrrole was the only notable interference, indole and azulene would also be expected to react. These interferences are of slight importance in the determination of succinaldehyde and its precursors since they would probably not be found in substantial amounts in succinaldehyde-polluted environments. No loss in sensitivity was found when formaldehyde was present in amounts five times greater than succinaldehyde. Replacement of *p*-dimethylamino-benzaldehyde with *p*-dimethylaminocinnamaldehyde gave a band at λ 628 nm with mε of 50. Spectra obtained in the procedure are shown in Fig. 98.

Table 57. Interference in the photometric procedure.[3]

Compound studied	Wavelength maximum (nm)	mε liters per μmol cm	Absorbance[a]
Succinaldehyde	546	71	0·71[b]
Pyrrole	546	35	0·35[b]
Acetaldehyde	—	—	0·00
1,3-dihydroxy-2-propanone	—	—	0·00
2,5-dihydro-2,5-dimethoxyfuran	545	0·1	0·25
Ethylene glycol	—	—	0·00
Formaldehyde	—	—	0·00
Furan	—	—	0·00
Glutaraldehyde	514	0·07	0·13
Isatin	—	—	0·00
Malonaldehyde	—	—	0·00
Thiophene	—	—	0·00

[a] At 546 nm; final concn., 2×10^{-3} M
[b] Final concn, 1×10^{-5} M.

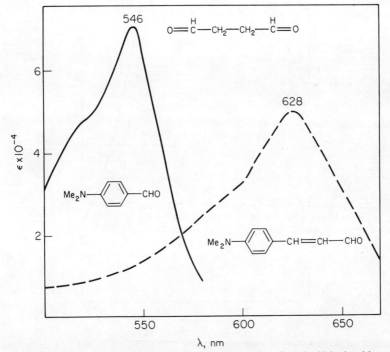

FIG. 98. Long wavelength bands obtained in determination of succinaldehyde with 4-dimethylaminobenzaldehyde (———) and 4-dimethylaminocinnamaldehyde (-----).

Replacement with *p*-diethylaminobenzaldehyde decreases the millimolar absorptivity to about 24. A freshly prepared aqueous solution of 2,5-dimethoxytetrahydrofuran used as the test solution gave negative results indicating that this compound must be hydrolysed to succinaldehyde before it will react with ammonium acetate.

Pyrrole is probably an intermediate in the procedure since millimolar absorptivities obtained with succinaldehyde and pyrrole (heating step

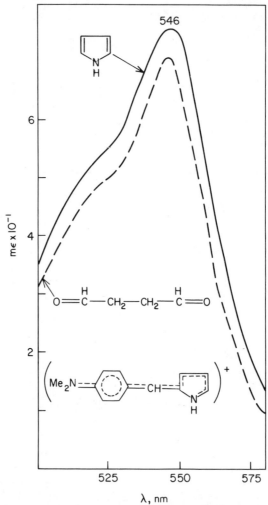

FIG. 99. Comparison of visible absorption spectra of chromogen obtained from determination of pyrrole (10^{-5} M) (———) and succinaldehyde (10^{-5} M) (-----) with 4-dimethylaminobenzaldehyde. Heating step omitted in pyrrole determination.

omitted) are 71 and 76, respectively, Fig. 99. In the procedure some pyrrole is lost as shown by the above results and by the fact that pyrrole in the procedure only gives an mε of 35. The postulated reactions are shown in Fig. 100 for the p-dimethylaminobenzaldehyde procedure.

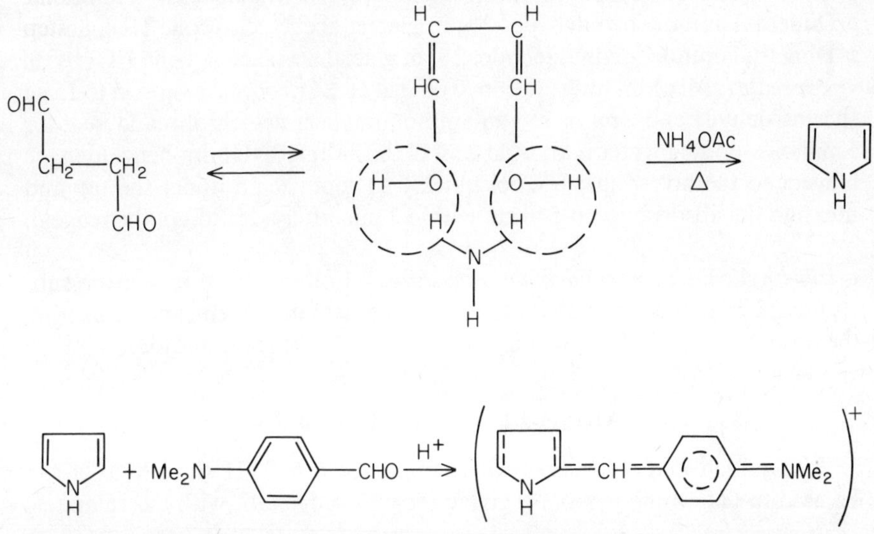

FIG. 100. Postulated reactions for determination of succinaldehyde with 4-dimethylamino-benzaldehyde.

In the p-dimethylaminocinnamaldehyde procedure the final chromogen is postulated to have the structure I. The hydrochloric acid content of the reagent is critical; 9 to 12% (v/v) afforded optimum absorbances. The absorbance drops from a high value of 0·72 to 0·64 in 35 minutes. The time to

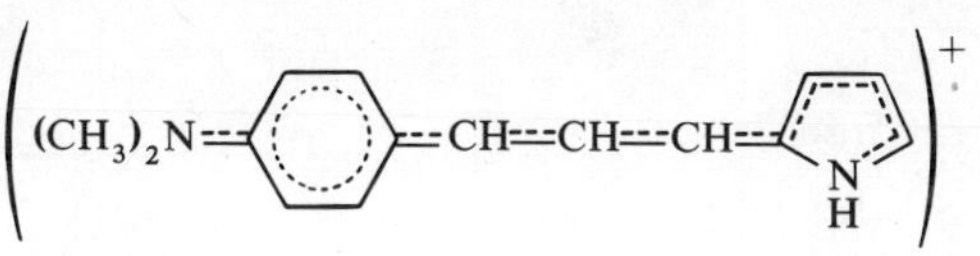

I

reach maximum absorbance depends on the percentage of hydrochloric acid in the reagent. Interferences are the same as in the p-dimethylaminobenz-aldehyde procedure. The standard deviation of the procedure is ±6·6%. Beer's law is not quite obeyed; the calibration line curves gradually. Milli-molar absorptivities of 75 and 63 were obtained with 0·86 and 12·9 μg of 2,5-dimethoxytetrahydrofuran, respectively. When pyrrole was determined by this procedure but with the heating step omitted, the spectral envelope was exactly the same as that obtained with succinaldehyde. The millimolar absorptivity at the wavelength maximum of 628 nm, however, was 91. It is believed that this procedure could be further improved.

p-Dimethylaminobenzaldehyde determination of succinaldehyde.[3] *Reagents.* *p*-Dimethylaminobenzaldehyde: 2% in glacial acetic acid–conc HCl, 85:15. *p*-Dimethylaminocinnamaldehyde: 2% in glacial acetic acid–conc HCl, 91:9.

Procedure. Mix 1 ml test solution (0·05 M in H_2SO_4) containing 0·35 to 15 µg succinaldehyde and 2 ml of 7% aq ammonium acetate solution and heat for 5 min on a boiling water bath. Add 2 ml of the *p*-dimethylaminobenzaldehyde reagent to the hot solution. Cool quickly to room temp under the tap and measure the absorbance at 546 nm within 2 min after addition of the reagent.

p-Dimethylaminocinnamaldehyde procedure.[3] Follow above procedure substituting 2 ml of the *p*-dimethylaminocinnamaldehyde reagent, and measuring the absorbance at 628 nm within 5 to 10 min after reagent addition.

B. 3-Methyl-2-benzothiazolinone hydrazone

Succinaldehyde could also be determined with MBTH since MBTH can be used to determine pyrrole[4] giving the chromogen, **II**, with mε 16 and 34

II

at λ 600 and 664 nm, respectively, for R = H, and mε 37 and 49 at λ 612 and 673 nm, respectively, for R = CH_3.

Succinaldehyde could also be determined directly with MBTH or through the formed formazan.

C. o-Phenylenediamine

In the fluorimetric procedure, the fluorescence obtained is fairly stable, decreasing by 25% in 60 hours. Most aldehydes decreased the intensity of fluorescence when present in amounts ten times that of succinaldehyde. Beer's law is not obeyed and the standard deviation is about ±14%. It is believed that this method could be considerably improved. The fluorescence excitation and emission spectra obtained with succinaldehyde and with a blank are given in Fig. 101.

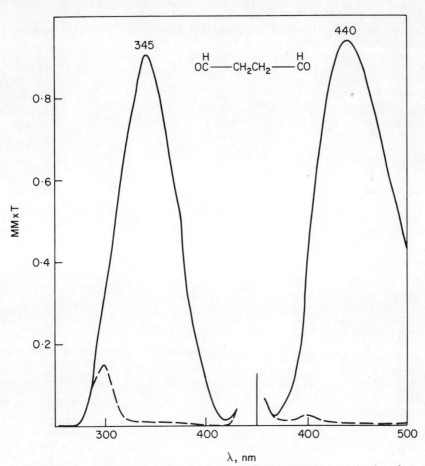

FIG. 101. Fluorescence excitation and emission spectra obtained in determination of succinaldehyde (final concentration 10^{-4} M) with o-phenylenediamine.

Fluorimetric estimation of succinaldehyde.[3] To 1 ml of test solution (aq or 0·05 M H_2SO_4) add 1 ml of o-phenylenediamine solution. Heat the mixture for 10 min on a boiling water bath. Cool and read the fluorescence at $F345/440$.

HBT and other reagents described in the aliphatic aldehyde section could be used in the assay of succinaldehyde.

REFERENCES

1. C. Izard-Verchere, P. Rumpf and C. Viel. *Bull. Soc. Chim. France* 2134 (1971).
2. G. Ohloff and W. Giersch. *Angew. Chem. Internat. Edit.* **12**, 401 (1973).
3. E. Sawicki and J. D. Pfaff. *Chemist-Analyst* **55**, 6 (1966).
4. E. Sawicki, T. R. Hauser, T. W. Stanley, W. Elbert and F. T. Fox. *Anal. Chem.* **33**, 1574 (1961).

61. SUCCINALDEHYDIC ACID
(SUCCINIC SEMIALDEHYDE OR
β-FORMYLPROPIONIC ACID)

$$HOOC-CH_2-CH_2-CHO$$

I. PHYSICAL AND SPECTRAL PROPERTIES

B.p. 134–6° at 14 mm; D_{23}^{23} 1·2568; n_D^{23} 1·4487. Soluble in water, alcohol, ether and benzene. Volatile in steam. Dimerizes on standing.

This aldehyde has a low intensity band derived from an $n \rightarrow \pi^*$ transition in the ultraviolet, e.g. in water, dioxane[1] and aq alkali[2] at λ 280, mε 0·0045, λ 289, mε 0·012 and λ 280, mε 0·0089, respectively. The bands are of such low intensity that they are useless in trace analysis.

3,5-Diaminobenzoic acid has been used in the determination of the aldehyde. Compounds containing the structure, RCH_2CHO, would also react.

A. Estimation of succinaldehydic acid with 3,5-diaminobenzoic acid[3]

Heat equal volumes of the aq test solution and 0·25 M 3,5-diaminobenzoic acid at 60° for 60 minutes. Read at $F400/500$.

Reagents described in the aliphatic aldehyde sections could be used here. An example is MBTH which could form either **I** or **II**.

An enzymatic colorimetric or fluorimetric method based on the measurement of NADPH could also be used. For example, in the following reaction as catalysed by succinate-semialdehyde dehydrogenase (succinate-semialdehyde: NAD(P) oxidoreductase, EC 1.2.1.16). NADP is 8·2 times as active as NAD.[4, 5]

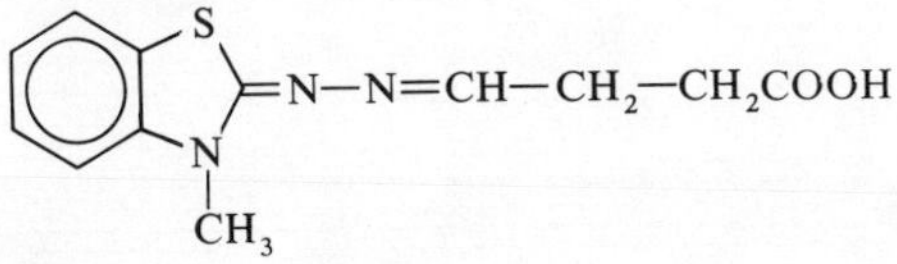

I

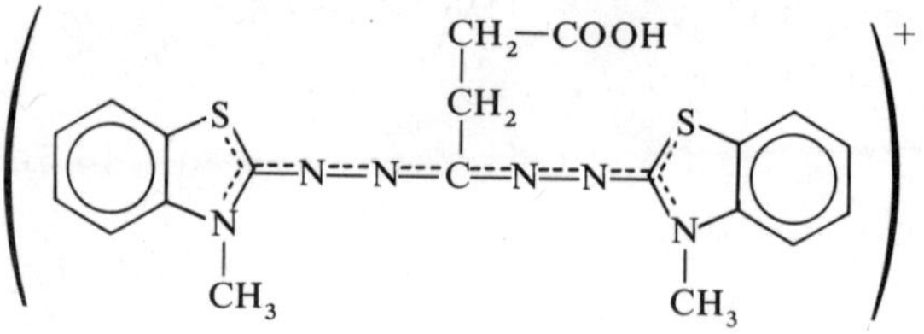

$$\left(\underset{\substack{\text{S} \\ \text{N} \\ | \\ \text{CH}_3}}{\bigcirc} C \text{—N}\text{=}\text{N}\text{=}\text{N}\text{—}\underset{\substack{\text{CH}_2\text{—COOH} \\ | \\ \text{CH}_2 \\ |}}{C}\text{=}\text{N}\text{=}\text{N}\text{—}C\underset{\substack{\text{N} \\ | \\ \text{CH}_3}}{\bigcirc} \right)^{+}$$

II

Succinate-semialdehyde + NADP$^+$ + H$_2$O = succinate + NADPH

Succinate-semialdehyde: NAD$^+$ oxidoreductase (EC 1.2.1.24) could also be used,[6] but NAD$^+$ would be the reactant and NADH would be measured.

REFERENCES

1. P. Pino *et al. Ann. Chim. (Rome)* **51**, 785 (1961).
2. F. Piacenti and P. Pino. *Ann. Chim. (Rome)* **51**, 803 (1961).
3. R. A. Salvador and R. W. Albers. *J. Biol. Chem.* **234**, 922 (1959).
4. W. B. Jakoby. *Methods in Enzymology* **5**, 774 (1962).
5. W. B. Jakoby and E. M. Scott. *J. Biol. Chem.* **234**, 937 (1959).
6. R. W. Albers and G. J. Koval. *Biochim. Biophys. Acta* **42**, 29 (1961).

62. TEREPHTHALALDEHYDE

$$\text{OHC} - \langle \bigcirc \rangle - \text{CHO}$$

I. PHYSICAL AND SPECTRAL PROPERTIES

M.p. 116°; b.p. 245–8°/771 mm; soluble in 5000 parts of cold water or 80 parts hot water, soluble in ether and alkaline solutions, very soluble in ethanol; sublimes; difficultly volatile in steam.

This aldehyde could be determined by some of the procedures described in the aromatic aldehyde and benzaldehyde sections.

An example of a procedure is the following method which has not as yet been optimized.

A. Estimation of terephthalaldehyde with *p*-nitrophenylhydrazine

To 1 ml of a dimethylformamide test solution add 1 ml of 0·1% *p*-nitrophenylhydrazine in 10% aq HCl. After 5 min add 1 ml of ethanolic 25% tetraethylammonium hydroxide and dilute to 10 ml with dimethylformamide. In 5 min read the absorbance at λ_{max} 595 nm. An mɛ of 69 was obtained at this wavelength with pure terephthalaldehyde.

63. TEREPHTHALALDEHYDIC ACID
(4-FORMYLBENZOIC ACID)

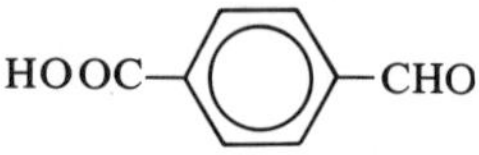

$$HOOC-\langle\bigcirc\rangle-CHO$$

I. PHYSICAL PROPERTIES

M.p. 256°. Sparingly soluble in water, ether or chloroform. Sublimes.

In hexane this aldehyde absorbs at λ_{max} 249, 257, 279, 288 and 298 nm with mε 17·4, 15·5, 1·7, 2·0 and 1·6, respectively.[1]

When terephthalic acid is esterified with ethanediol to give the bis-(2-hydroxyethyl)ester, terephthalaldehydic acid originally present in terephthalic acid remains unchanged and can be determined with Tollen's reagent (*Anal. Abstr.* **15**, 6738 (1968)) by the following procedure.[2] The time required for a determination is 30 min, and the coefficient of variation is 3·6% for 0·14% of the aldehyde in the ester.

A. Determination of terephthalaldehydic acid[2]

To 0·2 g test sample add 4 ml of 3% NaOH and heat at 100° for 10 min. Cool and treat a 1 ml aliquot with 2 ml of Tollen's reagent. Measure the absorbance at 440 nm.

REFERENCES

1. J. C. Dearden and W. F. Forbes. *Can. J. Chem.* **36**, 1362 (1958).
2. N. Oda, S. Ono, H. Matsumori and K. Norishima. *Japan Analyst* **18**, 226 (1969).

64. 2-THIOPHENECARBOXALDEHYDE

$$\left\langle\!\!\!\!\!\!\underset{S}{\overset{}{\frown}}\!\!\!\!\!\right\rangle\!\!-CHO$$

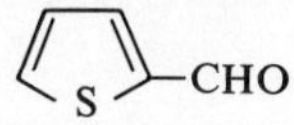

I. PHYSICAL AND SPECTRAL PROPERTIES

B.p. 198°; n_D^{20} 1·5900.

This aldehyde has the following λ_{max} and mϵ values in ethanol: 260 (11·0), 285 (7·1)[1-3] and in hexane; 265 (10·5), 278 (6·9).[3] The analogous 2-seleno-phenecarboxaldehyde absorbs at λ 271 (11·8) and 304 (5·1) in ethanol and at λ 268 (11·2) and 299 (11·2) in hexane.[4]

The aldehyde phosphoresces at $P$255, 280/480 in EPA at 77°K. The limit of determination is about 0·2 µg/ml.

The compound could also be determined by some of the methods described in the benzaldehyde, furfural and aromatic aldehyde sections.

REFERENCES

1. S. Gronowitz. *Arkiv. Kemi* **13**, 239 (1958–1959).
2. R. Andrisano and G. Pappalardo. *Boll. Sci. Fac. Chim. Ind. Bologna* **14**, 100 (1956).
3. G. Pappalardo. *Gazz. Chim. Ital.* **89**, 540 (1959).
4. L. Chierici and G. Pappalardo. *Gazz. Chim. Ital.* **88**, 453 (1958).

65. TRIFORMYLMETHANE
(FORMYLMALONALDEHYDE)

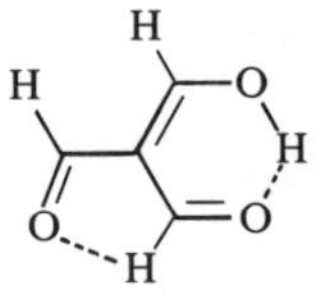

I. PHYSICAL AND SPECTRAL PROPERTIES

This compound could be determined by reaction with 1-alkyllepidinium, quinaldinium or analogous conjugated quaternary ammonium compounds. It could be treated with the analogous neutral bases, e.g. reaction at room temperature with 1,3,3-trimethyl-2-methyleneindoline gives the chromogen I.[1] A zwitterionic resonance structure of this type shows a strong shift

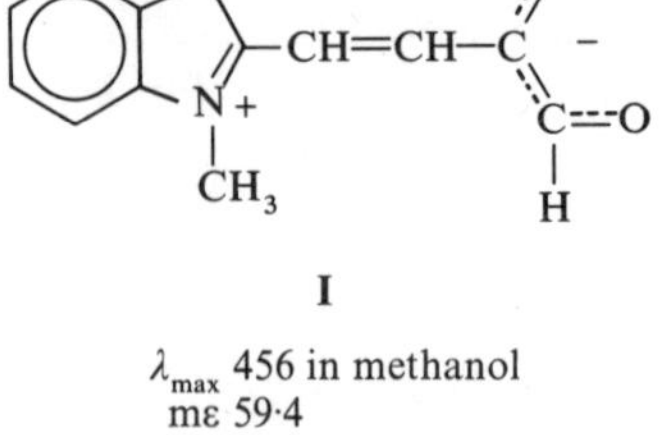

I

λ_{max} 456 in methanol
mε 59·4

toward shorter wavelengths and decreasing intensity with increasing polarity of the solvent. An example of this effect can be given for the lepidinium analogue of I, formed by the reaction of a 1-alkyllepidinium salt with triformylmethane, e.g. **II**.

276

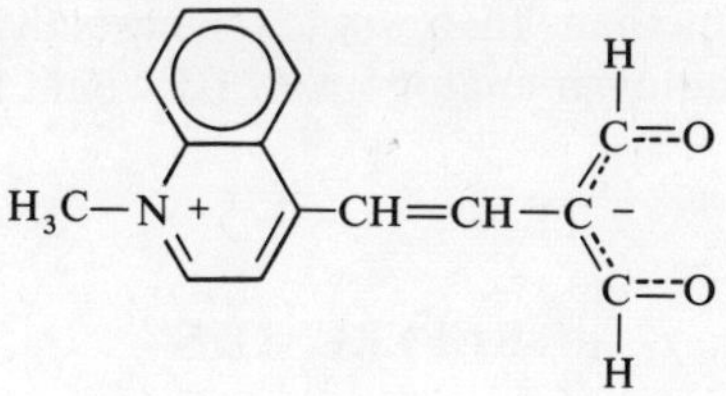

II

Solvent	λ_{max}	$m\varepsilon$
Benzene	588	~90
Methanol	511	37·1
Water	462	~23

If 2 or 3 equivalents of a reagent, such as 1,3,3-trimethyl-2-methylene-indoline are treated with one equivalent of triformylmethane, then **III** or **IV** could also result depending on the conditions of reaction.[1]

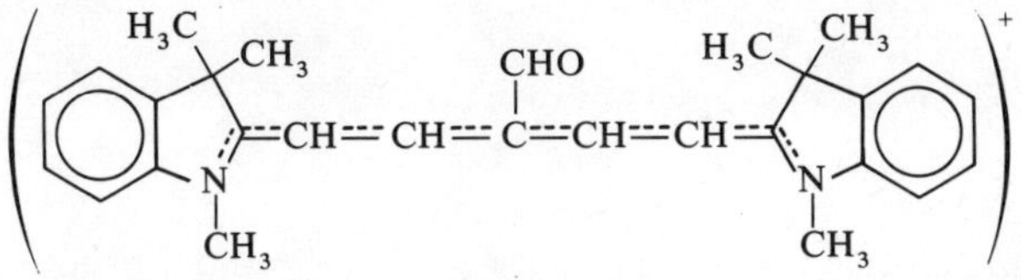

III

λ_{max} 596 nm, $m\varepsilon$ 99·3 in methanol

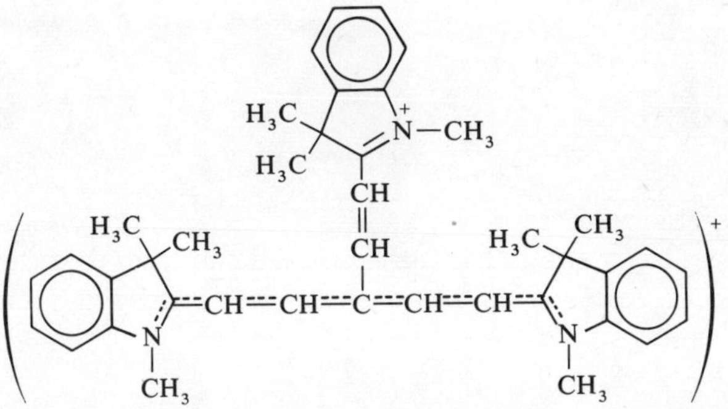

IV

λ_{max} 635 nm, $m\varepsilon$ 160 in methanol

For all these examples spectral data is given for the pure compounds. As yet none of these reactions have been applied to analytical studies.

MBTH and *p*-nitrophenylhydrazine could be expected to react more readily with triformylmethane than would the bases that have been discussed. With MBTH the chromogen analogous to **III** would be expected to absorb near 600 nm.

REFERENCES

1. C. Reichardt and W. Mormann. *Chem. Ber.* **105**, 1815 (1972).

66. α,β-UNSATURATED ALDEHYDES

$$\underset{H}{\overset{\displaystyle >}{C}}=\overset{|}{C}-C=O$$

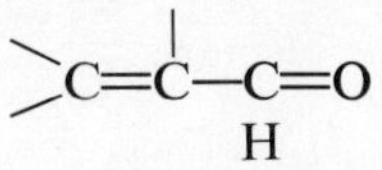

I. INTRODUCTION

Some of these aldehydes have been discussed, e.g. acrolein, crotonaldehyde, cinnamaldehyde, etc. In this section we will discuss some general methods for their analysis.

II. SPECTRAL PROPERTIES

Conjugated aldehydes absorb in the ultraviolet. Data for the simple α,β-unsaturated aldehydes are given in Table 58. The effect of various substituents are shown. Taking 207 nm for the wavelength maximum in alcohol

Table 58. Spectral data for α,β-unsaturated aldehydes

Aldehyde	Structure	Solvent	λ_{max}[a]	mε	Ref.
	CH$_2$=CH—CHO Type				
Acrolein		EtOH	207	11·2	1
		Water	210	12	2, 3
		Hexane[b]	203	12	1
		H$_2$SO$_4$	238	9·3	6
	CH$_2$=CR—CHO Type				
α-Methylacrolein		EtOH	216	11·0	1
		Hexane	213	11·2	1
	RCH=CH—CHO Type				
Crotonaldehyde		EtOH	218	18·0	1
			219	13·8	7
			220	14·8	8
			219·5	16·6	2
			223	15·1	9
		Water	220	12·6	3

279

Table 58—*continued*

Aldehyde	Structure	Solvent	λ_{max} [a]	mε	Ref.
			224	17·0	10
		Hexane	213	17·4	1
			217	15·9	11
			214	12·9	9
		Heptane	213	15·9	9
			212	14·8	12
		Isooctane	214	15·9	13
		97% H_2SO_4	258	23·4	7
2-Hexenal		Isooctane	215	17·4	14
		Hexane	216	19	15, 16
4-Methyl-2-pentenal		EtOH	219	17·8	17
2-Heptenal		EtOH	219	13·2	18
2-Octenal		Hexane	225s	8·9	19
	RCH=CR—CHO Type				
2-Methyl-2-butenal		EtOH	226	16·1	1
2-Methyl-2-pentenal		Heptane	222	17·4	12, 20
		Isooctane	222·5	9·4	21
		EtOH[c]	229	13·5	22
		MeOH	227·5	13·8	23
2-Ethyl-2-hexenal		Heptane	224	15·5	12, 20
		EtOH	230	20·0	24
2,4-Dimethyl-2-pentenal		EtOH	226	8·5	25
2,4-Dimethyl-2-hexenal		EtOH	229	14·1	25
	R_2C=CH—CHO Type				
3-Methyl-2-butenal		Cyclohexane	222·5	16·6	1
		Hexane	230	6·5	11
		EtOH	226	16·2	1
3,7-Dimethyl-2-octenal		EtOH	239	14·8	26, 27
	R_2C=CR—CHO Type				
2,3-Dimethylcrotonaldehyde		Hexane	239	13·5	1, 11
		EtOH	245	12·9	1
	RO—CH=CH—CHO Type				
3-Ethoxyacrolein		EtOH	242·5	13·8	28
	RO—CH=CR—CHO Type				
2-Pentyl-3-ethoxyacrolein		EtOH	253	14·8	29
	RO—CH=C(OR)—CHO Type				
2-Methoxy-3-hydroxyacrolein		EtOH	257	13·5	30
	$^-$O—CH=CH—CHO Type				
3-Hydroxyacrolein		Aq. alkali	267·5	26·9	30

Table 58—*continued*

Aldehyde	Structure	Solvent	$\lambda_{max}^{\;a}$	mε	Ref.
	⁻O—CH=C(OR)—CHO Type				
2-Methoxy-3-hydroxyacrolein	EtOH–NaOEt	277	24·6		31
	R₂N—CH=CH—CHO Type				
3-Dimethylaminoacrolein	CH₂Cl₂	283	37·2		30

ᵃIn addition an $n \rightarrow \pi^*$ band ranging from about 305 nm in water to 330 nm in heptane with an mε ranging from 0·05 in water to 0·02 in heptane and the band in the non-polar solvents containing much fine structure.

ᵇIn isooctane λ354 fs, mε 0·02,[4] in cyclopentadiene λ320, mε 0·02 and in chloroform λ330, mε 0·025.[5]

ᶜ2-Heptenal in alcohol absorbs at shorter wavelength, λ_{max} 223, mε 14·1.

of the basic acrolein chromophore, substitution of α-alkyl or β-alkyl results in a 10 or 12 nm red shift. Substitution of alkoxy, oxyanion or dimethylamino groups results in even greater red shifts because of the increasing internal basicity of these groups.

Increasing the chain length of conjugation results in further red shifts, Table 59. Another conjugated double bond shifts the wavelength maximum about 50 nm, e.g. acrolein λ 207 and 2,4-pentadienal λ 258. An additional double bond shifts the band another 58 nm, e.g. 2,4,6-octatrienal, λ 316. As a rule, for all these compounds the $\pi \rightarrow \pi^*$ band shifts to longer wavelength with increasing polarity of the solvent while the much less intense $n \rightarrow \pi^*$ band shifts to shorter wavelength under these conditions.

Where the aldehyde is saturated or is not conjugated with the unsaturated part of the molecule a $\pi \rightarrow \pi^*$ band is not found in the ultraviolet region. For example, in *trans*-6-octen-4-ynal in cyclohexane a band is found at λ 225 nm, mε 13·5 which is derived from the enyne chromophore.[54]

Where there are two insulated conjugated systems, $\pi \rightarrow \pi^*$ bands from both systems are usually present. For example, nuciferal, p-tolyl—CH(CH₃)CH₂—CH₂—CH=C(CH₃)—CHO, is an α,β-unsaturated aldehyde with bands in ethanol at λ_{max} 223, 229, 265, 267, 273 and 280 nm with mε 15·7, 14·3, 0·95, 0·8, 0·8 and 0·37, respectively.[55]

III. TECHNIQUES

A. Anthrone and N,N-dimethyl-p-phenylenediamines

Reagents useful for the analysis of these types of aldehydes have been discussed in the aliphatic aldehydes, acrolein, cinnamaldehyde and croton-aldehyde sections.

Table 59. Spectral data on unsaturated aldehydes containing the structure $(C{-}C)_n{-}CHO$

Aldehyde	Solvent	λ_{max}	$m\varepsilon$	Ref.
2,4-Pentadienal	EtOH	258·5[a]	27·5	32
	EtOH	258	28·8	33, 34
trans-	Hexane	250	33·9	35
cis-	Hexane	255	25·1	35
	EtOH	259·5	19·1	35
trans-2-Methyl-2,4-penta-dienal	Hexane	258·5	24·0	35
	EtOH	268	14·8	35
cis-2-Methyl-2,4-penta-dienal	Hexane	257·5	19·1	35
	EtOH	265	14·5	35
2,4-Hexadienal	i-Octane	260·4	28·8	36
	Hexane	263	26·9	37
	CH_3CN	269	31·6	36
	EtOH	271	30·9	32
	MeOH	271·2	30·2	36
	$CHF_2CF_2CH_2OH$	277·9	29·5	36
	H_2O	279·7	29·5	36
5-Methyl-2,4-hexadienal	MeOH	285	28·8	38
2,4-Heptadienal	EtOH	272·5	32·4	32
2,4-Octadienal	EtOH	273·5	31·6	32
2,4-Nonadienal	EtOH	274	30·2	32
2,4-Decadienal	EtOH	274	31·6	32
2,4-Hendecadienal	EtOH	274	32·4	32
2,4-Dodecadienal	EtOH	274	33·1	32
2,3-Dimethyl-2-penten-4-ynal	EtOH	271	16·2	39
5-Hydroxy-2,4-pentadienal	Aq. alkali	365	$\sim$50	40
	EtOH–NaOH	362·5	50	41
	DMF^b–3%Et_3N	362·5	56·2	30
2,4,6-Octatrienal	Hexane	306	40·7	42
	EtOH	316	37·2	8, 43
	$CHCl_3$	319	34·7	44
2,4,6-Nonatrienal	Ether	306	31·6	45
2,4-Heptadien-6-ynal	Ether	283[c]	40·7	46
3,6-Dimethyl-2,6-heptadien-4-ynal	EtOH	295·5	12·6	47
3-Methyl-2,6-heptadien-4-ynal	EtOH	300[d]	11·5	48
$(CH_3)_2N{-}(CH{=}CH)_n{-}CHO$,				
n = 1	$CHCl_3$	283	37·0	30
n = 2	$CHCl_3$	362	51·0	30
n = 3	$CHCl_3$	422	56·0	30
n = 4	$CHCl_3$	463	65·0	30
n = 5	$CHCl_3$	492	68·0	30
n = 6	$CHCl_3$	513	72·0	30
$C_6H_5(CH{=}CH)_n{-}CHO$,				
n = 0	AcOH	250	1·0	49
n = 1	AcOH	287	2·3	49

Table 59—*continued*

Aldehyde		Solvent	λ_{max}	$m\varepsilon$	Ref.
	$n = 2$	AcOH	325	4·0	49
	$n = 3$	AcOH	360	5·1	49
	$n = 4$	AcOH	387	6·1	49
	$n = 5$	AcOH	410		49
	$n = 6$	AcOH	430		49
$O_2N\!=\!C_4H_2O\!-\!(CH\!=\!CH)_n CHO^e$,					
	$n = 0$	H_2O	310	11·5	50
	$n = 1$	EtOH	347	23·2	51
	$n = 2$	EtOH	375	24·0	51
	$n = 3$	EtOH	401	45·2	51
	$n = 4$	EtOH	425	59·0	51
$4\text{-}CH_3OC_6H_4(CH\!=\!CH)_n\!-\!CHO$,					
	$n = 0$	EtOH	277	15·5	52
	$n = 1$	$CHCl_3$	322	30·5	53
	$n = 2$	$CHCl_3$	352	42·0	53
	$n = 3$	$CHCl_3$	382	52·0	53
	$n = 4$	$CHCl_3$	403	61·5	53
	$n = 5$	$CHCl_3$	425	68·7	53
	$n = 6$	$CHCl_3$	440	78·0	53
	$n = 7$	$CHCl_3$	457	90·2	53

[a] $n \to \pi^*$ band at 325 nm, $m\varepsilon$ 0·051.
[b] DMF = dimethylformamide.
[c] Also band at λ 295, $m\varepsilon$ 38·9.
[d] Also bands at λ 220, $m\varepsilon$ 8·9; 282, $m\varepsilon$ 12·0; and 292, $m\varepsilon$ 12·0.
[e] $n = 0$ is 5-nitro-2-furfural.

Anthrone can be used for the analysis of these unsaturated aldehydes.[56] The reaction details, procedure and fluorescence spectra are given in the acrolein section.

N,N-Dimethyl-*p*-phenylenediamine can also be used in the analysis of these unsaturated aldehydes.[57] The procedure needs optimization. The

Table 60. Spectral data of α-furylpolyenals and their dimethylaminoanils.[57]

Furylpolyenal	RCHO λ_{max}	$R\!-\!CH\!=\!\overset{+}{N}H\!-\!C_6H_4N(CH_3)_2$ λ_{max}
$n = 0$	270	480
1	312	510
2	346	530
3	366	542
4	389	553
5	412	570

Table 61. Colours of some polyenal dimethylaminoanils.[57]

$$p\text{-}[R(CH{=}CH)_n{-}CN{=}\overset{+}{N}H]{-}C_6H_4N(CH_3)_2$$

n	R = CH$_3$	R = C$_6$H$_5$
0	colourless	rose
1	yellow	red
2	raspberry red	blood-red
3	blue–red	blue–red
4	violet	violet
5	warm blue	blue–violet
6	cold blue	blue

formation of the chromogens shifts the wavelength maxima of the unsaturated aldehydes to much longer wavelengths, Table 60. The reagent was also reacted with $CH_3(CH{=}CH)_nCHO$ and $C_6H_5(CH{=}CH)_nCHO$, Table 61.

B. Hydrazines

2,4-Dinitrophenylhydrazine and 4-nitrophenylhydrazine can also be used for the analysis of unsaturated aldehydes. Spectral data for the dinitrophenylhydrazones of these unsaturated aldehydes is given in Table 62.

Table 62. Long wavelength bands of α,β-unsaturated aldehyde 2,4-dinitrophenylhydrazones

Aldehyde	Solvent	λ_{max}[a]	mε	Ref.
Acrolein	CHCl$_3$	366	27·5	58
	CHCl$_3$	368	26·9	59
	EtOH	369	25	60
	i-C$_8$H$_{18}$	347	19·1	61
	EtOH-Base	459	29·5	58
	NaOEt–EtOH–CHCl$_3$	459	28·8	59
Crotonaldehyde	CHCl$_3$	373	29·5	58
	CHCl$_3$	373	28·8	62, 63
	CHCl$_3$	373	26·9	59
	CHCl$_3$	360	27·5	64
	EtOH	377	26·3	64
	EtOH	376[b]	27·5	65
	EtOH	373	28·2	66
	EtOH, dil. KOH	451	30·2	64
Methacrolein	CHCl$_3$	367	31·6	67
	EtOH	370[c]	20	68
	EtOH	368	26·3	69
2-Pentenal	EtOH–10%CHCl$_3$	373	28·8	58

Table 62—*continued*

Aldehyde	Solvent	λ_{max}^{a}	mε	Ref.
	$CHCl_3$	374	28·8	58
	EtOH	374	28·8	70
	EtOH-Base	458	29·5	58
3-Methyl-2-butenal[d]	$CHCl_3$	376	27·5	59
	EtOH	382	30·9	69
	EtOH	377	27·5	64
	EtOH	380	28	71
	EtOH	382	29·5	72
	NaOEt–EtOH–$CHCl_3$	458	28·8	59
2-Methyl-2-pentenal	—	375	28·2	73
3-Methyl-2-pentenal	—	383	27·5	74
	$CHCl_3$	382	28·8	75, 76
4-Methyl-2-pentenal	$CHCl_3$	373	28·2	77
2-Hexenal	EtOH–10%$CHCl_3$	373	28·8	58
	$CHCl_3$	374	28·8	58
	EtOH-Base	458	29·5	58
2-Heptenal	EtOH–10%$CHCl_3$	373	30·2	58
	$CHCl_3$	374	30·2	58
	EtOH-Base	458	29·5	58
2-Octenal	$CHCl_3$	374	28·8	19
	$CHCl_3$	375	29·5	58
	EtOH-Base	458	30·2	58
3,4,4-Trimethyl-2-pentenal	EtOH	384	30·9	78
2-Nonenal	EtOH–10%$CHCl_3$	374	28·8	58
	$CHCl_3$	375	28·8	58
	EtOH–Base	459	30·9	58
2-Methyl-2-octenal	$CHCl_3$	380	28·2	79
2-Decenal	EtOH–10%$CHCl_3$	374	28·8	58
	$CHCl_3$	375	28·8	58
	EtOH–Base	458	29·5	58
2-Undecanal	EtOH–10%$CHCl_3$	375	28·8	58
	$CHCl_3$	376	28·2	58
	EtOH–Base	459	30·2	58
2,4-Dimethyl-2-pentenal	$CHCl_3$	382	30·2	25
3,4,4-Trimethyl-2-pentenal	EtOH	384	30·9	26
2,4-Dimethyl-2-hexenal	$CHCl_3$	383	29·5	25
3,7-Dimethyl-2-octenal	EtOH	384	30·2	26

[a] In neutral solution other bands around 250, 288s, and 450s while in alkaline solution shoulder near 540s.

[b] Also bands at 244, mε 16 and 282, mε 8·9. The corresponding 4-nitrophenylhydrazone absorbs at λ 285, mε 7·8 and 400, mε 30 in ethanol.

[c] Also band at 250, mε 13·8.

[d] Or Senecioaldehyde or Tiglaldehyde.

Alkyl substitution in the aldehyde shifts the long wavelength band to longer wavelengths; anion formation shifts it even further. However, the chromogen anion is less stable than the neutral chromogen.

Isonicotinic acid hydrazide can also be used to determine α,β-unsaturated aldehydes.[80–82] A yellow chromogen, **I**, is believed to be formed. Beer's

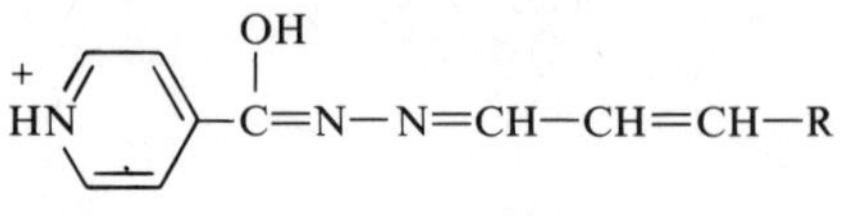

I

law is obeyed from 100 to 500 µg of aldehyde in the presence of 2,3,5-triphenyl-tetrazolium chloride. Aromatic aldehydes also react. The method is not very sensitive, but the sensitivity could probably be increased considerably with further optimization.

Isonicotinic acid hydrazide estimation of unsaturated aldehydes.[82] To 1·0 ml of aq test solution add 1 ml of $4\,\text{N}\ H_2SO_4$, followed by 6 ml water and 2 ml of a solution containing 1% of the hydrazide and 1% of the tetrazolium salt. Dilute to 100 ml with water and read the absorbance at the wavelength maximum.

MBTH can also be used to determine unsaturated aldehydes. Two types

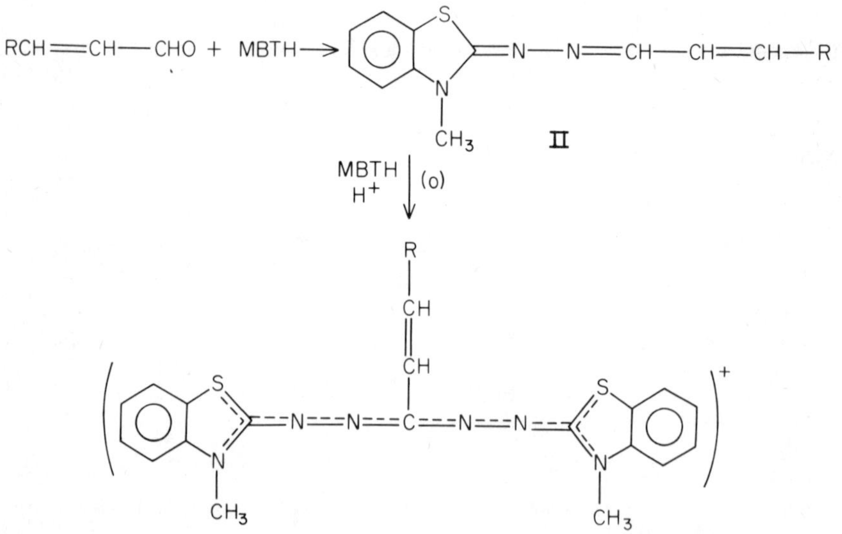

Fig. 102. Reaction of α,β-unsaturated aldehydes with MBTH.

of chromogens can be formed as shown in Fig. 102. **II** absorbs at a shorter wavelength than **III**. The data obtained for a few of these aldehydes is shown in Table 63.

Table 63. Spectral data for some MBTH derivatives of α,β-unsaturated aldehydes.[83]

| Aldehyde | λ_{max} (mε) | |
	II	**III**
Acrolein	326 (25)	670 (29·4)
2-Butenal	330 (30)	670 (29·4)
2-Methyl-2-butenal	331 (24)	670 (27)
2,4-Hexadienal	362 (33)	—

MBTH determination of unsaturated aldehydes.[83] *Spectrophotometric method.* To 0·8 ml of aq test solution add 1 ml of 0·1 M glycine buffer, pH 4, and 0·2 ml of 0·1 % aq MBTH . HCl. Incubate at 40° for 1 h (for 2-methyl-2-butenal 10 h is necessary). Read the absorbance at the wavelength maximum.

Colorimetric method. To 0·8 ml of aq test solution add 0·2 ml of 1 % MBTH . HCl. Heat at 100° for 3 min, cool, and add 2·5 ml of fresh 0·2 % aq ferric chloride. After 5 min at room temp add 6·5 ml of pure acetone, mix, and read the absorbance at 670 nm.

C. 2-Thiobarbituric acid

In the evaluation of the flavour of fats and oils in terms of malonaldehyde precursors the thiobarbituric acid procedure has been found to be of some value. In this test a peak is frequently found at 452 nm in addition to the peak at 532 nm derived from malonaldehyde. However, it is stated that dienals also give a peak at 532 nm.[84–86] Enals would then give a band near 490 nm.

D. Girard-T reagent

α,β-Unsaturated aldehydes can also be determined with Girard-T reagent, trimethylacethydrazide ammonium hydrochloride.[87] Citral and cinnamaldehyde give bands at λ 281 and 313, respectively. Oils of caraway, carvone, cinnamaldehyde, cinnamon bark, cinnamon leaf, citral, dill, lemon and lemon grass have been analysed for citral and cinnamaldehyde by refluxing the oil with an alcoholic solution of Girard-T reagent, adding ether, extracting the chromogen with water and reading the absorbance at 281 nm for citral and 313 nm for cinnamaldehyde. Other carbonyl compounds interfere.

E. High pressure liquid chromatography

High pressure liquid chromatography can be applied to the determination of α,β-unsaturated aldehydes through utilization of a 12 ft. $\times \frac{1}{4}$ in. (o.d.) stainless steel column packed with Poragel 60A and elution with methylene chloride flowing at the rate of 100 ml hr^{-1}.[88] 2,4-Pentadienal was detected at 254 nm. A plot of sample weight v peak area for duplicate analyses showed the response to be linear up to 1·5 µg of sample. The authors claim that this simple gel permeation chromatographic method should be of considerable value in the study of unstable low molecular weight chemicals. It is preferred over internal standard gas chromatography since polymerization or decomposition during analysis is less likely and, after the initial calibration, no pure sample component is required for subsequent quantitative analyses.

REFERENCES

1. W. F. Forbes and R. Shilton. *J. Am. Chem. Soc.* **81**, 786 (1959).
2. A.P.I. Research Project No. 44 **1**, 330 (1949).
3. G. Mackinney and O. Temmer. *J. Am. Chem. Soc.* **70**, 3586 (1948).
4. A.P.I. Research Project No. 44. **1**, 100 (1949).
5. B. A. Arbuzov and A. I. Konovalov. *Izvest. Akad. Nauk S.S.S.R.* 1290 (1965).
6. J. Rosenbaum and M. C. R. Symons. *J. Chem. Soc.* 1 (1961).
7. M. H. Palmer and D. S. Urch. *J. Chem. Soc.* 174 (1963).
8. E. R. Blout and M. Fields. *J. Am. Chem. Soc.* **70**, 189 (1948).
9. N. S. Bayliss and E. G. McRae. *J. Phys. Chem.* **58**, 1006 (1954).
10. A.P.I. Research Project No. 44 **1**, 332 (1949).
11. E. A. Braude and E. A. Evans. *J. Chem. Soc.* 3334 (1955).
12. P. Y. Blanc. *Helv. Chim. Acta* **44**, 1 (1961).
13. A.P.I. Research Project No. 44 **1**, 331 (1949).
14. F. L. Greenwood. *J. Org. Chem.* **24**, 1735 (1959).
15. S. J. Moss and H. Steiner. *J. Chem. Soc.* 2372 (1965).
16. M. Winter and F. Gautschi. *Helv. Chim. Acta* **45**, 2567 (1962).
17. Y. Chretian-Bessiere and H. Leotte. *Compt. rend.* **255**, 723 (1962).
18. L. Crombie and A. G. Jacklin. *J. Chem. Soc.* 1632 (1957).
19. L. Crombie. *J. Chem. Soc.* 1007 (1955).
20. P.-Y. Blanc, A. Perret and F. Teppa. *Helv. Chim. Acta* **47**, 567 (1964).
21. A.P.I. Research Project No. 44 **1**, 337 (1949).
22. C. Asselineau and J. Asselineau. *Bull. Soc. Chim. France* 1776 (1960).
23. A.P.I. Research Project No. 44 **1**, 338 (1949).
24. R. Heilmann, G. Gaudemaris, P. Arnaud and G. Scheurbrandt. *Bull. Soc. Chim. France* **24**, 112 (1957).
25. P. Caubére. *Bull. Soc. Chim. France* **31**, 161 (1964).
26. R. Heilmann and R. Glenat. *Bull. Soc. Chim. France* **22**, 1586 (1955).
27. C. C. Price and J. A. Pappalardo. *J. Am. Chem. Soc.* **72**, 2613 (1950).
28. L. A. Yanovskaya and V. F. Kucherov. *Izvest. Akad. Nauk S.S.S.R.* 667 (1962).

29. V. F. Kucherov, L. A. Yanovskaya and B. G. Kovalev. *Doklady Akad. Nauk S.S.S.R.* **133**, 370 (1960).
30. S. S. Malhotra and M. C. Whiting. *J. Chem. Soc.* 3812 (1960).
31. B. Eistert and F. Haupter. *Chem. Ber.* **92**, 1921 (1959).
32. E. L. Pippen and M. Nonaka. *J. Org. Chem.* **23**, 1580 (1958).
33. R. W. Kierstead, R. P. Linstead and B. C. L. Weedon. *J. Chem. Soc.* 1799 (1953).
34. H. Bader, B. C. L. Weedon and R. J. Woods. *J. Chem. Soc.* 3099 (1951).
35. E. E. Boehm and M. C. Whiting. *J. Chem. Soc.* 2541 (1963).
36. E. M. Kosower and T. S. Sorenson. *J. Org. Chem.* **28**, 692 (1963).
37. P. Y. Blanc. *Helv. Chim. Acta* **44**, 607 (1961).
38. I. N. Nazarov and Z. A. Krasnaya. *Zhur. Obshchei Khim.* **28**, 2440 (1958).
39. M. V. Mavrov and V. F. Kucherov. *Izvest. Akad. Nauk S.S.S.R.* 546 (1965).
40. G. Scheibe, D. Bruck and F. Dorr. *Chem. Ber.* **85**, 867 (1952).
41. S. Sarel and J. Rivlin. *Tetrahedron Letters* 821 (1965).
42. G. W. H. Cheeseman *et al. J. Chem. Soc.* 2031 (1949).
43. B. C. L. Weedon and R. J. Woods. *J. Chem. Soc.* 2687 (1951).
44. W. Krauss and H. Grund. *Z. Elektrochem.* **59**, 872 (1955).
45. F. Bohlmann and H. Jastrow. *Chem. Ber.* **95**, 2939 (1962).
46. F. Bohlmann *et al. Chem. Ber.* **97**, 809 (1964).
47. L. A. Yanovskaya *et al. Izvest, Akad. Nauk S.S.S.R.* 674 (1962).
48. E. R. H. Jones and B. C. L. Weedon. *J. Chem. Soc.* 937 (1946).
49. J. F. Thomas and G. Branch. *J. Am. Chem. Soc.* **75**, 4793 (1953).
50. R. F. Raffauf. *J. Am. Chem. Soc.* **72**, 753 (1950).
51. H. Saikachi and H. Ogawa. *J. Am. Chem. Soc.* **80**, 3642 (1958).
52. A. Burawoy and J. T. Chamberlain. *J. Chem. Soc.* 2310 (1952).
53. D. Marshall and M. C. Whiting. *J. Chem. Soc.* 4082 (1956).
54. L. Crombie *et al. J. Chem. Soc.* 4970 (1963).
55. T. Sakai, K. Nishimura and Y. Hirose. *Tetrahedron Letters* 1171 (1963).
56. E. Sawicki, R. A. Carnes and R. Schumacher. *Mikrochim. Acta* 929 (1967).
57. S. Hunig, J. Utermann and G. Erlemann. *Chem. Ber.* **88**, 708 (1955).
58. F. Stitt *et al., Spectrochim. Acta* **17**, 51 (1961).
59. L. A. Jones, J. C. Holmes and R. B. Seligman. *Anal. Chem.* **28**, 191 (1956).
60. R. H. Hall and E. S. Stern. *J. Chem. Soc.* 490 (1950).
61. I. N. Nazarov, C. A. Kazitsyna and I. I. Zaretskaya. *Zhur. Obshchei Khim.* **27**, 606 (1957).
62. O. Wiss and G. Bettendorf. *Z. Physiol. Chem.* **306**, 145 (1957).
63. G. D. Johnson. *J. Am. Chem. Soc.* **75**, 2720 (1953).
64. J. D. Roberts and C. Green. *J. Am. Chem. Soc.* **68**, 214 (1946).
65. F. Bohlmann. *Chem. Ber.* **84**, 490 (1951).
66. L. Bateman, J. I. Cunneen and J. Ford. *J. Chem. Soc.* 3056 (1956).
67. D. Lavie, Y. Shvo and D. Willner. *J. Am. Chem. Soc.* **81**, 3062 (1959).
68. J. J. Ritter and D. Ginsburg. *J. Am. Chem. Soc.* **72**, 2381 (1950).
69. P. R. Enslin, J. M. Huge, K. B. Norton and D. E. A. Rivett. *J. Chem. Soc.* 4779 (1960).
70. D. A. Thomas and W. K. Warburton. *J. Chem. Soc.* 2988 (1965).
71. N. L. Wendler and H. L. Slates. *J. Am. Chem. Soc.* **72**, 5341 (1950).
72. H. Marxmeier and E. Pfeil. *Chem. Ber.* **97**, 815 (1964).
73. K. Mori, S. K. Roy and D. M. S. Wheeler. *J. Chem. Soc.* 5815 (1964).
74. M. Julia. *Ann. Chim. Paris* 5, 595 (1950).
75. M. Julia and J. M. Surzur. *Bull. Soc. Chim. France* **23**, 1615 (1956).

76. M. Julia and J. M. Surzur. *Compt. rend.* **238**, 2426 (1954).
77. M. Julia and G. Tchernoff. *Compt. rend.* **245**, 1246 (1957).
78. R. Heilmann and R. Glenat. *Ann. Chim. Paris* **8**, 175 (1963).
79. R. Ahmad and B. C. L. Weedon. *J. Chem. Soc.* 2125 (1953).
80. H. L. Hale, K. Losee, J. Martins, M. Holsing, M. Perry and J. Bernstein. *J. Am. Chem. Soc.* **75**, 1935 (1953).
81. P. P. T. Sah and S. A. Peoples. *J. Am. Pharm. Ass.* **43**, 513 (1954).
82. M. H. Hashmi, A. Rashid, H. Ahmad, A. A. Ayaz and F. Azam. *Anal. Chem.* **37**, 1027 (1965).
83. M. A. Paz, O. O. Blumenfeld, M. Rojkind, E. Henson, C. Furfine and P. M. Gallop. *Arch. Biochem. Biophys.* **109**, 548 (1965).
84. H. C. K. Taufel and R. Zimmerman. *Fette, Seifen, Anstrichmittel* **63**, 226 (1961).
85. G. A. Jacobson, J. A. Kirkpatrick and H. E. Goff, Jr. *J. Am. Oil Chemist's Soc.* **41**, 124 (1964).
86. B. G. Tarladgis, A. M. Pearson and L. R. Dugan. *J. Am. Oil Chemist's Soc.* **39**, 34 (1962).
87. J. B. Stenlake and W. D. Williams. *J. Pharm. Pharmacol.* **9**, 900 (1957).
88. J. P. Walradt and C. Shu. *J. Agric. Food Chem.* **21**, 547 (1973).

67. VANILLIN
(4-HYDROXY-3-METHOXYBENZALDEHYDE)

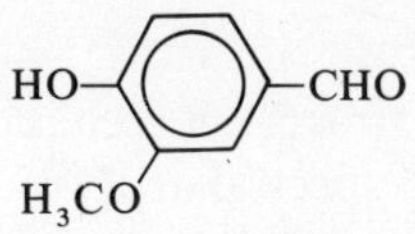

HO—⟨O⟩—CHO
H₃CO

I. PHYSICAL PROPERTIES

There are two crystalline forms, m.p. 77 to 79° and 81 to 82°; b.p. 170° at 15 mm, and 140 to 145° at 6 mm. Very soluble in ethanol, ether, acetic acid, chloroform, carbon disulphide and pyridine. Moderately soluble in hot ligroin and benzene. Insoluble in cold ligroin. Soluble in 90 parts of water at 14°, 20 parts at 75°.

II. SPECTRAL PROPERTIES AND APPLICATIONS

Since vanillin absorbs in the ultraviolet in neutral, acid and alkaline solution with some intensity, it can be determined through this physical property. Some of this spectral data is seen in Table 64. As can be seen from

Table 64. Spectral data for vanillin

Solvent	$\lambda_{max}(m\varepsilon)$	Ref.
Dioxane	277(10·0), 308(7·9)	1, 2
Ethanol	208 (12), 232(14·5), 279(10·2), 309(10·6)	3–8
Ethanol, pH 2·91	235(15·1), 280(10·7), 315(9·1)	9
Ether	206(12·8), 228(16·6), 273(12·3), 301(9·3)	8
Water	230(15·1), 279(10·7), 310(9·1)	10
0·01 N HCl	231(13·5), 281(10), 312(9·1)	11
0·1 N HCl	206(14·8), 230(15·5), 279(11·2), 309(10)	8
Ethanol, KOH	250(8·9), 295(3·0), 353(29·5)	5, 6
Ethanol, pH 10·93	245(9·1), 345(25·7)	9
0·02 N alkali	348(28·2)	7
0·1 N NaOH	249(9·8), 347(25·7)	10
0·01 N NaOH	249(8·1), 352(25·1)	11
95% H₂SO₄	238(7·4), 336(19·1)	10

L*

this data vanillin can be analysed in its neutral form or as the cationic or anionic salts, Fig. 103.

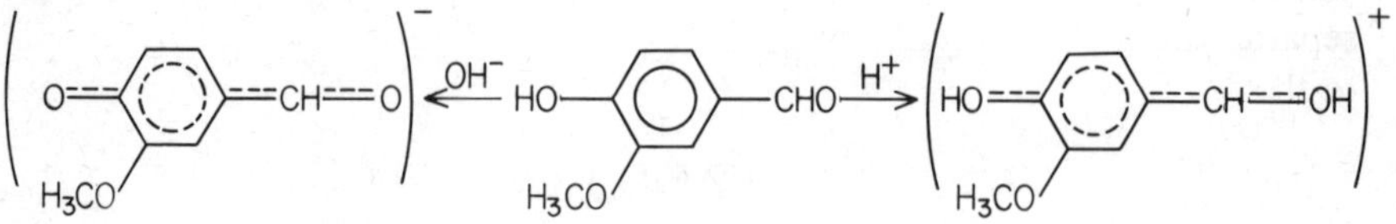

FIG. 103. Structure of vanillin in neutral, acid and alkaline solution.

In the analysis of vanilla extracts not containing ethylvanillin or coumarin, direct ultraviolet absorption spectral analysis is possible.[12] The band near 230 nm has been used for analysis[13] since it is the most intense band in neutral solutions. However, interferences are a greater problem at this low wavelength.

Because of the many interferences in the Folin–Denis method for vanillin,[14, 15] a variety of direct ultraviolet methods for this aldehyde have been tried.[5, 13, 16–20] To cancel out many of the interferences one method is based on the difference between the absorbances of the neutral and alkaline solutions of the phenolic substances at the wavelength maximum of the anion.[16, 17, 20] The isosbestic points at wavelengths 238, 259 and 316 nm[9] can also be used in this pH difference type of assay or in the assay of vanillin at intermediate pH values. Analysis can also be undertaken by measurement at a pH less than 5·0 or more than 9·7. Analyses at pHs between 5·0 and 9·7 would have to be done at the isosbestic points since the pK of vanillin is 7·3.[9] Thus, either an acidic or basic solution can be used to analyse a mixture of vanillin and propenylguaethol.[18] In the determination of a mixture of vanillin and vanitrope measurements can be made at 256 and 295 nm at pH 4·6 or at 256 and 347 nm at pH 9·0.[19] In the latter case wavelength settings are critical. Accuracy is about $\pm 5\%$. In alkaline mixtures containing vanillin and p-hydroxybenzaldehyde a two-component equation can be used involving the absorbance differences at the wavelength maxima for vanillin, λ 348 nm, and p-hydroxybenzaldehyde, λ 336 nm, the concentrations of these aldehydes being calculated from the data.[5]

III. PAPER CHROMATOGRAPHY

Paper chromatography has been used to separate vanillin from its interferences prior to analysis by ultraviolet spectroscopy.[21–28] For example, in one method which took 2 h for a separation the mobile solvent was cyclohexane–ethyl acetate–methanol, 100:30:20 and the immobile solvent, 10% dimethylformamide in ether.[23] A solution of 0·4% aq sodium carbonate was used for elution of the spots. Analysis was at 348 nm. The method does not separate vanillin from p-hydroxybenzaldehyde but this compound is present to the extent of 5% of the vanillin.

IV. THIN LAYER CHROMATOGRAPHY

Thin layer chromatography can also be used to separate vanillin from its interference prior to ultraviolet spectral analysis.[29–34] An example is the separation of vanillin from p-hydroxybenzaldehyde, o-vanillin, methyl-vanillin, ethylvanillin, m-hydroxybenzaldehyde, 2,4-dimethoxybenzaldehyde, benzylvanillin, p-methoxybenzaldehyde, piperonal, o-methoxybenzaldehyde and vanitrope (1-ethoxy-2-hydroxy-4-propenylbenzene) on a silica gel G thin layer plate with chloroform–ethyl acetate, 98:2, as the developer.[32]

V. LIQUID–SOLID, LIQUID–LIQUID, GAS–SOLID AND GAS–LIQUID CHROMATOGRAPHY

Conventional column chromatography has also been used for cleanup purposes prior to ultraviolet spectral analysis.[35–38] An example of this type of determination is the separation of a variety of aldehydes in sulphite spent liquors by ion exchange chromatography prior to spectral determination at 347 nm.[35] The compounds are taken up from the liquor on an anion ex-changer (Dowex 1-X8) in its bisulphite form and separated by elution with sodium bisulphite. An example of the separation is given in Fig. 104. The sulphite spent liquor was added to the columns in 10 to 100 ml amounts. After the sorption step the columns were washed with one to two column volumes of water followed by elution with bisulphite solutions of increasing concentrations (0·2 to 0·8 M). For vanillin the eluant contained 20% ethanol (v/v).

Vanillin and ethylvanillin can be determined in alcoholic solution by gas–liquid, gas–solid, liquid–liquid and liquid–solid chromatography.[39] A high pressure liquid chromatograph operated isothermally at 37° and having a UV detector at 254 nm was used for both the liquid–liquid and liquid–solid chromatographic analyses.

In the liquid–liquid chromatographic method, the mobile phase consisted of hexane–chloroform (3:1) at a flow rate of 1 ml min^{-1} and a flow pressure of 250 lb in^{-2}. The stationary phase was 1·8% Carbowax 400 on Porosil C with a mesh size of 36 to 75 μm diameter. In the liquid–solid chromatographic method, the mobile phase consisted of hexane–chloroform (1:1) at a flow rate of 0·8 ml min^{-1} and a flow pressure of 1250 lb in^{-2}. The stationary phase was sil-X of mesh size 37–75 μm diameter.

The best separation of vanillin and ethylvanillin was obtained using the liquid–liquid chromatographic method, while the best peak sharpness, best

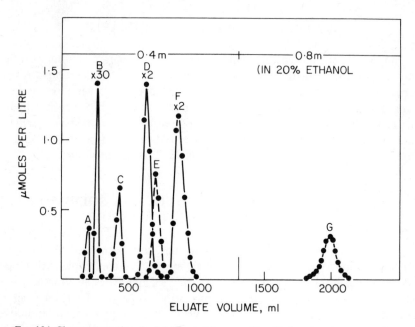

FIG. 104. Chromatography of sulphite spent liquor, with added carbonyl compounds, on Dowex 1-X8 in bisulphite form.
Column size 11 × 81 mm.
Bead size   200–300 mesh
Eluants   0·4 to 0·8 (20% ethanol) 1 M NaHSO$_3$.
Flow rate   0·72 to 0·68 ml cm^{-2} min^{-1}.
Fraction size 21 to 20 ml.
A. Acetaldehyde   E. 5-Hydroxymethylfurfural
B. Formaldehyde   F. Furfural
C. Pyruvic Acid   G. Vanillin
D Pyruvaldehyde

resolution and highest efficiency for both vanillin and ethyl vanillin were achieved using liquid–solid chromatography.[39] The authors state that under the most ideal conditions in gas chromatography it is difficult to exceed 400 number equivalent theoretical plates/ft, while using liquid–solid chromatography, it is relatively easy to obtain more than 700.

VI. PROBLEMS IN ULTRAVIOLET ASSAY

Some of the problems in the ultraviolet assay for vanillin include decomposition of vanillin and interferences. Vanillin slowly oxidizes in dilute aqueous solution to vanillic acid.[40] This reaction is a source of low ultraviolet assays. Vanillin can be determined alone, with coumarin or with syringaldehyde in artificial vanilla extracts.[41] The method depends upon shifts to longer wavelength of the long wavelength bands of vanillin and p-hydroxyaldehydes and p-hydroxyketones. Coumarin can be detected in these mixtures in two ways. Alkaline solutions of coumarin undergo rapid spectral changes when water is present. The 275 nm band disappears and a band develops at 330 nm. When neutral or acidic solutions of vanillin, ethylvanillin and coumarin are made alkaline, the dull yellow–green fluorescence is decreased, except for coumarin which acquires a brilliant green fluorescence.[12]

VII. PHOSPHORIMETRY

Vanillin could also be determined phosphorimetrically. In EPA at liquid nitrogen temperature 0.2 ng μl^{-1} could be determined at P230, 275, 305/440, 460, the long wavelength excitation and emission bands being best for analysis.

VIII. REAGENTS

A. Acetone

Vanillin can also be assayed by reaction with acetone in alkaline solution to give a red–brown chromogen[42] or by reaction with isobutanol in conc H_2SO_4 to give a blue–red chromogen.[43]

N,N-Dimethyl-p-phenylenediamine has been used to determine unsaturated aldehydes and ketones.[44–46] Other aldehydes also react. Essentially 1 ml of an acetic acid test solution is reacted with 2 ml of a 2% solution of the oxalate of N,N-dimethyl-p-phenylenediamine in acetic acid at 5 to 10°. The absorbance is read immediately at 460 nm.[46] Vanillin gives a band at this wavelength with mε = 18.

B. 2,4-Dinitrophenylhydrazine

Vanillin can also be determined with 2,4-dinitrophenylhydrazine directly.[47, 48] Other aldehydes interfere strongly, ketones moderately. Determination can be made by means of the neutral chromogen, I, or its anion, II.

$$O_2N-\!\!\!\bigcirc\!\!\!-NH-N\!=\!CH-\!\!\!\bigcirc\!\!\!-OH$$
$$NO_2 \qquad\qquad OCH_3$$

I

$$\downarrow OH^-$$

$$\left(O_2N\!=\!\!\!\bigcirc\!\!\!=\!N\!=\!N\!=\!CH\!=\!\!\!\bigcirc\!\!\!=\!O\right)^{--}$$
$$NO_2 \qquad\qquad OCH_3$$

II

Procedures utilizing the neutral chromogen and its anion are the following:

DNPH determination of vanillin, A.[48] To 1 ml of acetic acid test solution add 5 ml of 0·1% 2,4-dinitrophenylhydrazine in acetic acid containing 0·5% of conc HCl (v/v). After 1 h read the absorbance at λ 412 nm. An mε of 19·5 is obtained. The pure chromogen, **I**, absorbs at λ_{max} 393 nm, mε 68·1 in chloroform.[49]

B.[47] To 1 ml of reagent (50 mg of DNPH suspended in 30 ml of carbonyl-free methanol) add 1 ml of aq test solution. After 30 min add 5 ml of alkaline mixture (mix 4 volumes of pyridine kept over KOH, 1 ml of water and 1 ml of 10% KOH in 80% aq methanol). After 10 min., read the absorbance at the wavelength maximum.

In mixtures containing other carbonyl compounds, vanillin or its dinitrophenylhydrazone have to be separated before colorimetric analysis. Paper,[50, 51] thin layer[52] and column[53] chromatography can be used.

In the paper chromatographic method vanillin (and sometimes ethylvanillin) is extracted from pudding powder, some spices, cocoa, vanilla oils, etc., converted into its dinitrophenylhydrazone and separated by paper chromatography with benzene as an ascending solvent in an atmosphere saturated with ammonia. The vanillin spot is eluted with warm ethanol and determined in chloroform solution at 394 nm.

In another method column and thin layer chromatography are used.[53] The method was applied to the analysis of ice-cream, evaporated and pasteurized milk and other food products. The determination takes about 6 to 7 hours. Essentially, vanillin and ethylvanillin are converted into their dinitrophenylhydrazones by the addition of a 2% methanolic solution of 2,4-dinitrophenylhydrazine containing 4% of conc H_2SO_4 to a chloroform extract of the food product. After concentration, the oily residue containing the two derivatives is applied to an alumina column, and the oil and excess of reagent are eluted with acetone. The band containing the two derivatives is then eluted with 2% conc HCl in acetone, and their total content is measured spectrophotometrically (395 nm) to within $\simeq \pm 1\%$. The ratio of the two derivatives present is determined by thin-layer chromatography on silica gel, with ethyl acetate–benzene (1:19) as solvent; the accuracy is within $\simeq \pm 10\%$.

C. Indole

Indole can also be used for the determination of vanillin.[54, 55] The colour produced in the following procedure reaches a maximum in about 3 min and begins to fade after about 15 minutes. A standard should be run in the procedure. Beer's law is obeyed. Ethylvanillin reacts similarly.

Indole determination of vanillin.[55] *Reagents.* Lead acetate solution: Dissolve 8 g normal lead acetate in water and dilute to 100 ml. Indole solution: Dissolve 0·1 g indole in 10 ml alcohol and dilute to 100 ml with water. Standard vanillin solution: Dissolve 0·2 g in a small amount of alcohol and dilute to 100 ml with water.

Procedure: Transfer 2 ml single-strength vanilla extract to 25 ml volumetric flask, dilute with *ca* 10 ml alcohol, and add 0·5 ml of the lead acetate solution. Mix, dilute to the mark with alcohol, and mix again. Centrifuge or filter (discarding the first few ml filtrate) and transfer 10 ml clear solution to 100 ml volumetric flask. Add *ca* 80 ml water and 0·2 ml saturated ammonium oxalate solution, dilute to mark, and mix. Let stand for 10 min, and if a precipitate forms, filter through Whatman #1 paper, discarding the first portion that comes through the filter. Transfer 2 ml to a 25 ml Erlenmeyer flask, add 10 ml H_2SO_4 (1 + 1), mix, and cool in a water bath to room temp. Add 2 ml of the indole solution, mix, and read absorbance at 500 nm in not less than 3 nor more than 10 min, using as a reference blank a mixture of 2 ml water, 10 ml H_2SO_4 (1 + 1), and 2 ml indole solution, treated in the same manner as the sample. Obtain the absorbance of the standard vanillin solution in the same way and calculate the vanillin content of the sample.

Samples containing more than 0·3 g vanillin per 100 ml should be diluted below this value with 35% alcohol.

D. Millon's reagent

The use of Millon's reagent in the analysis of vanillin and other phenols has been investigated in terms of the mechanism[56] and the specificity.[57] The violet colour obtained in this reaction is believed to be derived from the formation of a mercury chelate with a nitroso derivative of vanillin. Phenols give a band at 500 nm while compounds containing the structure **III** give a violet colour with λ_{max} 530 nm. The results obtained in this test are shown in Table 65.[57]

III

Table 65. Reaction of vanillin and its analogues with Millon's reagent.[57]

III, R	Name	Measured at 30 min. A at λ 530
—H	Vanillin	0·170
—OH	Vanillic acid	0·110
—OCH$_3$	Methyl vanillate	0·100
—N(C$_2$H$_5$)$_2$	N,N-Diethylvanillamide	0·105
—CH$_3$	Acetovanillone	0·150
—CH$_2$OH	α,4-Dihydroxy-3-methoxyacetophenone	0·095
—CHOH—CH$_3$	α-Hydroxypropiovanillone	0·105
—CH$_2$—CH$_2$OH	β-Hydroxypropiovanillone	0·160

E. *p*-Nitrophenylhydrazine

p-Nitrophenylhydrazine is another reagent that can be used to analyse vanillin in the absence of interferences or after separation from other carbonyl compounds. The *p*-nitrophenylhydrazone of vanillin absorbs at λ 426 nm, mε 31 in dimethylformamide and at λ 587 nm, mε 50 (also λ 565s, mε 48) in dimethylformamide containing 2 % of 1 M methanolic tetra-*n*-butylammonium hydroxide.

F. Phosphomolybdic acid

In the past phosphotungstic–phosphomolybdic acid reagent has been used to determine vanillin.[14, 58–65] Because of the lack of specificity the method has been replaced by other photometric procedures. The method depends on the ability of vanillin to reduce the reagent. However, other reducing agents could have the same result. Consequently, the method usually gives fairly high results. However, in some instances it could be used but only in knowledgeable hands.

Phosphomolybdic–phosphotungstic acid determination of vanillin. Dilute 1 ml of the vanilla extract to 40 ml with water. Add 1 ml of a filtered lead acetate solution containing 50 g each of a neutral and basic lead acetate in 1 litre of water. Dilute to 250 ml with water, mix, and filter, discarding the cloudy portion of the filtrate. To 10 ml of this clear aliquot (containing up to 20 mg of,vanillin) add 5 ml of reagent. (For preparation reflux for 2 h 750 ml water, 100 g sodium tungstate, 20 g phosphomolybdic acid and 50 ml of phosphoric acid.) Mix and let stand for 5 minutes. Add 10 ml of 25% sodium carbonate solution, mix, and let stand for 10 minutes. Dilute to 100 ml with water, mix, and filter, discarding the cloudy portion of the filtrate. Read the absorbance immediately at 610 nm.

Obviously, this method could be considerably improved, if necessary.

G. 2-Thiobarbituric acid

Thiobarbituric acid can also be used to determine vanillin.[66, 67] Beer's law is followed from 1 to 25 µg/ml when 2 N HCl is the media and from 1 to 40 µg when phosphoric acid is used.[63]

TBA determination of vanillin.[66, 67] Add 2 ml of 0·36% 2-thiobarbituric acid in 9·8% H_3PO_4 to the aq test solution. Dilute to 10 ml and read the absorbance at 433 nm.

REFERENCES

1. F. Wessely and J. Kotlan. *Monatsh. Chem.* **84**, 291 (1953).
2. I. A. Pearl. *J. Am. Chem. Soc.* **71**, 2331 (1949).
3. Y. R. Naves. *Helv. Chim. Acta* **32**, 1351 (1949).
4. W. D. Kumler and P. P. T. Sah. *J. Am. Pharm. Ass., Sci. Ed.* **41**, 375 (1952).
5. H. W. Lemon. *J. Am. Chem. Soc.* **69**, 2998 (1947).
6. D. W. Glennie, H. Techlenberg, E. T. Reaville and J. L. McCarthy. *J. Am. Chem. Soc.* **77**, 2409 (1955).
7. G. de Stevens and F. F. Nord. *J. Am. Chem. Soc.* **75**, 305 (1953).
8. F. Meyer and E. Meyer. *Arch. Pharm.* **290**, 109 (1957).
9. D. T. Englis and L. A. Wollermann. *Anal. Chem.* **29**, 1151 (1957).
10. O. Goldschmid. *J. Am. Chem. Soc.* **75**, 3780 (1953).
11. R. A. Robinson and A. K. Kiang. *Trans. Faraday Soc.* **51**, 1398 (1955).
12. F. J. Feeny. *J. Ass. Offic. Agric. Chem.* **47**, 555 (1964).
13. D. T. Englis and D. J. Hanahan. *Ind. Eng. Chem., Anal. Ed.* **16**, 505 (1944).
14. O. Folin and W. Denis. *J. Ind. Eng. Chem.* **4**, 670 (1912).
15. D. M. Smith. *J. Ass. Offic. Agric. Chem.* **47**, 808 (1964).
16. L. G. Ensminger. *J. Ass. Offic. Agric. Chem.* **36**, 679 (1953).
17. G. Aulin-Erdtman and L. Hegborn. *Svensk Papperstidn.* **60**, 671 (1957).
18. L. A. Wollermann. *Diss. Abs.* **16**, 940 (1956).

19. D. T. Englis and L. A. Wollermann. *Food Res.* **20**, 567 (1955).
20. D. M. Smith. *J. Ass. Offic. Agric. Chem.* **48**, 509 (1965).
21. R. M. Way and W. R. Gailey. *J. Ass. Offic. Agric. Chem.* **34**, 726 (1951).
22. W. H. Stahl, J. H. Sullivan and W. A. Voelker. *J. Ass. Offic. Agric. Chem.* **44**, 549 (1961).
23. J. Fitelson. *J. Ass. Offic. Agric. Chem.* **47**, 1161 (1964).
24. R. ter Heide and J. F. Lemmens. *Perfume Essent. Oil Record* **45**, 21 (1954).
25. T. C. Chou and B. W. Tharp. *J. Dairy Sci.* **46**, 237 (1963).
26. M. H. Anwar. *Anal. Chem.* **35**, 1974 (1963).
27. F. M. Kunze and B. L. Espinoza. *J. Ass. Offic. Agric. Chem.* **46**, 899 (1963).
28. J. E. Stone and M. J. Blundell. *Anal. Chem.* **23**, 771 (1951).
29. J. M. Brand. *J. Chromatog.* **21**, 424 (1966).
30. J. M. Pepper and M. Siddiqueullah. *Can. J. Chem.* **38**, 2324 (1960).
31. K. von Kratzl and G. Puschmann. *Holzforschung* **14**, 1 (1960).
32. E. Sundt and A. Saccardi. *Food Technol.* **16**, 89 (1962).
33. S. Kahan and J. Fitelson. *J. Ass. Offic. Agric. Chem.* **47**, 551 (1964).
34. G. H. N. Towers and W. S. G. Maass. *Phytochemistry* **4**, 57 (1965).
35. K. Christofferson. *Svensk Papperstidn.* **67**, 540 (1967).
36. K. Christofferson. *Anal. Chim. Acta* **33**, 303 (1965).
37. K. Christofferson. *Anal. Chim. Acta* **31**, 233 (1964).
38. "Official Methods of Analysis", 9th Ed., Association of Official Agricultural Chemists, Washington, D.C. 1960. Section 19.014–19.022.
39. G. E. Martin, G. G. Guinard and D. M. Figert. *J. Agric. Food Chem.* **21**, 544 (1973).
40. D. T. Englis and M. Manchester. *Anal. Chem.* **21**, 591 (1949).
41. H. W. Lemon. *Anal. Chem.* **19**, 846 (1947).
42. E. K. Nikitin and S. A. Vershinskiĭ. *J. Gen. Chem.* (USSR) **7**, 1306 (1937).
43. T. von Fellenberg. *Mitt. Lebensm. Hyg.* **6**, 267 (1915).
44. S. Hunig, J. Utermann and G. Erlemann. *Ber.* **88**, 708 (1955).
45. S. Hunig and J. Utermann. *Ber.* **88**, 1201, 1485 (1955).
46. M. Pesez and J. Bartos. *Talanta* **10**, 69 (1963).
47. H. Bohme and O. Winkler. *Z. Anal. Chem.* **142**, 1 (1954).
48. M. Pesez. *J. Pharm. Pharmacol.* **11**, 475 (1959).
49. G. D. Johnson. *J. Am. Chem. Soc.* **75**, 2720 (1953).
50. D. E. Bland and C. Stamp. *Aust. J. Appl. Sci.* **6**, 353 (1955).
51. P. H. Joppien. *Z. Lebensmitt. Untersuch.* **115**, 20 (1961).
52. G. Ruffini. *J. Chromatog.* **17**, 483 (1965).
53. D. I. Rees. *Chem. and Ind.* 16 (1965).
54. M. Sandler and C. R. J. Ruthven. *Lancet* **2**, 114 (1959).
55. J. Fitelson. *J. Ass. Offic. Agric. Chem.* **48**, 913 (1965).
56. E. Neuzil, H. Jensen and J. Josselin. *Ann. Pharm. France* **25**, 127 (1967).
57. E. Neuzil, J. Josselin, H. Jensen and G.-O. Cesaire. *Ann. Pharm. France* **25**, 215 (1967).
58. S. A. Castro. *Anales farm. bioquim.* (Buenos Aires) **13**, 53 (1942).
59. V. A. Rozanova. *Obschchestvennoe Pitanie* **9**, 19 (1941).
60. J. M. B. Wilson. *J. Ass. Offic. Agric. Chem.* **25**, 155 (1942).
61. L. G. Ensminger. *J. Ass. Offic. Agric. Chem.* **34**, 330 (1951); **35**, 264 (1952).
62. "Official and Tentative Methods of Analysis of the Association of Official Agricultural Chemists", 7th edition, p. 306, Association of Official Agricultural Chemists, Washington, D.C. (1950).
63. "Official Methods of Analysis of the Association of Official Agricultural Chemists",

8th ed., pp. 319–20. Association of Official Agricultural Chemists, Washington, D.C. (1955).

64. H. J. Lynch and N. Deahl. *J. Ass. Offic. Agric. Chem.* **23**, 429 (1940).
65. A. L. Curl and E. K. Nelson. *J. Ass. Offic. Agric. Chem.* **22**, 684 (1939).
66. G. S. Bains, N. S. Kapur and D. S. Bhatia. *J. Sci. Ind. Res. (India)* **17B**, 462 (1958); through *Chem. Abstr.* **53**, 11706 (1959).
67. N. S. Kapur, W. M. Narayana, G. S. Bains and D. S. Bhatia. *Chem. Ind.* 1272 (1957).

AUTHOR INDEX

Numbers in italics refer to the pages where references are listed; numbers in parentheses are reference numbers and are included to assist location in the text.

Abendschein, P. A.   71(48), *84*
Abrahamson, E. W.   234(20), 235(21), *248*
Acheson, E. D.   160(55), *161*
Adamiak, J.   7(84), *19*
Adams, E.   185(44), 200(44), *202*, 207(29, 36, 55), 208(29), 209(29), 211(36), 212(36), 221 (55), *222, 223*
Adams, G. A.   4(55), *18*
Adams, R. G.   239(47, 50), *249*
Adkins, H.   37(2), *41*
Aeschlimann, F.   4(62), 5(62), 6(62), *19*
Agrawal, T. N.   258(29), *259*
Ahmad, H.   286(82), *290*
Ahmad, R.   285(79), *290*
Ahrens, H.   194(72), *202*
Aito, Y.   23(8), *26*
Akhtar, M.   234(18), 237(40), *248, 249*
Albers, R. W.   271(3), 272(6), *272*
Albert, J. D.   191(69), *202*
Albrecht, A. M.   65(37), *83*
Aldenhoff, S. M.   230(34), *232*
Alekseeva, G. L.   148(14), *149*
Alexander, N. M.   226(19), 230(19), *232*
Alexander, P. W.   252(1), *259*
Alfthan, M.   71(50), *84*
Altshuller, A. P.   16(122), *20*
Ames, S. R.   242(57), 244(77), *249*
Anderson, P. J.   23(1), 25(1), *26*
Andrisano, R.   3(7, 14), *17*, 275(2), *275*
Angelino, N.   194(72), *202*
Angell, F. G.   4(40), *18*
Anger, V.   131(48), *137*, 157(42, 43), *161*, 258(28), *259*
Anwar, M. H.   292(26), *300*
AOAC   7(93), *19*, 293(38), 298(62, 63), 299(63), *300*
A.P.I.   86(2, 5, 6), *87*, 164(2), *167*, 279(2), 280(10, 13, 21, 23), 281(4), *288*
Arbuzov, B. A.   281(5), *288*
Arens, J. F.   235(25), *248*
Ariga, N.   66(13), 70(13), *83*
Arnaud, P.   280(24), *288*

Arnon, D. I.   34(9), *35*
Arya, S. S.   135(62), *137*
Aryama, N.   226(3), *232*
Asada, K.   65(6), 66(6), 67(6), 68(6), *83*
Asmus, E.   130(52), *137*
Aso, A.   23(8), *26*
Asselineau, C.   280(22), *288*
Asselineau, J.   280(22), *288*
Aulin-Erdtman, G.   292(17), *299*
Austin, F. L.   3(12), 5(12), 6(12), *17*, 148(5), *149*
Ayaz, A. A.   286(82), *290*
Azam, F.   286(82), *290*

Bacon, N.   121(37), *136*
Baden, M.   36(1), *36*
Bader, H.   282(34), *289*
Badger, L.   185(18), 187(18), 188(18), *201*, 207(27), 208(27), *222*
Badre, R.   81(82, 83), *84*
Baer, E.   226(21), *232*
Baglioni, C.   185(21), 190(21), *201*
Bains, G. S.   299(66, 67), *301*
Balasubramaniyan, P.   239(52), 243(67), *249*
Balasubramaniyan, V.   239(52), 243(67, 73, 74), *249*
Balke, D. E.   236(38), 245(38), *249*
Ball, S.   235(22, 28), 237(44), 239(44), 240(44), *248, 249*
Bally, O.   127(45), *136*
Bancher, E.   43(17), 52(17), *58*, 116(19), 132 (53), *136, 137*
Bandow, F.   3(21, 22), *18*
Banks, B. E. C.   205(8), *222*
Banks, T.   37(4), *41*, 48(33), *58*
Banner, M. R.   66(19), 74(19), *83*
Bannuscher, H.   208(61, 62), *223*
Barber, E. D.   157(50), *161*
Barltrop, J. A.   86(10), *87*
Barrensheen, H.   226(9), *232*
Barrick, P. L.   93(3), 94(3), *104*
Barta, L.   4(57), *18*

303

M

SUBJECT INDEX

Since practically every chapter contains data on the absorption spectra of the aldehyde concerned, these spectra are not referenced in the subject index. The Table of Contents and the Subject Index complement each other.

321

M*